CHROMOSOME DIAGNOSTICS
IN
CLINICAL MEDICINE

Publication Number 610

AMERICAN LECTURE SERIES®

A Monograph in

The BANNERSTONE DIVISION *of*
AMERICAN LECTURES IN LIVING CHEMISTRY

Edited by

I. NEWTON KUGELMASS, M.D., Ph.D., Sc.D.

Consultant to the Departments of Health and Hospitals
New York, New York

CHROMOSOME
DIAGNOSTICS
IN CLINICAL MEDICINE

By

ROBERT R. EGGEN, M.D.

Chief Pathologist, San Diego County (Coroner)
Associate Pathologist and Director of Cytogenetics Laboratory
Grossmont Hospital
Consulting Pathologist, U.S. Naval Hospital
San Diego, California

CHARLES C THOMAS • PUBLISHER
Springfield • Illinois • U.S.A.

Published and Distributed Throughout the World by

CHARLES C THOMAS • PUBLISHER

BANNERSTONE HOUSE

301-327 East Lawrence Avenue, Springfield, Illinois, U.S.A.

NATCHEZ PLANTATION HOUSE

735 North Atlantic Boulevard, Fort Lauderdale, Florida, U.S.A.

With THOMAS BOOKS careful attention is given to all details of manufacturing and design. It is the Publisher's desire to present books that are satisfactory as to their physical qualities and artistic possibilities and appropriate for their particular use. THOMAS BOOKS will be true to those laws of quality that assure a good name and good will.

Printed in the United States of America

S–4

To Doris, Jim and Cathy,
whose patience and forbearence
made it possible, this work
is dedicated

FOREWORD

OUR Living Chemistry Series was conceived by Editor and Publisher to advance the newer knowledge of chemical medicine in the cause of clinical practice. The interdependence of chemistry and medicine is so great that physicians are turning to chemistry, and chemists to medicine in order to understand the underlying basis of life processes in health and disease. Once chemical truths, proofs and convictions become sound foundations for clinical phenomena, key hybrid investigators clarify the bewildering panorama of biochemical progress for application in everyday practice, stimulation of experimental research, and extension of postgraduate instruction. Each of our monographs thus unravels the chemical mechanisms and clinical management of many diseases that have remained relatively static in the minds of medical men for three thousand years. Our new Series is charged with the *nisus élan* of chemical wisdom, supreme in choice of international authors, optimal in standards of chemical scholarship, provocative in imagination for experimental research, comprehensive in discussions of scientific medicine, and authoritative in chemical perspective of human disorders.

Dr. Eggen of San Diego presents the principles and practice of clinical cytogenetics in simplified form for bedside application by pediatrician and physician. It encompasses the entire field from the normal mechanism of cell division through basic genetics to the clinical sequelae of chromosome abnormalities in man. Human chromosomes are amenable to direct studies for establishing the diagnosis of congenital malformations and sexual abnormalities. Fetal-cell chromosome studies bring to light malformed infants in the making while newborn-cell studies identify affected families to prevent congenital abnormalities in the future. Autosomal chromosome abnormalities may involve deviations in number or in morphological appearance of the chromosomes or both. Nuclear sex is determined by examination of buccal smears, white blood cells or skin biopsy material. Sex chromatin at variance with the sex of the phenotype indicates an underlying sex chromosome abnormality but a concordant sex-chromatin result does not necessarily connote a normal sex chromosome constitution. Chromosomal aberrations viewed by current techniques represent gross genetic damage to the cell, for the smallest detectable deletion involves large numbers of genes while molecular cytogenics unravels submicroscopic molecular arrangements reflecting altered genic material in human mutations. All this and more is embodied in this practical manual on clinical chromosome analysis, complete with methods, indications, interpretations and limitations.

Maupertuis (1730) first advanced the theory of heredity based on the direct transmission of chemical particles from each parent. Brown (1831) of Brownian movement distinction, discovered the cell nucleus—the site of the chromosomes. In the nucleus the apparatus of cell government is at rest; in the chromosomes it is in movement. Hereditary characters are carried to the nucleus rather than the cytoplasm, and more specifically in the chromosomes of the nuclei. DNA in the cell is confined to the nucleus while most of RNA, a misnomer, by contrast in the cytoplasm. Chromosomes are among the largest molecules whose chemistry is pursued, the smallest living structures whose transformations are followed. Their maneuvers in mitation and fertilization were first observed about a century ago following the development of analine dyes and high power magnification. Weisman (1883) evolved the germ plasm theory in which chromosomes formed the basis of heredity and development. Roux (1883) considered them specific hereditary determiners in the cell nucleus presaging molecular genetics. Yet, Mendel (1866) had already demonstrated the principle of heredity in an eight-year experiment with sweet peas to prove the correctness of his graduate contention and thus vindicate his licentiate failure in agriculture science. But the data was not discovered until the turn of the century by de Vries and others in the obscure Brünn journal of the Abbey, rejected for publication in the national journal by the leading biologist who flunked him. Affirmante, non neganti, incumbit probatio. With his transcendent capacity of taking trouble he proved his point and deduced Nature's laws in wretched seclusion.

Mendelian genetics is indispensable for interpretation of pedigrees of disease. But human genetics extends beyond mendelian bounds that inherited characteristics are transmitted from generation to generation in ratios of simple whole numbers. Biochemical genetics has progressed so far that it is now possible in some cases to pin-point the precise function of a gene. For example, the only detectable difference between normal and sickle hemoglobin is that in the latter valene has been substituted for glutamic acid in the peptide, a simple change that marks the difference between health and disease. It has its origin in either the abnormal DNA derived from the parent, which directs the formation of an abnormal RNA that serves as a template for the biosynthesis of abnormal protein, or from an error in the copying of the normal parental DNA which leads to the same sequence of abnormal reactions. The biochemical basis of genetically transmitted diseases is viewed in terms of the components that transmit genetic information and the phenotypes that determine molecular aberration. The author enables chromosome visualization by simple separation in hypotonic media to swell cell nuclei, by flattening the cell nuclei under slide pressure, by blocking cell division in mitosis with cytostatic agents to define the individual karyotype and by other ingenious methods. Cytogenic techniques applied to clinical problems create genetic syndromes by delineating individuals in particular positions of the homo sapiens spectrum in health and disease as the analytical answer to the uniqueness, unpredictability and unrepeatability of human beings. Clinical medicine is thus becoming a form of experimental and applied biology in the everyday service of our strange species.

> *"But beyond the bright searchlights of science,*
> *Out of sight of the windows of sense,*
> *Old riddles still bid us defiance,*
> *Old questions of why and whence."*

I. NEWTON KUGELMASS, M.D., PH.D., SC.D., *Editor*

PREFACE

IT IS a regrettable fact that human chromosome analysis is still generally regarded as an interesting laboratory curiosity rather than as a practical diagnostic medium. However regrettable this fact may be, it is not entirely astonishing.

The very rapidity with which these techniques have evolved militates to some degree against ready recognition of their value by clinicians. In less than a decade, human cytogenetics has become a discipline of most appreciable breadth.

To an even greater degree, a comparative inaccessibility of information must be held responsible for this lack of recognition. In the United States particularly, pertinent articles in this field are extremely infrequent in the most widely read medical journals where they appear only as sporadic case reports. A scan of the publications listed in the bibliography will reveal few of everyday familiarity. Even the few comprehensive review articles published have appeared in specialty journals.

There is, of course, a natural tendency on the part of specialists in any field to communicate with their fellows. Much of the pioneer investigation in cytogenetics has been performed by geneticists and cytologists, an appreciable number of whom are not clinicians (and not a few of whom are not in the medical sciences at all). Thus we have articles written by cytogeneticists about cytogenetics for the edification of other cytogeneticists *via* appropriate journals. This has proven a moderately successful method of keeping the field from the attention of the majority of practicing physicians.

My own experience has emphasized to me the difficulty in gleaning a comprehensive view of this subject by perusing the literature. The task is one of considerable magnitude if one is equipped with no sounder basic knowledge than a half-forgotten course in elementary college genetics. For, as will soon become apparent to others who make such an attempt, geneticists writing for other geneticists made the tacit assumption that the reader already knows a good deal about genetics. This assumption is not always warranted.

It is now essential, in my opinion, that a concise source of reference material be available to physicians in all of the medical specialties. The techniques of cytogenetics are increasing in sophistication at an almost geometric pace. It is not unrealistic to predict that twenty years hence that man's chromosome pattern will be known with an exactitude now the exclusive province of the megachromosomal insects.

The purposes of this monograph are thus twofold:

1) To identify the clinical situations in which cytogenetic techniques are of proven diagnostic value and to show how best to apply them to maximum advantage.

2) to provide clinicians with a sufficiently detailed fund of basic genetic and cytologic knowledge that they may approach the literature in this field with enhanced assurance and comprehension.

In short, this is a monograph by a clinician for clinicians. I sincerely hope that it will fulfill its stated objectives.

ROBERT R. EGGEN, M.D.

ACKNOWLEDGMENTS

To THE many pioneers in the field of cytogenetics, whose work forms the basis of this monograph, goes my most heartfelt thanks. Specifically, I am most indebted to

Dr. Murray L. Barr
Dr. Gerald H. Holman
Dr. Irene Uchida
Dr. Fred W. Bauer
The Canadian Medical Association Journal, and
The New England Journal of Medicine

for their courtesy in allowing me to reproduce their illustrations.

My thanks are also due the medical librarians without whose aid many references would have eluded me: Miss M. Cranny of the San Diego County Medical Society Library, Mrs. M. Le Compte of San Diego State College Library and Mrs. S. Fraser of University of California (La Jolla) Library.

I must also acknowledge the heroic efforts of my secretary, Mrs. Opal Hollister, in the preparation of the manuscript.

To Charles C Thomas, Publisher go my thanks for their cooperation and aid in this project.

R. R. E.

CONTENTS

Page

Foreword vii

Preface xi

Acknowledgments xiii

Chapter

I. CHROMOSOME STRUCTURE AND THE CHEMISTRY OF HEREDITY . 3
  Visible Chromosome Structure 4
  Special Chromosome Types 9
  The Chemistry of Heredity 10
  Deoxyribonucleic Acid (DNA) 10
  Replication of DNA 13
  The Genetic Code 14
  Ribonucleic Acid (RNA) 18
  The Transfer of Genetic Information 20
  The Nature of the Gene 21
  The Operon 24
  Histones 25
  Heterochromatin 26
  Mutations 27
  Cell Differentiation 27

II. NORMAL CELL DIVISION 30
  Mitosis 31
  Meiosis 35
  First Meiotic Division (Meiosis I) 36
  Second Meiotic Division (Meiosis II) 42
  Meiosis in Man 44

III. PRINCIPLES OF INHERITANCE 47
  Mendel's First Law 48
  Mendel's Second Law 50

Chapter   *Page*

Linkage and Crossing-over 51
Sex Linked Genes 54
Patterns of Inheritance 55
    Dominant Inheritance 56
    Autosomal Recessive Inheritance 56
    Sex-linked Dominant Inheritance 56
    Sex-linked Recessive Inheritance 56
Other Variations on the Mendelian Theme 57
    Association *vs.* Linkage 57
    Multiple Alleles 57
    Expressivity and Penetrance 58
    Position Effects 58
    Affinity 59
    Gene Balance 59
    Structural Chromosome Abnormalities 60
    Gene Effects on Gametes 60
    Gene Control of Segregation 60
    Environmental Factors 61
The Pedigree Chart 61

IV. SEX DIFFERENTIATION AND THE CHROMATIN TEST 63
Sex Differentiation in Man 63
    Function of the Sex Chromosomes 66
The Chromatin Test 68
    Recognition of Sex Chromatin 68
    Origin of the Sex Chromatin—The Lyon Hypothesis . 70
    Interpretation of Barr Chromatin Tests 73
    The Neutrophil Appendages 76

V. IDENTIFICATION OF HUMAN CHROMOSOMES 80
Technical Methods 81
    Collection of Samples 82
    Culture Media 83
    Phytohemagglutinin 84
    Colchicine 85
    Other Steps 86
Chromosome Identification 87
    The Denver Nomenclature 88
    Identification of Individual Chromosomes 89
Chromosome Mapping in Man 102

Chapter *Page*

VI. ANEUPLOIDY AND NONDISJUNCTION 104
   Nondisjunction 105
      Meiotic Nondisjunction 107
      Determining the Source of Nondisjunctive Gametes . 111
      Mitotic Nondisjunction 113
      Chimerism 115
      Secondary Nondisjunction 116
   Other Causes of Aneuploidy 116
      Anaphase Lagging 117
   Supernumerary Chromosomes 117
   Clones 118

VII. STRUCTURAL ABNORMALITIES OF CHROMOSOMES 119
   Genesis of Structural Alterations 119
   Single Chromosome Breaks 123
   Deletions 124
   Translocations 125
   Duplications 130
   Isochromosomes 130
   Ring Chromosomes 132
   Inversions 132
   Insertions 134
   Partial Trisomy 136

VIII. ETIOLOGY AND CLASSIFICATION OF HUMAN CHROMOSOME AB-
   NORMALITIES 137
      Age 138
      Genetic Complement 138
      Nucleolus Organizers 139
      Sex Chromosomes 139
      Structural Anomalies 139
      Radiation 139
      Chemicals 141
      Viral Infections 142
      Chronic Disease 145
   Classification of Human Chromosome Defects 145

IX. INDICATIONS FOR CYTOGENETIC TESTING 148
   Congenital Abnormalities 149
   Genetic Counselling 150

Chapter   *Page*
    Differential Diagnosis of Intersex 152
    Primary Amenorrhea 154
    Female Infertility 155
    Male Infertility 155
    Blood Dyscrasias 156
    Dysproteinemia 156
    Medicolegal Applications 156
    Antenatal Sex Determination 157
    The "Biological Dosimeter" 157
    Cytology of Effusions 158
    Habitual Abortion 158
    Future Developments 158

  X. Mongolism and Other Autosomal Aneuploidy Syndromes 160
    Sporadic Mongolism (Trisomy-21) 161
    Group D. Trisomy Syndrome (Patau's Syndrome) . . 165
    Group E Trisomy Syndrome (Edwards' Syndrome) . . 170
    Occasional Trisomy "Syndromes" 176
      Group C Autosomal Trisomy 176
      Group F Trisomy 177
      Trisomy-22 177
    Monosomy and Polysomy 178
    Complex Aneuploids 178
      Triploidy 179
      Partial Trisomy 179
    Autosomal Mosaics 180
      Mosaicism in Mongolism 181
      Mosaicism in D-Trisomy Syndrome 181
      Other Autosomal Mosaics 182
    Chimeras 183
    Secondary Nondisjunction 183
    Supernumerary Chromosomes 184

  XI. Clinical Effects of Autosomal Structural Anomalies . 185
    Autosomal Translocations 187
      Translocation Mongolism 188
      Other Autosomal Translocations 193
    Autosomal Deletions 196
    Autosomal Duplications 198
    Autosomal Isochromosomes 198

Autosomal Inversions 198
Other Autosomal Structural Defects 199
  Alterations in Size 200
Complex Autosomal Anomalies 201
Clones 201

XII. CLINICAL EFFECTS OF SEX CHROMOSOME ABNORMALITIES . . 203
  General Clinical Features 204
  Clinical Presentation of Sex Chromosomal Alterations . 205
  Chromosomally Induced Intersex 206
    True Hermaphroditism 206
    The "Ultimate Hermaphrodite" 207
    Is There an X-Y Translocation? 208
    Mosaicism in Intersex States 208
    Non-chromosomal Intersex 210
  Chromosomally Induced Impairment of Female Sex Differentiation 210
    Turner's Syndrome 210
    Chromatin Positive Gonadal Dysgenesis 214
    Primary Amenorrhea 216
    Oligomenorrhea and Sterility 217
    XXX and XXXX 217
    X Chromosome Mosaicism 218
    Morphologic Abnormalities of the X Chromosome . . 219
  Chromosomal Impairment of Male Sex Differentiation . 219
    Klinefelter's Syndrome 220
    Other Defects 224
  Sex Chromosome Defects and Mental Deficiency . . . 224

XIII. UNRELATED CHROMOSOME ABNORMALITIES IN FAMILIES AND INDIVIDUALS 226
  In Individuals 226
  In Families 227
  Implications 229

XIV. CHROMOSOMAL CHANGES IN NEOPLASIA 232
  Chronic Myelocytic Leukemia and the Ph1 Chromosome . 235
  Other Leukemias 238
  Chromosomal Alteration in Solid Tumors 241
  Detection of Malignant Cells Using Cytogenetic Techniques 241

Appendix   *Page*

I. GLOSSARY 243

II. TECHNICAL METHODS 252
    Demonstration of Sex Chromatin 252
    Karyotype Analysis—Peripheral Blood 256
        Peripheral Blood—Micro method 262
        Peripheral Blood—Mail-in Method 264
    Karyotype Analysis Using Bone Marrow 265
        Bone Marrow—Ultra-short Method 266
    Karyotype Analysis Using Solid Tissues 267
    Accentuation of Secondary Constrictions 269
    Autoradiography 270
    Reagents 270

III. SOURCES OF ERROR 273
    Technical Defects 273
        Chromatin Preparations 273
        Karyotype Preparations 274
    Sources of Interpretive Error 278
        Sex Chromatin (Barr) Tests 278
        Polymorphonuclear Leukocyte Appendages . . . 279
        Karyotypes 279
    Reporting 280

IV. CONVERSION OF PERSONAL NOMENCLATURES TO DENVER TERMINOLOGY 282

V. CLASSIFICATION OF KNOWN CHROMOSOMAL DEFECTS (WITH REFERENCES) 283

References 293

Index 339

CHROMOSOME DIAGNOSTICS
IN
CLINICAL MEDICINE

CHAPTER I

CHROMOSOME STRUCTURE AND THE CHEMISTRY OF HEREDITY

THERE are few sciences in which basic principles can be enunciated as succinctly as can those of genetics. Nor are there many branches of science in which basic principles form so readily discernible a theme, scarcely obscured by even the most complex variations of the science. Thus, at the outset, it would be well to summarize the single basic concept upon which the whole science of genetics is based—the gene concept of inheritance.

Briefly stated, *the gene concept of inheritance* attributes the physical and chemical individuality of organisms to the action of hereditary material which is derived in equal parts from each parent. The hereditary material maintains its identity from generation to generation and resides in the nucleus. Here it is borne on the chromosomes as a series of factors, or *genes*, each of which controls a specific cellular function. The microscopically visible variations on this basic theme constitute the subscience of *cytogenetics* and it is with this field that this monograph is primarily concerned.

Minute intranuclear bodies, first demonstrated in the middle of the nineteenth century (about 1850), were given the name "chromosome" because of their affinity for certain basic dyes. The remarkable behavior of these strange little bodies stimulated a great deal of scientific interest and, by 1880, the mechanisms of chromosome behavior during cell division had been fairly well elaborated. Probably the earliest depiction of chromosomes in human material was made by Arnold in 1879 (in tumor tissue).

By 1885, the constancy of chromosome number within species and from generation to generation had become recognized. The mechanism which maintained this numerical constancy was dis-

3

covered during the study of germ cells. This proved to be a special type of cell division which was named *"meiosis,"* to distinguish it from ordinary cell division (*mitosis*). Familiarity with the behavior of chromosomes during cell division was sufficiently intimate that by 1902, when Mendel's laws (*q.v.*) were rediscovered, the unique synchrony between the observed activity of chromosomes and that predicted by Mendel was immediately apparent. This synchrony established both the Mendelian theory and the chromosome theory of inheritance with a firmness which has not been seriously challenged. This wedding of theories provided the science of genetics with the firm base upon which it rests today.

Subsequent scientific advances in genetics have proceeded more or less autonomously at three biologic levels—the family (pedigree genetics), the cell (cytogenetics) and, more recently, the nucleoprotein (molecular genetics). A summary of advances in all of these fields would indeed be of encyclopedic proportions. This monograph deals with the circumscribed field of human cytogenetics. The following discussions of molecular and pedigree genetics will be of only sufficient depth to make subsequent allusions to these fields comprehensible.

VISIBLE CHROMOSOME STRUCTURE

Chromosomes, as they are studied clinically, are usually in the metaphase stage of mitosis (*q.v.*), and the model chromosome which we will describe is a metaphase chromosome (see figure). A metaphase chromosome is composed of two identical longitudinal halves which are united at pale or unstained area. Each half is called a *chromatid* and the pale point of union is the *centromere*. Depending upon the position of the centromere, the metaphase chromosomes assume the characteristic "X" and "wishbone" shapes in which they are usually depicted. It is important that the distinction between *chromosomes* and *chromatids* be thoroughly familiar if confusion is to be avoided.

It is also appropriate to emphasize the fact that in sexually reproducing organisms chromosomes occur in essentially identical pairs; only one member of a pair is shown in the diagram. With the exception of the sex chromosomes, the members of each pair

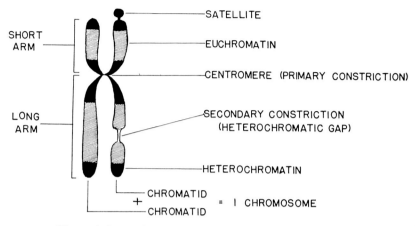

Figure 1. Parts of a Hypothetical Metaphase Chromosome.

are identical (*homologous*) and it is this feature which has given these pairs the name *autosomes*. Since only the sex chromosomes can occur in dissimilar pairs ("heterosomes"), the term "autosome" is used synonymously with "non-sex (or somatic) chromosome."

Each chromatid is composed of a tightly wound spiral thread of deoxyribonucleic acid (DNA), histone and incomplete protein called a *chromonema*. These threads are generally so tightly wound by metaphase that their spiral configuration is not apparent. *Spiralization* can be demonstrated with appropriate special techniques and is a feature common to all chromosomes. The direction of the spiral of the chromonema is variable and has no special significance.

In early prophase, before spiralization has occurred, the chromonemata can be seen to bear small "granules" of varying size strung along their length much like a string of beads. These granules are called *chromomeres* and their size and distribution along the chromonema seems to be fairly characteristic. Though the view has since been disproved, the chromomeres were regarded for a time as being the genes themselves.

Each chromatid is divided into two segments, or *arms*, by the centromere. In general, each chromatid arm is somewhat club shaped with its narrower portion near the centromere. In metaphase chromosomes, staining is usually fairly uniform along the

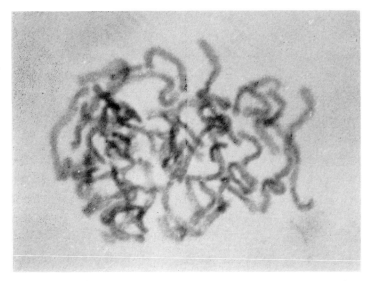

Figure 2. A Prophase Nucleus. The distinction between euchromatin and hetero-chromatin is most readily apparent at this stage. Early spiralization is present.

entire length of the chromatid though more darkly staining portions of chromosomes (or even entire chromosomes) may sometimes be noted. These asynchronously stained ("condensed") regions are more prominent during earlier stages of cell division and are referred to as *heterochromatic* regions and the component chromosomal material referred to as *heterochromatin*.

Other segments of chromosomes retain a uniform staining character throughout cell division and are called *"euchromatic"* segments. Heterochromatic segments may always be darker than euchromatin (positive heteropyknosis) or may vary in staining properties, occasionally becoming paler than euchromatin (negative heteropyknosis). It is generally believed that euchromatin is genetically more active than heterochromatin.

Studies in molecular genetics (*vide infra*) are shedding some light on the differences between heterochromatin and euchromatin. There is reason to believe that the question *"what* is heterochromatin?" might be more correctly rephrased *"why* is heterochromatin?" Heterochromatinization seems related more closely to physical than to chemical differences in the structure of the chromatid. Some of these differences are explored in the discussion of molecular genetics.

Heterochromatin is distributed most consistently near the centromere and near the ends of the chromatid arms, though blocks of heterochromatin are also seen in other regions. Fractures which occur in chromatids and lead to structural anomalies are more prone to occur at heterochromatin-euchromatin junctions. Heterochromatinization is an important structural and functional characteristic of the X chromosome in females (see Chapter IV).

The centromere is an autonomous and constant area of pallor or complete lack of staining at which the chromatids remain united in the metaphase chromosome. This area is also referred to as the *kinetochore* or the *primary constriction*. These are the terms in most common use and each, reflecting either a physical or functional characteristic of the area, has its adherents. The term "centromere" is most widely employed and will be used throughout the monograph. The principal function of the centromere is to serve as the chromosomal point of attachment for the spindle apparatus and, presumably, as the spindle organizer. There is growing evidence that the centromere, rather than being genetically "inert" as has been thought, does have a specific genetic identity (see "Affinity," p. 59).

Occasionally, other areas of pallor (*heterochromatic gaps* or *secondary constrictions*) may be present and lead to confusion as to which area is the true centromere. The constancy of the position of centromere is a most useful distinction. Another distinctive feature is the ability of the chromosome to bend at the centromere. Bending is rarely, if ever, seen at the site of a secondary constriction. The functional significance of secondary constrictions is obscure; most investigators feel that they function as sites of nucleolus formation. Some secondary constrictions occur with sufficient constancy to be useful in chromosome identification (see Chapter V).

The position of the centromere is a physical characteristic useful in chromosome identification and classification. All naturally occurring centromeres are interstitial, i.e., they do not occur at the ends of chromatids. A chromosome bearing a terminal centromere (*telocentric* chromosome) is an unstable form which quickly undergoes structural rearrangement. Fragments which lack a centromere (*acentric* fragments) lack a spindle attachment and are generally lost during cell division. The normal positions for centromeres are central (*metacentric* chromosomes), slightly eccentric (*submetacentric* chromosomes) or almost terminal (*acrocentric* chromosomes). Eccentric centromeres divide the chromosomes into readily distinguishable long and short arms, the measurements of which are useful in chromosome identification.

Chromosomes which have nearly terminal centromeres, the acrocentric chromosomes, not infrequently bear *satellites*. These structures, borne at the ends of the short arms, have two possible microscopic configurations:

1) Small areas of negative heteropyknosis at the ends of the short arms.

2) Heterochromatic (usually positively heterochromatic) knobs whose length does not exceed their width attached to the short arms of the chromosomes by slender chromatin stalks.

> There is reluctance on the part of some cytologists to accept the negatively heteropyknotic structures as true satellites. However, these structures *do* occur and there has been no satisfactory alternative terminology proposed. The term "satellite" is thus used in its broader sense throughout.
>
> Theoretically at any rate, any part of a chromosome which is distal to a secondary constriction may be properly termed a satellite. Since secondary constrictions are in themselves fairly characteristic features, there seems to be little justification for making the terminology all *that* inclusive.

Though they are microscopically indistinguishable from the remainder of the chromatid, free chromatid ends possess characteristics which are sufficiently unique to justify their separate identification as *telomeres*. Evidence is accumulating that these areas do, in fact, have a specific chemical composition. The most important attribute of the telomere is its inability to unite with broken chromatid ends or with other telomeres. It is incapable of assuming an interstitial position. The implications of this behavior will become apparent in later discussions (see Chapter VII).

Special Chromosome Types

Two specialized types of chromosomes have been of singular significance in genetic research. Both of these types occur in lower animal forms and studies of each type have made unique contributions to present genetic knowledge.

Salivary Gland Chromosomes

Within the salivary and intestinal epithelial nuclei of the larval forms of some members of the order *Diptera*, there are specialized and highly characteristic huge banded and beaded chromosomes. The most widely studied are those found in *Drosophila sp.*, the fruit fly. The combined advantages of highly specialized chromosomes and rapid breeding have made these tiny flies among the most important of genetic research media.

The chromosomes found in these insects are called *polytene* chromosomes and are formed as a consequence of repeated replications of DNA without cell division. As a result, many chromonemata come to lie side by side with their chromomeres aligned and so assume a banded appearance. These bands are predictably situated and serve as markers whose alterations can be correlated with hereditary changes in the affected flies. These bands are easily discernible with the light microscope and their study has provided the basis for much of our present knowledge of structural chromosome changes.

"Lampbrush" Chromosomes

Another highly specialized form of megachromosome is present in the cells of some newts of the genus *Triturus*. These chromosomes have a highly characteristic "feathery" appearance which, with high magnification, proves to be a consequence of separation of the chromosome into two strands. The separated strands form lateral loops along which chromomeres are spaced.

The relatively slow reproductive cycle of *Triturus sp.* has made these spectacular chromosomes an object of less intense study than their counterparts in *Drosophila*. Greatest use has been made of lampbrush chromosomes in radioisotope tagging techniques.

The ability to form such polytene chromosomes is related to an inherent tendency to polyploidy present in these same nuclei. Polyploidy is a consequence of chromosome division without cell division. Both lampbrush chromosomes and salivary gland chromosomes show characteristic areas of "puffing" (*Balbiani rings*) which are areas of high chromosomal metabolic activity.

THE CHEMISTRY OF HEREDITY

The correlation of Mendelian theory with observed chromosomal activity alluded to earlier made it seem that in a matter of only a short time the chemical secrets of heredity would be discovered. The basic chemical components of chromosomes had, after all, been known for almost forty years by the time this correlation was made. For almost another forty years, biological chemists stood upon the threshold of discovery, struggling vainly to open the door with a protein key!

While the glamorous proteins commanded the attention of the biological chemists of the day, another well known chromosomal constituent, deoxyribonucleic acid (DNA), remained relegated to the role of a secondary compound of rather dubious significance. Not a few chemists assigned to DNA the role of a rather unusually complex intranuclear buffer. In 1944, the work of Avery, MacLeod and McCarty proved conclusively that DNA, *functioning alone*, was capable of inducing genetic alterations in *Pneumococcus*. The identity of the hereditary material was finally established.

The research of the past twenty years has elaborated the role of DNA in protein synthesis and the transfer of genetic information. Its complex interrelationships with its sister classes of compounds, the ribonucleic acids (RNA), have been aptly summarized in the phrase "*DNA makes RNA and RNA makes protein.*" Behind the disarming simplicity of this euphonious little slogan lies the most fascinating detective story in biological science. And the most significant.

Deoxyribonucleic Acid (DNA)

Deoxyribonucleic acid is one member of the large class of biological compounds derived by the polymerization of simple constituent molecules into giant macromolecules. It has a number of completely unique properties whose satisfactory explanation posed great difficulty for the chemists attempting to determine its structure. To be adequate, any proposed structural formula must

1) Explain the ability of the molecule to reproduce itself.

2) Accommodate the constant sugar:phosphate ratio seen in DNA from all species.

3) Accommodate the vast variations in base (adenine, thymine, guanine and cytosine) ratios seen between species.

4) Explain the constancy of the ratio of adenine:thymine and guanine:cytosine seen in all types of DNA, and,

5) Explain the ability of the molecule to transmit genetic information.

Devising a structure for a fibrous macromolecule some fifteen hundred times as long as wide within the limits of such criteria is obviously no minor challenge.

The component parts of the molecule are well known. They include a comparatively simple five-carbon sugar (deoxyribose), phosphate, and four organic bases (two purines—adenine and guanine, and two pyrimidines—cytosine and thymine). The fibrous character of the molecule is evident from its physical properties and from electron microscope findings.

Wilkins, a physicist studying the molecule using polarized light, found that its structure is crystalline. Wilkins' X-ray crystallographic studies of DNA from various species further revealed that the crystalline structure is identical in all forms.

Incorporation of all these known facts into a single workable structural scheme was the Nobel prize-winning accomplishment of J. D. Watson and F. H. C. Crick. The Watson-Crick model, accommodating as it has all the known chemical facts, has also provided rational chemical explanations for the unique physiological properties of the molecule. Its accuracy has become well accepted.

The Watson-Crick version of the DNA molecule is that of a long double helix wound around a central axis. The "backbone" of the helices are chains of—phosphate—sugar—phosphate—linkages to which the organic bases are attached, oriented to the *inside* of the helix. The double strands are united by hydrogen bonding between the bases.

One of the most significant features of the structural formula is the precise relationship maintained by the purine and pyrimidine bases. Bonding occurs only between adenine and thymine (A-T linkages) or between guanine and cytosine (C-G linkages). This highly specific bonding accounts for the equal proportions of

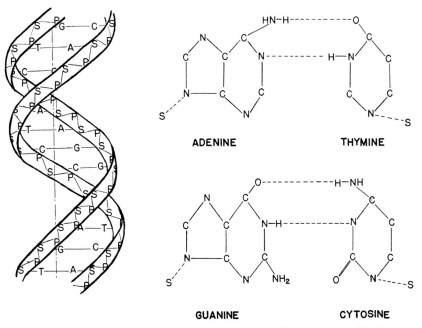

ADENINE   **THYMINE**

GUANINE   **CYTOSINE**

Figure 3. Structure of D.N.A. (*Left*) The phosphate (P) and sugar (S) "back-bones" are wound around a common longitudinal axis, with the nucleotide bases adenine (A), thymine (T), cytosine (C) and guanine (G) oriented to the center of the molecule. (*Right*) Chemical structure of the nucleotide bases showing the sites of bonding between the bases.

adenine and thymine and of guanine and cytosine which was alluded to earlier. More important, this specificity ensures that each strand of the helix is an exact complement of the other.

It must be emphasized that the coils of the DNA helix are *not* analogous to the coils of the chromonemata in the chromosomes. The DNA molecule itself is coiled and the chromonema most probably represents a coiled-coil of an already helical molecule. Evidence for the complexity of the coiling within the chromonemata has been derived from both electron microscope study and from the behavior of chromonemata in low ionic strength solutions, where they dissociate into several distinct strands.

The specificity of the base pairing also explains the physiological properties of the molecule—self-replication and storage of genetic information. One of the few disadvantages of the proposed structure, which its authors were among the first to point out, is that in order for the molecule to function, it must first unwind. Unwinding is apparently required either for replication or for nuclear function. In view of the wide dispersal of chromosomal material within the nucleus which is not actively dividing, the objection does not seem of sufficient magnitude to negate the validity of the proposed structural formula.

Replication of DNA

Replication of the DNA molecule has two phases, unwinding of the molecule and synthesis of complementary strands. The parent strands must first separate at the hydrogen bonds before synthesis of a new complementary chain can occur. Whether replication occurs in an orderly end-to-end ("zipper") fashion or in a patchy fashion along the course of the molecule has not been determined with certainty. Studies using radioactive thymidine, which becomes incorporated into the new DNA strands as synthesis proceeds, suggest that replication is patchy in type. Evidence has also been derived from studies of lampbrush chromosomes which indicate that interstitial unwinding and separation of the DNA helix is entirely possible.

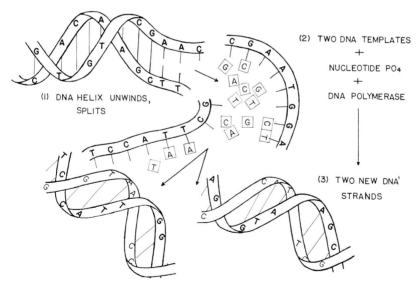

Figure 4. Replication of D.N.A. The two new D.N.A.' strands which form are identical with the original D.N.A. molecule.

The synthesis of complementary strands is a chemical process which is mediated by an enzyme, *DNA polymerase*. In the presence of adequate supplies of nucleotide phosphate and a DNA template (the original strand), a reaction occurs which may be summarized as

$$4^n \text{ nucleotide-PO}_4 \xrightarrow[\text{template DNA}]{\text{DNA polymerase}} \text{DNA}'$$

This reaction has been carried out *in vitro* by many investigators and, in all instances, the DNA′ produced has had a structure identical with that of the template DNA (or primer DNA) in the reaction system.

Thus, when replication is complete, two new helices have been formed, each of which contains one original (template) strand and one new strand. Each of the two new helices is chemically identical to the original helix from which it was derived. This type of reaction is called a semiconservative duplication. (In a conservative duplication, the original strands would remain united —in a dispersive duplication there would be fragmentation of the DNA strands.) This mechanism has much experimental support, particularly from isotope labelling techniques.

The Genetic Code

With the exception of some of the viruses (which use RNA) all organisms studied have DNA as the basic hereditary determiner. Since the major difference between the DNA of various species lies in the proportions of organic base carried, it is apparent that it is in the nucleotide base sequence that the information transport system of DNA resides. It is also a generally accepted fact that the mediation of all genetic information is through protein and enzyme synthesis. These proteins and enzymes, in turn, mediate development of the physical and chemical attributes of the individual.

Since proteins and enzymes are, for the most part, polymers of amino acids it is also apparent that the "genetic code" of the DNA molecule is concerned with the sequential arrangement of amino acids into functional protein molecules. Most elegant and elaborate studies of amino acid production by DNA and RNA templates have at last yielded considerable insight into the nature of the genetic code.

The bulk of these synthetic and natural template studies have been applied to bacterial systems. Some writers have urged caution in extrapolating the findings in bacterial systems directly to man and suggest that the code in bacteria is not necessarily equivalent to the code in mammalian cell systems. Although the ubiquity of the DNA hereditary determiners suggests that hereditary mechanisms in all organisms are essentially similar, it is well to bear in mind that present knowledge of the genetic code is knowledge of the bacterial code and *not necessarily* the human. Errors deriving from overenthusiastic extrapolation of experimental data are not unknown.

With the above reservation in mind, the following generalizations concerning the nature of the genetic code may be made:

It is a "triplet" code, each series of three bases coding an amino acid.

It is a non-overlapping code.

It is a "degenerate" code with some amino acids being coded by more than one triplet.

The code is read from a fixed starting point and the reading proceeds in an orderly rather than random fashion.

The code is punctuated by interspersed "nonsense" regions in which the nucleotide sequence codes no useful information.

These generalizations have not met with anything approaching unanimous scientific accord. They are, however, the most widely accepted generalities at present. The supportive evidence for them, and some alternatives, are explored below.

The Triplet Code

Since there are some twenty amino acids which must be coded, and the available code consists of four letters (bases), it is obvious that neither single bases nor base pairs provide sufficient combinations to encode all the amino acids. A three letter "word" code utilizing a four letter alphabet is capable of encoding sixty-four (4^3) different amino acids. The triplet code easily meets the test of numerical adequacy.

Another strong piece of evidence in favor of the three letter code word is derived from experiments in which one or more molecules of extraneous base are added to the end of a DNA or RNA molecule whose coding capability is known. It has been found that addition of one or two such extraneous molecules impairs the function of the DNA. However, addition of a third such extraneous base reactivates the DNA. This strongly suggests a reaction of the type:

U.C.G....U.C.G.. etc. → amino acid

U.C.G....U.C.G.. etc. + B → B.U.C....G.U.C.. etc. → no activity

U.C.G....U.C.G.. etc. + 2B → B.B.U....C.G.U.. etc. → no activity

U.C.G....U.C.G.. etc. + 3B → B.B.B....U.C.G.. etc. → amino acid

The Non-overlapping Code

The strongest argument in favor of the non-overlapping nature of the genetic code resides in the fact that alterations of a single base molecule in a DNA chain produce an alteration in only one of the amino acids of the peptide chain which is coded. If the code were an overlapping type, two, or even three of the amino acids should be altered. Schematically:

Non-overlapping—

   AmAcA   AmAcB

..C.*T*.A....C.G.T...   Replacement of T alters
                              only amino acid A

Overlapping—

   AmAcA   ⌐AmAcC

.C.T.*A*.G.C.G.T.   Alteration of A alters
   AmAcB   amino acids A, B and C

Other Alternatives

Other coding probabilities have been advanced from time to time. Though the evidence cited above most strongly favors a three letter code, it is equally applicable to codes of more than three letters. Such longer codes may also be of the overlapping type and still fulfill the criteria discussed provided that the code word is long enough that any overlap still leaves three "letters" between each overlap. A five letter code, for instance, may have a two-letter overlap and be indistinguishable from a three-letter code.

Non-random Reading of the Code

Experimental methods such as the terminal base additions, which provide evidence of the triplet nature of the code, also indicate that the code must be read from a fixed starting point, displacement of which makes reading impossible.

There is also evidence from some of the protein syntheses which occur in nature. The hemoglobin molecule, for instance, is synthesized in a linear fashion commencing with one terminal NH^2—group and ending with the terminal −COOH of the other end of the chain.

Not only are individual protein molecules constructed in an orderly fashion, but the entire chromosomal complex of genes (*genome*) appears to be decoded in an orderly fashion. Studies of E. *coli* phage T^3 have shown that distinguishable groups of RNA are synthesized at predictable times during the metabolic activity of this organism.

The code words which have been established, at least tentatively, for various amino acids are outlined in the table. In the words listed, only the letters present are indicated—the order of the letters in the words has not yet been established for any of the amino acids except in a preliminary manner. The technique of terminal addition of base to an RNA whose product is already known has suggested the order of letters for at least some of the amino acids. Poly-U RNA, for instance, codes polyphenylalanine. Addition of a terminal unit of A (adenosine) to poly-U RNA induces formation of one molecule of tyrosine which is attached to the end of the polyphenylalanine molecule which normally results. This indicates that the code sequence for tyrosine is AUU.

There is abundant evidence that the code words so far discovered, while not necessarily incorrect, almost certainly form an

TABLE I

GENETIC CODE FOR AMINO ACIDS*

Alanine	U C G	Leucine	U U C
Arginine	U C G	Lysine	U A A
Asparagine U U A or U A C		Methionine	U A G
Aspartic Acid	U A G	Phenylalanine	U U U
Cysteine	U U G	Proline	U C C
Glutamic Acid	U A G	Serine	U U C
Glutamine	U C G	Threonine	U C C
Glycine	U G G	Tryptophan	U G G
Histidine	U A C	Tyrosine	U U A
Isoleucine	U U A	Valine	U U G

U—uracil   C—cytosine   A—adenine   G—guanine

*Only the letters present have been determined—their *order* is not known.

*After: Speyer, J. F., *et al.*: *Proc. Nat. Acad. Sci.*, *48*:441-448, 1962.)

incomplete dictionary. Each of the code words so far discovered contains at least one molecule of uracil. If a code word is devised for a protein whose amino acid sequence is known, this RNA word will contain about fifty percent uracil. This proportion of uracil is not found in any of the RNA which occurs in nature. There are a number of possible explanations. Most pertinent is the fact that the analytic techniques currently in use are incapable of detecting non-U words. It is most probable that the code is a great deal more degenerate than it now appears and that a large number of non-U words have yet to be discovered. An alternative explanation suggests that U- words are confined to the structural subgenes and that non-U words are confined to operator or regulator subgene loci (see "Operon," below). The latter seems a less probable explanation.

Ribonucleic Acid (RNA)

The knowledge that DNA carries the genetic information within the cell and that it is the principal mediator of cell activity, while very significant, is obviously not the whole story. Regardless of the functional state of the cell, the protein content of the nucleus remains relatively unchanging. If protein is not synthesized in the nucleus, some mechanism must exist by which the information of the nuclear DNA is transported to the site of protein synthesis in the cytoplasm. The search for the information transfer mechanism drew the attention of biological chemists to another fascinating group of compounds, the ribonucleic acids.

Ribonucleic acid has been recognized almost as long as has DNA. Originally, since its concentrations seemed highest in plants (yeast), it was regarded as the plant counterpart of DNA. This has, of course, been disproved long since. Its chemical structure is very similar to that of DNA, having only a minor alteration in the sugar component (ribose instead of deoxyribose) and in the complement of its bases (thymine of DNA is replaced by uracil in RNA). More recently, a helical molecular structure has been suggested similar to that of DNA.

Three general types of RNA have been recognized—ribosome RNA, messenger RNA and transfer RNA. These will be described individually.

Messenger RNA

Though messenger RNA was the last to be discovered, it is more appropriate to describe this type first. Messenger RNA was brought to the attention of investigators by its instability. Of the nucleoproteins, messenger RNA is by far the most labile and is the only type which is found in both the nucleus and the cytoplasm in significant concentrations (other RNA is principally cytoplasmic). Messenger RNA functions as the "carrier" of genetic information from nuclear DNA to the cytoplasm.

Messenger RNA is a nucleic acid with a molecular weight of approximately 3×10^5 and is synthesized in the nucleus. In the presence of a DNA template (or primer) molecule, an adequate supply of nucleotide and a synthesizing enzyme, an RNA molecule is formed which exactly recapitulates the base sequence of the DNA template. In RNA, however, each molecule of thymine in the DNA template is represented by a molecule of uracil.

Ribosome RNA

Ribosomes are intracytoplasmic nucleoprotein particles which are the principal site of protein synthesis in the cell. Ribosome RNA has a structure and a replication mechanism similar to that of DNA. In the presence of template RNA, adequate nucleotide supply and RNA polymerase, new ribosomal RNA is elaborated which recapitulates the structure of the template molecule.

Ultracentrifugal studies of ribosome RNA show that two distinct classes of this compound exist—"heavy" ribosome RNA (100 S) and "light" ribosome RNA (70 S). Recent research has correlated this weight variation with differences in functional activity. It is currently thought that "heavy" ribosome RNA is metabolically active and that its increased weight reflects binding of messenger RNA to the ribosome molecule.

Ribosome RNA thus serves two functions in the cytoplasm. It serves as a point of attachment for the messenger RNA molecule. As a consequence, it is the site of cytoplasmic protein synthesis. With the termination of protein synthesis, messenger RNA is released and ribosome RNA reverts to its "light" form.

Transfer RNA

A third type of RNA is built up in the cytoplasm from about ninety nucleotide units and has a specific terminal structure of

G - - - - - - C.C.A. The other bases in the molecule form a sequence
which has a specific affinity for one of the amino acids. At least
one individual type of transfer RNA exists for each of the twenty
or so amino acids.

Transfer RNA (soluble RNA or s-RNA) is thought to have
the configuration of an elongated "U" with hydrogen bonding
between the bases on the limbs of the U. Some of the bases, at
the bend of the U, have no partners to bond with and are thought
to be the bases which attach to the specific amino acid. Transfer
RNA carries amino acids to the ribosome-messenger RNA complex where the amino acids become oriented in accordance with
the information coded by the messenger RNA molecule.

The Transfer of Genetic Information

The transfer of genetic information from nucleus to cytoplasm
and the synthesis of protein employ all of the classes of DNA
and RNA alluded to. The sequence of intracellular protein synthesis has been fairly well determined and commences with
unwinding of the DNA helix and separation of its strands. Messenger RNA molecules are formed (using the unwound and
separated DNA strands as templates) and diffuse into the cytoplasm.

In the cytoplasm, messenger RNA molecules attach themselves
to ribosomes. Multiple units of transfer RNA, one for each amino
acid, transport amino acids to the ribosomes where the amino
acids become aligned along the messenger RNA molecule in
accordance with the sequence coded by the nucleotide base
sequence of the RNA molecule. Upon completion of protein
synthesis, the messenger RNA-protein complex is released from
the ribosome, the messenger RNA breaks down and the newly
synthesized protein is released to assume its function in the cell.

The striking similarities between the synthesis of RNA and the
synthesis of DNA pose an interesting problem, the solution to
which has been only imperfectly elucidated. What mechanism
determines which synthesis takes precedence (DNA synthesis or
RNA synthesis) when the nuclear template DNA unwinds and
separates? There must be constant competition between DNA and
RNA synthesis when the DNA template is formed. The outcome

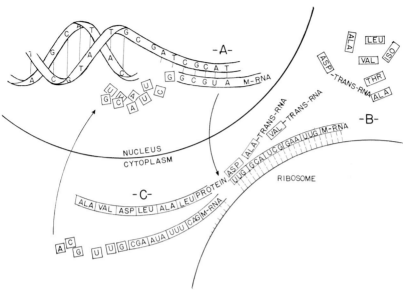

Figure 5. Transfer of Genetic Information. (*A*) Nuclear D.N.A. unwinds and splits to form templates upon which messenger R.N.A. (M-RNA) forms. (*B*) M-RNA becomes attached to a ribosome and amino acids, transported by transfer R.N.A., become aligned in accordance with the "code" of the M-RNA. (*C*) When protein synthesis is completed, M-RNA breaks down and its constituent bases become available for synthesis of new M-RNA molecules. (Modified from Siminovitch, L.: *Canad. M.A.J.*, *58*:1137-1142, 1962.)

of this competition will determine whether the cell will continue its metabolic activity (RNA synthesis) or will divide (DNA synthesis). Superficial insights into this mechanism have been gained with elucidation of the "repressor" concept (*vide infra*).

"DNA makes RNA and RNA makes protein."

THE NATURE OF THE GENE

The elegant research which has broadened scientific knowledge of the functional interdependence of DNA and RNA has provided increasingly strong evidence supporting the validity of the gene concept of inheritance. The outcome of such research has demanded increasing sophistication in the concept of gene structure and gene function but the basic concept, "one gene—one enzyme," remains inherently accurate.

Some general features of gene activity might be profitably explored at this point. In sexually reproducing organisms chromosomes occur in identical pairs, one member of each pair derived from the ovum (maternal) and one from the sperm (paternal). The paired chromosomes are not only physically identical but are, to a certain extent, chemically identical in that they bear the same genes at the same positions.

The paired genes may be identical both chemically and functionally and an individual carrying such an identical gene pair is *homozygous* in respect to that gene. If a mutation has occurred at some point in the evolution of the gene under consideration, the members of a gene pair carried by an individual may be structurally and functionally dissimilar and the individual is *heterozygous*. Genes which occupy the same position (*locus*) on paired chromosomes, and which regulate the same class of reactions, but which are functional variants are called *alleles* (or *allelomorphs*). There are a number of human gene loci in which evolution has led to the development of many variants (alleles)—one excellent example is the hemoglobin locus.

The interaction of the paired genes in the genetic complement is variable. In the homozygous individual, the combined activity of the paired identical genes may be additive or may not exceed the effect of a single gene acting alone. In the latter instance, one member of the gene pair may undergo preferential inactivation or the activity of the pair may be governed by the concentration of metabolite produced by the locus (via the regulator site).

In the heterozygous individual, each of the dissimilar genes may obtain independent expression (as in the human blood groups), or one of the pair may be expressed and the other suppressed. In the latter instance, the member of the heterozygous pair which is expressed is the *dominant* allele, the suppressed member the *recessive* allele.

In addition to variability in the expression of genes, there are demonstrable differences in the manner in which gene activity is mediated. Although the transfer of DNA coded genetic information to the cytoplasm is essential in initiating gene action, there are some genetically controlled reactions which can continue more or less autonomously once they have been initiated. The autonomous existence of a genetically controlled reaction has been demonstrated using the effects of Actinomycin D, which inhibits RNA messenger transfer. One easily demonstrable naturally occurring autonomy of this nature is the synthesis of hemoglobin (gene initiated and directed) by anuclear reticulocytes.

Much of the recent modification of the concept of gene action derives from the fact that early geneticists were concerned only with the physical manifestations of gene action. Physical characters mediated by gene action are now known to be dependent upon some underlying chemical reaction at the cell level. The magnitude of the physical alterations produced by alterations (mutations) in genes depends upon the ubiquity of the chemical reaction affected by the mutations.

In contemporary terms, a gene may be defined as "a finite section of a chromosome which contains the information necessary to control a particular chemical reaction or class of reactions." Estimates have been made of the physical length of genes in some of the bacteria and viruses. The phosphatase locus of *E. coli*, for instance, is thought to contain some two thousand nucleotide pairs and to measure about 0.68 microns. The limits of the gene are fairly sharply defined. On a similar basis, the total gene complement of one *E. coli* virus (the T_2 phage) has been estimated to be one hundred. Only thirty active loci have been identified in this phage, the remainder of the phage DNA presumably being occupied by "nonsense" punctuation areas.

The human chromosome complement is estimated to contain some 10^{10} nucleotide pairs or, using the same length calculated for the *E. coli* phosphatase locus, about 5×10^6 individual genes. This should provide a sufficient number of loci to encode even the very complex biochemical complement of this species.

Until fairly recently, it has been assumed that the gene represented the smallest indivisible unit of inheritance. This view has been considerably revised. Studies of one viral locus (γII of T-phage) indicate that this locus is divisible into some four hundred detectable genetic subunits. Similar intragene structure has been demonstrated by changes in irradiated *Drosophila*. All of these "subgenes" (*sites* or *cistrons*) are concerned with the same chemical reaction or class of reactions but each is capable of modifying the

INDUCIBLE-

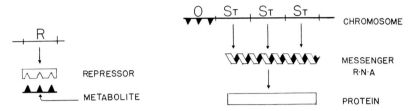

REPRESSIBLE-

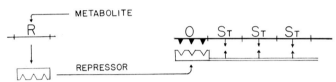

Figure 6. The Operon. In an inducible (*above*) system, a small molecule metabolite blocks the repressor substance produced by the regulator site (R) and permits function of the operator (O) and structural (ST) sites. In a repressible system (*below*), the metabolite activates the regulator site and therefore inactivates the operator and structural sites. (Modified from Jacob, F., and Monod, J.: *J. Molec. Biol.*, *3:*318, 1961.)

expression of the gene as a whole. Evidence so far accumulated indicates that each of these "subgenes" has a physical length approximately equivalent to that of three nucleotide bases.

The Operon

Discovery of the multiple site structure of the gene opened the way for the development of the *operon* concept of gene structure as recently proposed by Jacob and Monod. According to their concept, each gene locus is composed of a series of *structural* subgenes (sites) which are concerned with the construction of the protein controlled by the locus. Adjacent to the structural sites, and an inherent part of the gene locus, is an "*operator*" site whose integrity is essential to the function of the entire locus. A third site, the "*regulator*" site, may or may not be situated within the gene locus, but is thought to produce a "suppressor" substance, which, by becoming fixed at the operator site, can inactivate both the operator and the structural sites in the locus.

Operator sites are active only when they lie on the same chromosome and within the gene locus which they affect (*cis* position). Regulator sites, on the other hand, may funtion even when they are on different chromosomes than the locus which they affect (*trans* position). Two different systems may affect the structural sites in the gene locus.

"*Repressible*" systems—a small molecule metabolite which is produced by the structural sites may activate the regulator locus, and in consequence, inactivate the structural sites themselves.

"*Inducible*" systems—small molecule metabolites combine with the suppressor substance elaborated by the regulator site and inactivate it. Thus, the operator site is freed from the inhibitory control of the suppressor and activates the structural sites in the locus.

This complex of operator, structural and regulator sites is inclusively referred to as an *operon*. The operon concept of gene action does much to explain the complex "feedback" mechanisms which must necessarily exist to maintain the concentration of metabolites within the very narrow ranges which occur in nature.

The mechanisms, which are portrayed very diagrammatically in the figure, have their counterparts in human genetic mechanisms. The operon concept has been applied particularly to the human hemoglobins and haptoglobulins. Studies of hemoglobin synthesis, for instance, provide very good evidence that marked functional alterations of the molecule follow alterations of a single amino acid in the globin portion of the molecule. This, according to present knowledge, reflects alteration of a single base in one triplet of the DNA chain responsible for hemoglobin synthesis. In addition, studies of human hemoglobin have revealed inherited hemoglobin abnormalities which are presumably a consequence of disordered function of the operator site within the hemoglobin locus. In this type of defect, a structurally normal hemoglobin variant (fetal hemoglobin) is produced in abnormal quantities.

Histones

Following the discovery that DNA is the carrier of genetic information, the popularity of the protein components of chromosomes as research objects declined precipitously. Until recently, the histones have suffered much the same ignominy which was the lot of DNA in the past. There is, however, a recent resurgence of interest in these protein components of chromosomes.

Though much of the material relating to the function of histones in recent literature is speculative in type, some interesting functions have been proposed for these proteins. One such is a suggestion that the regulator site may inhibit the operator site of the operon through the mediation of a histone suppressor. The ability of histone to inhibit DNA-dependent RNA synthesis has been demonstrated experimentally. It has also been suggested that it is the incorporation of histone into a chromosome which is responsible for heterochromatin formation.

A demonstrable synchrony between histone synthesis and DNA synthesis is strong evidence that some functional interrelationship exists. There is also difference in the function of histones which can be correlated with their chemical structure. One class of histones (lysine rich) apparently does not have the same inhibitory effect on RNA synthesis that another class (arginine rich) does. Loss of arginine-rich histone from cells has been implicated in the etiology of neoplasia (see Chapter XIV).

Heterochromatin

Studies made of the chemical structure of chromosomes have yielded little evidence that any marked difference exists between the chemical structure of heterochromatin and that of euchromatin. Some authors have described a higher concentration of A-T linkages in heterochromatin, however most well recognized differences are physical rather than chemical. Heterochromatic portions of the chromosome show much tighter spiralization of the chromonema (not the DNA helix). DNA replication is also delayed in heterochromatic areas.

Heterochromatinization is a more or less permanent feature of some portions of the chromosome. In other areas, it is an induced state which, apparently, reflects inactivation of the DNA in that area. This is supported by investigations which indicate that histone concentration is higher in heterochromatic than in euchromatic areas. The ability of histone to inactivate RNA synthesis has already been commented upon.

In summary, it seems that heterochromatinization is a physical reflection of a genetically controlled inactivation system. The most striking instance of heterochromatinization is that which affects the X chromosome in mammalian females (see Chapter IV).

Mutations

A mutation is an heredity change in a gene. In general, the term is becoming restricted to chemical alterations and minute structural alterations (deletions, unequal crossing over, etc.) which are intragenic and which affect only a few sites within the gene locus.

Mutations may be either spontaneous or induced, the former being comparatively uncommon. The incidence of mutation may be increased by physical agents (X-ray, ultraviolet light) or by specific chemicals which either replace (e.g., 5-bromuracil) or alter (e.g., nitrous acid) bases in the DNA molecule.

Chemical alterations which make the code unreadable and thus render the entire locus functionally imperfect or totally nonfunctional have been categorized as "nonsense" types (base pair substitutions) or "gibberish" types (addition or loss of base which shift the starting point for reading the code). Such a distinction is not mere semantic frivolity for there is evidence that the former (base pair substitution) type may be more susceptible to reversal than the latter. *Suppressor* mutations, which overcome alterations produced by a previous mutation, are known to occur in bacteria.

Paramutation

The term "paramutation" has been coined to express alterations of gene activity in one chromosome as a consequence of the activity of an allele (gene partner in the chromosome pair) on the homologous chromosome of the pair. The allele concerned will effect a genetic change in one hundred percent of the cases in which such genes are present as alleles and is a predictable alteration of genetic expression.

Cell Differentiation

One fascinating problem in molecular biology whose solution is apparent only in most general terms is the phenomenon of cell (and, by inference, chromosome) differentiation. What facts account for the apparent anomaly of genetically identical nuclei performing widely varying functions in the mature organism? One possibility, not seriously entertained, is that the concept of genetically identical nuclei is itself erroneous. Should this be true, vast revision of the whole concept of heredity will be necessary.

Less disturbing explanations for the loss of functional uniformity of nuclei can be advanced. That there is a loss of uniformity has been shown repeatedly by nuclear transplantation experiments in which nuclei from differentiated cells are transplanted to embryonic cells. Such transplanted nuclei are functionally incompetent in the embryonic cell and are incapable of directing maturation of the embryonic cell (transplanted embryonic nuclei are functionally competent).

The mechanics of chromosome and cell differentiation probably depend upon the selective inactivation of various chromosome loci (by histone?) which are present in the totipotent embryonic nuclei. Such inactivation is thought to be initiated by the very subtle differences in oxygen tension, electrolyte and metabolic concentration and even pressure and temperature which exist between adjacent cells in a multicellular embryo.

Objective evidence of chromosome differentiation is available in studies of polytene chromosomes. These very large chromosomes bear characteristic "puffed" areas (Balbiani rings) at which chromosome metabolic activity is highest. The location of Balbiani rings in the chromosome varies in chromosomes derived from the nuclei of different tissues (e.g., salivary gland *vs.* intestinal). This at least suggests that different portions of the chromosome are functional in different body cells from the same organism.

Such considerations are not wholly philosophical, as they might at first appear. An extension of this line of speculative reasoning has, for instance, introduced a new concept of cell ageing which may be pertinent to carcinogenesis. The classic concept of the "old" cell is one which has remained for months or years without dividing. A newer concept, however, bases the age of the cell upon the number of generations which separate it from the unicellular zygote. By this criterion, rapidly dividing cells such as lymphocytes, which are separated from the zygote by thousands of generations in some instances, are mitotically "older" than the relatively stable neuron. Do the individually inconsequential errors which occur in mitosis have a cumulative effect from generation to generation which may ultimately terminate in carcinoma or in cell death (somatic ageing)? The concept is, to say the least, a most intriguing one.

CHAPTER II

NORMAL CELL DIVISION

THE complex mechanisms of cell division which are visible microscopically have as their sole purpose the distribution of genetic material in equal amounts to a new generation of cells. Cell division actually commences as a chemical phenomenon in the interphase ("resting") cell nucleus with the replication of the DNA helices within the chromosomes. The more dramatic physical changes of cell division apportion these duplicated DNA strands equally to two new cells.

In sexually reproducing organisms, the mechanism of cell division depends upon the type of cell which is to be produced. Production of two new body (*somatic*) cells within the same organism is accomplished by *mitosis*. If, however, cell division has as its ultimate objective the production of an entirely new organism, *gametes* are derived from *germ cells* by *meiosis*.

Before discussing the actual mechanisms of mitosis and meiosis, there are several terms which should be defined. The suffix -*ploidy* (or -*ploid*) refers, in general, to alterations in the number of *sets* of chromosomes carried by a cell. In man, the normal chromosome complement in body cells (except gametes) is twenty-three pairs. Cells bearing a single set of twenty-three chromosomes, the normal complement of *gametes* (ova or spermatozoa), are *haploid* (n). Somatic cells, with forty-six chromosomes, are *diploid*. Aberrant cells may have three (*triploid*), four (*tetraploid*) or even more (*polyploid*) sets of chromosomes.

Cells which bear a normal number of chromosomes are *euploid*, and cells which have an abnormal number of chromosomes are *aneuploid*. Numerical variations affecting individual chromosomes are designated by the suffix -*somy*. A somatic cell bearing a single

30

X chromosome, for example, shows *monosomy-X*. Aneuploid cells may bear three (*trisomy*) or even more (*polysomy*) identical chromosomes instead of the normal pair. Triploidy and other forms of polyploidy are types of aneuploidy affecting entire chromosome sets.

MITOSIS

Mitosis, sometimes referred to as "cleavage," produces two new (daughter) cells whose chromosome complement is numerically, physically and chemically identical with that of the parent somatic cell. Briefly stated, the chromosomes of the parent cell divide longitudinally and one half of each parent cell chromosome is distributed to a daughter cell. Since each parent cell contains a set of paired homologous chromosomes (2n), each daughter cell derived by mitotic division will also be diploid.

Mitosis is arbitrarily divided into five phases (interphase, prophase, metaphase, anaphase and telophase) which merge almost imperceptibly one with another.

Interphase

Almost all of the nuclei seen microscopically in tissue sections are in interphase (or so-called "resting" phase). The appellation "resting" phase is one of the most singularly inappropriate terms in modern biology and should be discarded. Interphase nuclei, far from "resting," are very active indeed—either governing cell metabolism or, in the mitotic cycle, replicating the DNA helix preparatory to cell division.

Two types of interphase nuclei may be distinguished—those which are incapable of further division such as neurons, and those which are merely going about their metabolic business until mitosis occurs. The former type show no periodic variation in nuclear DNA content. The latter, however, begin to show a progressive increase in DNA content prior to dividing and, immediately prior to prophase, have doubled their normal DNA content.

Accompanying the increase in DNA content, there is measurable enlargement of most nuclei prior to cell division. Immediately prior to prophase, premitotic nuclei are temporarily tetraploid

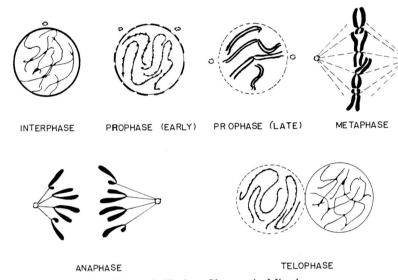

INTERPHASE   PROPHASE (EARLY)   PR OPHASE (LATE)   METAPHASE

ANAPHASE   TELOPHASE

Figure 7. Nuclear Changes in Mitosis.

(4n) in respect to their DNA content. This has led to some confusion in assessing the chromosomal status of rapidly dividing tissues (most particularly tumors) by indirect DNA assay methods. Using such methods, it is difficult to distinguish abnormal permanently tetraploid nuclei from premitotic nuclei.

Prophase

Visible mitosis begins with condensation of the dispersed nuclear chromatin of the interphase cell into recognizable elongated thread-like chromosomes. There is some question as to whether the chromonemal strands of early prophase are optically single or double. There is no question that replication of the DNA helices has been completed prior to prophase (during the S-period of interphase) and is, in fact, followed by a short two to three hour period of inactivity (G- period) prior to the onset of visible prophase.

Whether or not the chromosomes in early prophase are optically single or double, the string-of-beads configuration of chromomeres strung along the string-like chromonemata is best seen in early prophase. As prophase progresses, the chromonemata begin to form increasingly tight spirals and become progressively more condensed. By late prophase, the longitudinal division of the chromosomes into paired chromatids united at a centromere can be distinguished. At this point, the chromosomes resemble those of the metaphase with the exception that maximal spiralization has not yet been attained and the chromosomes have "fuzzy" and indistinct outlines. The staining differences between euchromatin and heterochromatin are most apparent from mid to late prophase.

Concomitant with these changes in the nuclear chromatin, changes are also occurring in other parts of the cell. During prophase, lysis of the nuclear membrane commences and the membrane becomes progressively less distinct as prophase continues. Lysis is complete, or nearly so, by the onset of metaphase and the chromosomes lie free in the cytoplasm of the cell.

Also during prophase, a cytoplasmic structure, the *centrosome*, splits and each half of the centrosome migrates to one or other pole of the cell. The centrosome cannot always be seen microscopically using ordinary methods. The centrosome, after splitting and moving to the cell poles, forms the origin and the point of attachment of the spindle body.

The distinction between late prophase and early metaphase is not at all sharp and, in fact, has been designated *prometaphase* by several authors. During this interval, the chromosomes arrange themselves in a disc in the center of the cell. This disc of chromosomes, all lying in the same plane, is the *equatorial plate*. It is generally stated that the chromosomes are arranged in a "random" fashion at the equatorial plate in a mitotic cell. Although the chromosomes are certainly not arranged in pairs, as they are in the meiotic equatorial plate, their arrangement does not seem to be entirely disordered.

The chromosomes in the equatorial plate tend to arrange themselves with the largest members at the periphery of the disc and the smaller members in the center. In addition, there is a measurable tendency for homologous chromosomes to lie closer to one another than to other chromosomes. Another form of association seen in the equatorial plate occurs between the satellited chromosomes which tend to associate with one another at their satellited ends. It is not at all unlikely that further careful observations of the mitotic equatorial plate will reveal a considerably more ordered arrangement than has been suspected to the present.

Metaphase

During metaphase, chromonemal spiralization reaches its maximum and the chromosomes and chromatids assume well defined, sharp outlines. If it has not already done so, the nuclear membrane becomes completely lysed in metaphase. The formation of the spindle apparatus is completed in metaphase. The spindle is a multithreaded, sticky, tenacious structure which is almost entirely protein in nature. One end of each of the threads of the spindle is attached to the centromeric region of a chromosome and the other to the centrosome. Some of the smaller chromosomes may be completely enveloped by the threads of the spindle.

The mechanics of spindle formation are poorly understood. Its formation appears to be the joint responsibility of both the centromeric portions of the chromosomes and of the centrosome. The spindle body, more than any other structure in the cell, has impaired investigation of the human chromosome complement. When cells with an intact spindle are squashed, there is a tangling and piling of chromosomes which makes individual chromosomes almost impossible to sort out. Colchicine acts as a spindle poison and by impairing spindle formation, arrests cell division in the metaphase (C-mitosis) and also makes chromosome dispersion much easier. Rediscovery of this property of colchicine has played a very prominent role in the development of satisfactory human cytogenic techniques.

Anaphase

The onset of anaphase is much more sharply defined than is the onset of metaphase. Anaphase begins with the splitting of the centromeres and separation of the chromatids. With severance of this final point of union between them, the chromatids migrate rapidly to opposite poles of the cell. Division of the centromere and the migration of the chromatids to the cell poles is referred to collectively as *disjunction*. Failure of this mitotic mechanism is responsible for the numerical variations which are encountered in chromosomal *mosaicism* (*q.v.*).

Telophase

Telophase has been aptly described as "reverse prophase," a term which neatly summarizes the changes which occur in the cell. When migration of the chromatids to the poles of the cell is complete, the nuclear membrane begins to re-form and the chromatids from this point function as new chromosomes. The chromosomes elongate, become very tenuous and are soon dispersed through a newly formed nucleus as nuclear chromatin.

Formation of the new nuclear membranes around the chromosome groups at each pole of the cell produces a temporarily binucleate cell. Two new cells are formed when a new cell wall develops between the two new nuclei.

The salient features of a mitotic cell division are outlined in the accompanying diagram.

MEIOSIS

The production of gametes requires a mechanism of considerably greater complexity than is necessary for the division of somatic cells. In order for the chromosome number to remain stable from generation to generation while each parent contributes equally to the chromosomal complement of the new individual, gametes must carry a single set of unpaired chromosomes, i.e., they must be haploid.

A complete meiotic cell division embraces two successive cell divisions (called *meiosis I* and *meiosis II* for convenience) and yields four haploid gametes, either ova or spermatozoa, from each diploid germ cell. Fertilization of a haploid ovum by a haploid spermatozoon thus produces a new diploid one-celled individual (*zygote*) which develops further by sucessive mitoses.

The two successive meiotic divisions are separated by a short period of inactivity (*interkinesis*) and each has four stages which are similar to those of a mitotic cell division. Prophase I (first meiotic prophase) is a very long phase in which a number of highly significant events occur. Because of its duration and complexity, prophase I is itself divided into five separate stages. A complete meiotic division thus has the following phases:

Meiosis I— Prophase I
Leptotene
Zygotene
Pachytene
Diplotene
Diakinesis
Metaphase I
Anaphase I
Telophase I
Interkinesis
Meiosis II— Prophase II
Metaphase II
Anaphase II
Telophase II

In the subsequent description of meiosis, only the chromosomal changes will be emphasized. As in mitosis, lysis of nuclear membranes, centrosome splitting and spindle formation proceed concomitant with the chromosomal changes. Subsequent reference to these associated phenomena will be less exhaustive than in the description of mitosis. This brevity in no way implies a lesser importance of these phenomena in the meiotic cycle.

First Meiotic Division (Meiosis I)

The first meiotic division is referred to as a *reductional* division. In the diploid cells of any organism, one of the chromosomes in each pair is of maternal and the other of paternal origin. The first meiotic division separates the maternal member of the pair from the paternal member, and distributes them to haploid daughter cells. The distribution is random and the daughter cells do not receive maternal or paternal chromosomes preferentially.

Prophase I

As previously noted, prophase I is a very long and a comparatively intricate stage of meiosis. It embraces mechanisms which are of very great significance in the hereditary mechanism. A thorough knowledge of the mechanisms of meiosis is imperative to the understanding of those chromosomal abnormalities which are a consequence of perversions of this mechanism.

Leptotene Stage

The leptotene stage of prophase I commences with condensation of the dispersed nuclear chromatin of the diploid interphase germ cell nucleus into recognizable strands. These strands, the chromonemata, are thin, tangled and bear many chromomeres. Whether or not optically visible separation into individual chromatids is detectable at this earliest stage is a subject of considerable debate.

Not infrequently, the ends of the threadlike chromosomes are concentrated at some point on the periphery of the nucleus, near the nuclear membrane. This configuration of looped strands radiating from a more or less common point is known as a "bouquet." The concentration of chromosome ends at a common area of the nucleus represents a non-specific type of attraction between the heterochromatic end segments of the chromosomes.

Zygotene Stage

It is at this stage of prophase I that the first of many very striking differences between mitosis and meiosis is noted. Though nuclear appearance changes little in this stage, the members of each chromosome pair arrange themselves in very close apposition with their homologues. This pairing, *synapsis,* affects the homologues in each pair throughout their entire length and seems to be the result of a specific attraction which exists between them.

Synapsis occurs rather slowly and commences at the ends of the chromosomes (which are close together in the "bouquet" to start with). This pairing is exquisitely precise. Studies on the inheritance patterns of proteins whose chemical composition is well known (particularly hemoglobin and haptoglobulin) show that not only do specific gene loci lie in apposition, but pairing extends at least to the subgene and most probably to the nucleotide level.

Completion of synapsis marks the end of the zygotene stage. The chromosome pairs which result from synapsis are called *bivalents.*

Pachytene Stage

During the pachytene stage of prophase I, the members of the bivalent become shorter and plumper and assume smoother outlines as spiralization of the chromonemata continues. The members of the bivalent lie in very close apposition, sometimes in direct physical contact with one another. During this stage, longitudinal splitting of the chromosomes into chromatids united at a centromere becomes apparent. The bivalent is thus converted into a figure composed of four chromatids, each pair of which is united by a centromere, lying in close apposition. The figure at this stage is called a *tetrad*.

Diplotene Stage

With the splitting of the chromosomes into their component chromatids, the mutually attractive force which binds the chromosome pairs through the early stages of prophase I is lost and is superseded by active repulsion between the chromosomes in each pair. There is active separation of the members of each chromosome pair (this occurs before attachment of the spindle apparatus and must, therefore, represent some active repulsive force).

The chromosome pairs, however, remain bound together at points of contact between their chromatids. These points of contact are *chiasmata* and each of these is assumed to be the site of an actual physical exchange of chromosomal genetic material between the members of each pair. This inter-chromosomal exchange of hereditary material is called *crossing-over*. Its genetic implications are more fully explored in Chapter III. No similar phenomenon has ever been proven to occur during mitosis.

There is a tendency for chiasmata to form at fairly predictable points within each chromosome pair—usually at a euchromatin-heterochromatin junction. The number of chiasmata which form in any given tetrad is a function of chromosome length. In man, the longest of the autosomal bivalents (studied during spermatogenesis) may contain as many as five chiasmata. In the total human complement, about sixty chiasmata can usually be seen.

The behavior of the non-homologous X and Y sex chromosomes of the human male differs significantly from that of other chromosome pairs during synapsis. In general, non-homologous sex chromosomes show end-to-end association rather than intimate side-by-side pairing, and there is little convincing evidence that chiasmata form between the X and Y chromosomes. The peculiarities of meiosis in ova (*vide infra*) make the incidence of chiasma formation between the paired X chromosomes of the female difficult to assess, though chiasma formation undoubtedly occurs.

The number of chiasmata formed, while largely a function of chromosome length, also appears to be under genetic control. Inbreeding in certain plants (*e.g. Delphinium*) has produced populations in whom both increased and decreased chiasma frequency has been noted. The total number of chiasmata in the total chromosome complement appears to be fairly constant and a decrease in chiasma frequency in one bivalent is associated with a compensatory increase in the number of chiasmata in the other bivalents of the complement.

The minimal physical distance between chiasmata is mechanically restricted by the stiffness of the chromatids. This minimal distance between chiasmata is called the *interference distance*. There also appears to be a similar minimum to the distance which the first chiasma may have from the centromere. This is the *differential distance*. These "irreducible" minima can be altered by physical agents of one kind or another. What role this type of alteration has in the induction of chromosomal defects by physical agents has not yet been established.

The amazing precision with which pairing occurs between homologues has been indicated in some of the studies on the inheritance patterns of the human haptoglobulins. Crossing over may occur within gene loci (*i.e.*, at the subgene level), but when it does, it usually occurs with such exquisite precision that there is no alteration in the length of the amino acid chain produced. Defects in the pairing mechanism which alter the length of the amino acid chains by as little as one amino acid may produce profound alterations in the function of the affected protein. The rarity of such defects indicates that normal synapsis and crossing-over are accurate not only in aligning genes and subgenes but are accurate even to the nucleotide level.

The phenomenon of crossing-over leads to some semantic complications. If one adheres to the definition of a reductional division as one in which maternal and paternal chromosomal material becomes separated, then crossing-over has some interesting sequelae. Since a portion of a maternal chromosome becomes attached to its paternal homologue and vice versa, the first meiotic division is reductional only for that portion of the chromosome pair in which

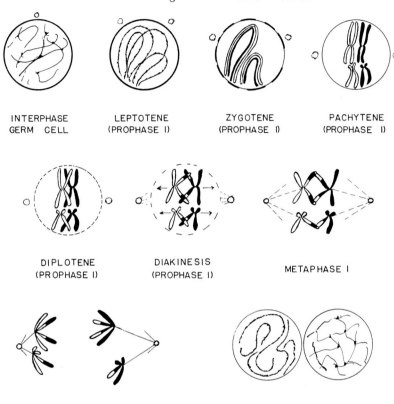

Figure 8. Nuclear Changes in Meiosis - Meiosis I. Two homologous pairs of chromosomes are depicted. The maternally derived member of each pair is shown in white, the paternally derived member in black (see discussion in text).

crossing-over has not occurred. Separation of the crossover segments does not occur until the chromatids separate in the second meiotic division which, by this definition, becomes the reductional division for the crossover segments.

Diakinesis Stage

The final stage of first meiotic prophase is marked by further separation of the members of the chromosome pair. As the pairs move farther and farther apart, the chiasmata "slide" along the chromatids until they approach the end of the chromosome arms. This *terminalization* of the chiasmata marks the end of the first meiotic prophase.

As these complex chromosomal activities are occurring, the ancillary mechanisms of prophase occur much as they do in a mitotic prophase. The nuclear membrane lyses and the spindle body begins to form. As in mitosis, the meiotic chromosomes arrange themselves at the equatorial plate. At this point another of the many differences between the two forms of cell division is noted. In mitosis, the centromere of each chromosome lies in the plane of the equatorial plate. In meiosis, however, the chromosomes are in pairs and the centromere of one member of the chromosome pair lies above the plane of the equatorial plate and the other below it.

Metaphase I

The mechanisms of the remainder of the first meiotic division are much the same as those of the corresponding phases of mitosis. In metaphase I, the chromosomal outlines attain maximum clarity, the spindle becomes completely organized and the centromeres become attached to it. The attachment of spindle threads to the centromeres varies from that of mitosis. In mitosis, a strand of the spindle extends from both centrosomes to each centromere i.e., the centromeres have a bipolar attachment. In first meiotic division, however, the centromeres have a unipolar attachment, with a single spindle strand extending from the centromere to the nearest centrosome.

Anaphase I

In this phase of first meiotic division, another of the differences between meiosis and mitosis is apparent; there is no division of the centromere during anaphase I. Following contraction of the spindle, since the centromeres of each chromosome remain unsplit, *whole chromosomes* (composed of two chromatids and a centromere) are drawn to the cell pole (*first meiotic disjunction*). Thus, the maternal and paternal members of each chromosome pair are distributed to opposite poles of the cell, earning meiosis I its designation as a reductional division. There is no tendency for maternal and paternal chromosomes to accumulate at a specific cell pole. The distribution of chromosomes to the cell poles is entirely random.

Telophase

In the final phase of first meiotic division, the chromosomes complete their migration to the poles of the cell, a new nuclear membrane forms and the chromosomal material becomes dispersed through the newly formed nucleus as nuclear chromatin. The two new nuclei, each of which contains a half-set of chromosomes, become separated by a newly developing cell wall and two separate *haploid* daughter cells are thus formed.

Second Meiotic Division (Meiosis II)

After a brief (sometimes nonexistent) resting phase or *interkinesis,* each of the haploid daughter cells of the first meiotic division again divides. The phases of the second meiotic division, the *equational* division, are similar in most respects to those of mitosis. Each of the unpaired chromosomes of the daughter cells splits at its centromere. The separated chromatids migrate to opposite poles of the cell and become enclosed by a new nuclear membrane.

Prophase II

The nuclear chromatin of the interkinetic nucleus once again condenses to form discrete *unpaired* chromosomes. Each of these exhibits a longitudinal division into two chromatids which remain united at the centromere.

Metaphase II

A new spindle forms and becomes attached to the chromosomes at the centromeric region. The attachment in this instance is bipolar, with one strand of the spindle extending from the centromere to each pole of the cell.

Anaphase II

As in a mitotic anaphase, anaphase of meiosis II is initiated by the splitting of the centromeres. Each of the chromatids then migrates to one or other pole of the cell, one chromatid from each chromosome going to each cell pole. This is the second instance of *disjunction* in the meiotic cycle.

Telophase II

Once again, the chromatids become enclosed in a new nuclear membrane and disperse to form the nuclear chromatin of the *gametes* (ova or spermatozoa).

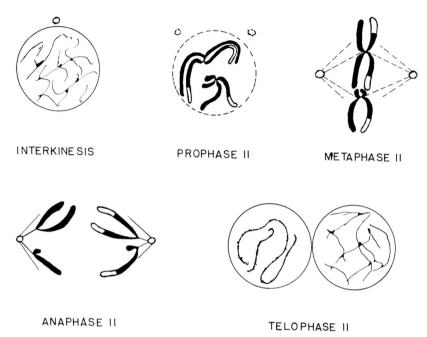

INTERKINESIS   PROPHASE II   METAPHASE II

ANAPHASE II   TELOPHASE II

Figure 9. Nuclear Changes in Meiosis - Meiosis II. Maternally derived genetic material is shown in white; paternally derived genetic material is shown in black.

Although each of the differences between mitosis and meiosis has been pointed out as the discussion progressed, there are some differences which are so important that they deserve brief recapitulation. The most significant single difference is that the products of mitosis are diploid while those of meiosis are haploid. In meiosis, though two successive cell divisions occur, the DNA helix is replicated only once. Thus the constancy of chromosome numbers within species is maintained.

The interchange of genetic material through crossing-over has never been conclusively demonstrated in mammalian mitosis and, in fact, somatic pairing of chromosomes is rarity. The contribution which crossing-over during meiosis makes to the genetic heterogeneity of randomly bred populations is obvious.

The complexity of meiosis, both in respect to crossing-over and in respect to the repeated occurrence of disjunction, makes susceptibility to mechanical error far greater than it is in mitosis.

This is reflected in the greater incidence of chromosomal abnormalities which can be ascribed to meiotic errors.

MEIOSIS IN MAN

In man, meiosis occurs in the germ cells of the testis and the ovary. Meiosis during spermatogenesis is a continuing process which commences about the time of puberty and affects successive generations of primary spermatocytes until the time of senescence. Each generation of primary spermatocytes, which arise from continuing mitotic activity in the testicular germ cells, proceeds through the meiotic cycle without appreciable interruption. Four functional gametes (spermatozoa) are produced by each primary spermatocyte.

Human oogenesis, though it follows the general mechanisms of meiosis just described, is endowed with a number of completely unique features. Unlike meiosis in the male testis, meiosis in the female ovary commences during *intrauterine* life and has, in fact, proceeded almost completely through first meiotic prophase before the female is even born. After germ cells migrate to the gonadal ridges in the female fetus, they undergo successive mitoses as they do in the male. At the fifth to sixth month of intrauterine life, however, mitotic activity in the fetal ovary ceases and the full complement of ovarian germ cells is established at this time.

The oocytes enter the first meiotic prophase at about the sixth intrauterine month. Before the end of gestation, the primary oocytes of the female fetus have reached the stage of diakinesis in prophase I. At this point, meiosis ceases, the chromosomes disperse through the nucleus and the primary oocytes enter a very long resting stage known as the *dictyotene* stage.

Thus, by the time gestation is complete, the infant female has her entire complement of primary oocytes and these have virtually completed first meiotic prophase. The dictyotene stage persists until the time of ovulation—some thirteen to fifty years, depending upon the time of ovulation of the particular oocyte in question. With the onset of puberty in the female, one or two primary oocytes per month complete the meiotic cycle and form functional ova.

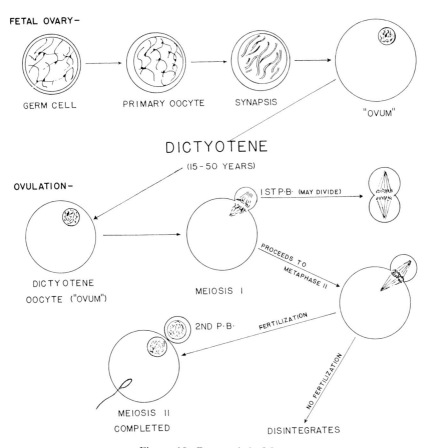

FETAL OVARY—

GERM CELL   PRIMARY OOCYTE   SYNAPSIS

"OVUM"

DICTYOTENE

(15–50 YEARS)

OVULATION—

DICTYOTENE
OOCYTE ("OVUM")

MEIOSIS I

IST P·B· (MAY DIVIDE)

PROCEEDS TO METAPHASE II

2ND P·B·   FERTILIZATION

MEIOSIS II
COMPLETED

NO FERTILIZATION

DISINTEGRATES

Figure 10. Oogenesis in Man.

Following ovulation, the maturing primary oocyte undergoes a rather specialized type of meiosis which results in the formation of only a single functional gamete (ovum). The nucleus of the dictyotene primary oocyte is situated eccentrically within the cell and, when meiosis is reinitiated after ovulation, the metaphase spindle is also situated eccentrically and the cytoplasm becomes unequally divided between the daughter cells of the first meiotic division. The smaller of the two daughter cells is the non-functional *first polar body* and the other, which receives the bulk of the cyto-plasm is the *secondary oocyte*.

The secondary oocyte and the first polar body both enter the second meiotic division quickly and reach metaphase II rather rapidly. The first polar body may either degenerate without further divisions or may complete its second meiotic division and then degenerate. The secondary oocyte will not complete metaphase II or the remainder of the second meiotic division unless fertilization occurs (although exceptions have been reported). Following fertilization, meiosis II is completed; again there is an unequal distribution of cytoplasm between the *ovum* and the nonfunctional *second polar body*. Without fertilization, the secondary oocyte breaks down.

In summary, meiosis in human oogenesis is initiated in the fetus, arrested in the dictyotene stage and reinitiated, one ovum at a time, at puberty. Further meiosis produces only one functional gemete which cannot complete the meiotic cycle without fertilization.

CHAPTER III

PRINCIPLES OF INHERITANCE

A SCIENTIFICALLY derived theory expressing the presently accepted principles of heredity was first promulgated by Gregor Mendel about 1850. The astute scientific historian can undoubtedly point to earlier theories, such as those of Luis Mercado (*ca.* 1600) which were similar to those of Mendel. Some of these more ancient theories have, in fact, a surprisingly contemporary tenor. Such earlier theories, however modern in sound, were derived on a wholly philosophical plane which, more often than not, reflected nothing more than the underlying preconceptions of their authors. The laws proposed by Mendel, on the other hand, were derived *after* long experimentation and so remain rightfully regarded as the first scientific expression of the laws which govern inheritance.

Mendel's work antedated by several years the elucidation of the mechanisms of cell division. The work, therefore, attracted very little attention and even less support. Rediscovery of Mendel's laws in 1910 has been followed by repeated proofs of their validity in the last half century.

Mendel's laws of inheritance form the foundation upon which the entire science of modern genetics rests. Thorough understanding of their implications is absolutely mandatory if any aspect of modern genetics is to be approached with true comprehension. Even in the most elaborate ramifications of modern genetic theory, these laws can be discerned with comparative clarity. Their importance and pertinence to any study of genetics cannot be overstated.

MENDEL'S FIRST LAW

Mendel's first law is commonly known as the "law of segregation" (or "non-mixing of alleles") and was derived from observation of the inheritance patterns in peas. Mendel noted that when individuals from pure lines were *crossed* (mated) as in a mating of pure Tall (T) and pure short (t) peas, all of the offspring were of one type (Tall, in this instance). However, when these offspring were bred with one another, pure lines similar to the original parental lines could be recovered.

From these observations, Mendel postulated that each individual received some "factor" from each parent, the interaction of which produced the physical characteristics of that individual. It was also apparent that these "factors" did not lose their identity as a consequence of their interaction but were recoverable, apparently unaltered, in later generations. The "factors" of Mendel have become the *genes* of modern genetics and have, indeed, been found to possess a specific chemical identity which normally remains unaltered from generation to generation.

In more modern terms, Mendel's first law encompasses several implications which warrant expansion. The control of heredity is now known to reside within the nuclear chromosomal material. The genes are arranged in a specific linear sequence along the chromosomes and are represented by "coded" arrangements of the nucleotide bases of the DNA molecule. The chromosomes, and hence the genes, are present in pairs one member of each pair being of maternal and one of paternal origin.

Through evolution, the same site (locus) on a chromosome may bear one of a number of different genes (alleles), each of which controls the same class of reactions. Not all of these alleles will operate with equal vigor and, generally, one member of a dissimilar (heterozygous) gene pair—the dominant allele—will be expressed in preference to the other (the recessive allele). Occasionally, each will show equality of expression and a mixed effect will result (as in the ABO blood groups).

The gene complement of an individual is known as the *genotype*. The physical characteristics produced by gene action are known as the *phenotype*. Genetic shorthand expresses genotype and phenotype in brief one or two-letter symbols in accord with a widely accepted convention. Phenotype symbols are set in standard type, with the phenotype attributable to action of a dominant gene in upper case letters. Genotype symbols are paired, one for each gene, and separated by a bar. They are set in italic type with dominant genes in upper case. Thus, an expression such as $T = T/t$ indicates that phenotype T is the result of the interaction of the dominant gene T and the recessive gene t.

The Monohybrid Cross

Occasional brief allusions to "pure lines" have been made. These are populations in which all of the individuals (at least in respect to the gene in question) are genotypically and phenotypically identical and show neither phenotypic nor genotypic variation from generation to generation when inbred. The members of such lines are, obviously, all homozygotes.

Hybridization follows the introduction of two dissimilar alleles into the genetic complement of an interbreeding population. The implications of the terms "hybrid" and "heterozygote" are very similar, suggesting as they do the possession of genes derived from parents of dissimilar genotype. Matings between heterozygous individuals are therefore alluded to as *hybrid crosses*. If the inheritance patterns are being studied in respect to only a single heterozygous locus, the cross is a *monohybrid cross*. The inheritance pattern which typifies the monohybrid cross provides a succinct summary of the findings embodied in Mendel's first law:

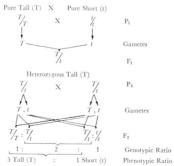

The genotypic and phenotypic ratios shown are characteristic of a monohybrid cross and when offspring are produced in this ratio, parental heterozygosis can be inferred. The enumeration (P_1, F_1) of generations is a standard genetic convention. Acquaintance with the pattern enables one to draw two conclusions when studying inheritance patterns. First, it allows one to predict the probability of an undesirable recessive gene being expressed in a mating between heterozygotes. Secondly, it permits accurate assessment of the parental genotype if sufficient offspring are present for study.

MENDEL'S SECOND LAW

Mendel's second law is often known as the "law of independent assortment" (or "random segregation"). Its basic premise is that when alleles at two or more loci are inherited, each is distributed to the offspring independently of the other. That is, under normal conditions, the distribution of one allele to the offspring is not influenced by the distribution of the other.

During gametogenesis, alleles (genes) are distributed to the gametes in a random fashion. The separation of the paired alleles of the germ cells and their distribution to the gametes is referred to as *assortment* or *segregation*. If assortment is truly random, a germ cell which is heterozygous at two loci can produce *four* different types of gametes in equal proportions. Thus, an individual of genotype $T/t,G/g$ can produce gametes of types TG, Tg, tG and tg. A cross between parents who are heterozygous at two loci is a *dihybrid* cross. The ratio of offspring is as characteristic as that of the monohybrid cross. Gross distortions of the dihybrid ratio are commonly indicative of linkage. The following is a typical dihybrid cross:

Plant Height Alleles — T (tall) and t (short)
Plant Color Alleles — G (green) and g (yellow)

Heterozygous Tall Green (TG)	X	Heterozygous Tall Green (TG)
$T/t \; G/g$	X	$T/t \; G/g$	P₁

TG, Tg, tG, tg TG, Tg, tG, tg Gametes
1 : 1 : 1 : 1   1 : 1 : 1 : 1   Gametic Ratio

Gametes	TG	Tg	tg	tG
TG	$T/T \; G/G$	$T/T \; G/g$	$T/t \; G/g$	$T/t \; G/G$
Tg	$T/T \; G/g$	$T/T \; g/g$	$T/t \; g/g$	$T/t \; G/g$
tg	$T/t \; G/g$	$T/t \; g/g$	$t/t \; g/g$	$t/t \; G/g$
tG	$T/t \; G/g$	$T/t \; G/g$	$t/t \; G/g$	$t/t \; g/g$

(Offspring contained in heavy lines have a similar phenotype)

$T/T \; G/G : T/T \; G/g : T/t \; G/g : T/t \; G/G$ 9 Tall Green (TG)
1 : 2 : 4 : 2

$T/t \; g/g : T/T \; g/g$ 3 Tall Yellow (Tg)
2 : 1

$t/t \; G/g : t/t \; G/G$ 3 Short Green (tG)
2 : 1

$t/t \; g/g$ 1 Short Yellow (tg)
1

Genotypic Ratio = 1 : 2 : 4 : 2 : 2 : 1 : 2 : 1 : 1
Phenotypic Ratio = 9 : 3 : 3 : 1

The characteristic 9:3:3:1 ratio was obtained by Mendel in his original experiments and was the basis from which he evolved the law of random segregation. Distortions of this ratio can be invaluable in chromosome mapping (*q.v.*). If the segregation of one allele affects the segregation of the other allele in the system, this is strong evidence of linkage (see below).

The Back Cross

If a heterozygous individual is mated with an individual who is a homozygous recessive at the loci in question (this is usually obvious from the phenotype), the proportion of offspring accurately reflects the genotype of the heterozygous parent. Such a mating between a heterozygote and a recessive homozygote is called a *back cross*. Matings of this type, when they occur in human populations, are extremely informative.

As an example, a plant which is Tall and Green (TG), may have any one of four genotypes: $T/T,G/G;$ $T/t,G/G;$ $T/t,G/g$ or $T/T,G/g$. A back cross with a short yellow (tg) plant of genotype $t/t,g/g$ will elucidate which of the genotypes is present in the Tall Green individual.

$T/T,G/G$ x $t/t,g/g$ — all offspring are Tall Green

$T/t, G/G$ x $t/t, g/g$ — all offspring are Green,
with 50% Tall, 50% short

$T/t,G/g$ x $t/t,g/g$ — produces a 1:1:1:1 phenotypic ratio
(TG = Tg = tG = tg)

$T/T,G/g$ x $t/t,g/g$ — all offspring are Tall, with 50% Green and
50% yellow

LINKAGE AND CROSSING-OVER

Is is obvious that Mendel's second law depends upon the loci under consideration being on different chromosomes (or rather far apart on the same chromosome—see below). Two genes which are situated on the same chromosome will, of course, tend to travel together during mitosis and meiosis. When two loci are present on the same chromosome, they may behave as a single locus—they show *linkage*. In this instance, a "dihybrid" cross involving the linked loci will produce offspring in a ratio which is typical of a monohybrid cross. In the example shown below, another convention in genetic shorthand is introduced, the use of a solid bar linking the symbols is the conventional expression of linkage between genes.

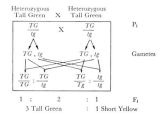

Examples of *complete linkage* such as the one illustrated above are invaluable in chromosome mapping. Complete linkage may be confirmed using an appropriate back cross. Unfortunately, all linkages are not as simple to detect and assess as the one exemplified. A mental review of meiosis will soon suggest that the phenomenon of crossing-over might introduce a small note of chaos into this otherwise tidy scheme. And so it does.

Two genes which are situated on the same chromosome may bear one of three relationships to each other in their inheritance patterns. The inheritance pattern is a function of the distance between the genes on the chromosome:

1) If the genes are very close together, they will always travel together (as in the example cited)—*complete linkage*.

2) If the genes are sufficiently far apart that crossing-over always occurs between them, the genes will segregate as if they were on separate chromosomes and their linkage will be inapparent.

3) If the genes are such a distance apart that crossing-over occurs between them only part of the time, they will exhibit *incomplete linkage*.

We have already examined the implications of complete linkage.

If crossing-over always occurs, the genes show what amounts to random segregation:

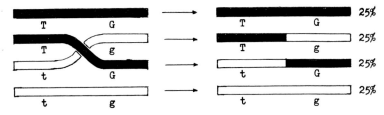

In the above diagram, the maternal chromatids are depicted in white, the paternal in black—the centromere has been ignored.

It can be seen that if crossing-over always occurs as shown, the genes are distributed to the gametes in the same proportion as obtains in the usual dihybrid cross. As a consequence of the phenomenon of crossing-over, *parts* of chromosomes may exhibit random segregation as readily as do complete chromosomes.

Crossing-over which occurs only part of the time produces still another variable in linkage patterns. In the example below, crossing-over between loci is assumed to occur 20 per cent of the time.

80% NON-CROSSOVER

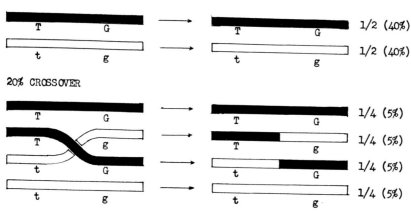

20% CROSSOVER

In this instance, the percentage of crossover gametes is 10 per cent and hence the incidence of crossover gametes is 10 per cent. On the basis of established genetic convention, the genes are said to be ten crossover units apart. The maximum theoretically measurable crossover distance is slightly less than fifty units (slightly under 100 per cent crossing-over). In practice, the maximum measurable crossover distance is considerably less than fifty units.

Since it is not the intention of this monograph to provide an exhaustive survey of all of the ramifications of modern genetics, only brief mention will be made of such added complexities of linkage as the *double crossover* and *three point linkage* studies. Both of these are of considerable interest to those who wish to attempt chromosome mapping.

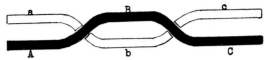

Double crossovers are of interest because they yield the apparently anomalous situation in which genes A and C exhibit complete linkage while there is random segregation in respect to genes A and B and genes B and C. Three point linkage studies are used to assess the distance between two genes which are on the same chromosome but which are too far apart to show linkage. By selecting an appropriate third gene which lies between the two in question, and with which both show linkage, the distance between the original two genes may be derived by addition.

SEX LINKED GENES

In those organisms in which sex is determined by specific sex chromosomes, another form of "linkage" is recognized. In actuality, the term *sex-linked* applies to genes which are borne on one of the sex chromosomes and does not necessarily imply demonstrable linkage between genes in the sense outlined above.

For all practical purposes, the term "sex-linked" as it applies to human genetics is confined to descriptions of those genes which are borne on the X chromosome. This frame of reference reflects the relative genetic ineffectuality of the human Y chromosome. With one possible exception, the human Y chromosome has not been shown to bear any genes other than those concerned with "maleness."

In man, females have paired X chromosomes (XX) and males have nonhomologous X and Y chromosomes (XY). Theoretically, three types of sex linkage can exist—X linkage, Y linkage and XY linkage. The latter (XY) linkage exists when the X and Y chromosome have segments which are homologous. There is no evidence yet that the human X and Y chromosomes bear any homologous segments. This type of sex linkage is difficult to discern since such genes do not segregate in relation to the individual's sex. Genes of this type become recognized as sex-linked genes when linkage (in the usual sense) between these and other sex-linked genes is demonstrated.

X-linked genes can be detected with ease only if they are recessive (dominants are expressed whether the individual is XX or XY). X-linked recessive genes are expressed phenotypically in one-half of the sons of phenotypically normal female carriers. They are never transmitted from father to son. Expression of such a gene occurs whenever it is present in the male, since the male has only one X chromosome (*hemizygous*). X-linked recessive genes are rarely expressed in the female since they must be homozygous to gain such expression. The example below illustrates the transmission of hemophilia, a human sex-linked recessive trait.

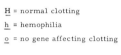

$\underline{H}$ = normal clotting

$\underline{h}$ = hemophilia

$\underline{o}$ = no gene affecting clotting

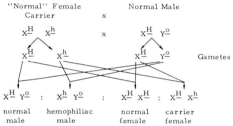

(Half of the sons are normal, half are hemophiliacs. All of the daughters appear normal, though half are carriers and will bear hemophiliac sons.)

Y-linked inheritance (*holandric*) has several distinctive features. A gene which is borne only by the Y chromosome is expressed whenever it is present and is transmitted by affected fathers to all sons but to none of the daughters. The gene is not transmitted by the female and the trait governed does not occur in females. The only example of holandric inheritance for which there is good evidence in man is the "hairy ear" trait. Even this trait is not accepted as an example of true holandric inheritance by all human geneticists.

PATTERNS OF INHERITANCE

From the foregoing discussion, it is apparent that any one of several major inheritance patterns may govern the transmission of any given set of alleles. Though these basic patterns may be obscured by a variety of genetic or environmental variables, one or another of them can be discerned in nearly all instances. In addition to summarizing the inheritance patterns we have discussed to this point, an enumeration of the major inheritance patterns will give some insight into the frequency with which such patterns are seen.

Dominant Inheritance

The effects of dominant genes are the commonest effects seen in any population. Dominant genes are passed from generation to generation without skipping. They are expressed phenotypically whenever they are present.

Autosomal Recessive Inheritance

Phenotypic expression of autosomal recessive genes is, in comparison to autosomal dominants, rather rare. In general, the recessive gene is expressed more frequently in sibships than it is in the general population (i.e., in brothers and sisters). To be expressed, these genes must be homozygous. When these genes are expressed, there is a fair possibility that the parents of the individual were related.

Sex-linked Dominant Inheritance

This is a comparatively rare inheritance pattern in human populations. The inheritance pattern is generally similar to that of an autosomal dominant gene with the exception that affected fathers transmit the trait to all of their daughters but to none of their sons. Affected mothers transmit the trait to half of their children, whether male or female.

Sex-linked Recessive Inheritance

Expression of sex-linked (X-linked) recessive genes is uncommon. A sex-linked recessive gene is characteristically expressed only in the male (who is hemizygous) but is not transmitted from the father to his sons. Sex-linked recessive genes are passed to successive generations by phenotypically normal-appearing "carrier" females. Sex-linked recessive genes characteristically "skip" generations in their expression.

OTHER VARIATIONS ON THE MENDELIAN THEME

Linkage, sex-linkage and crossing-over are not the only phenomena which modify the basic hereditary patterns exemplified by the monohybrid and dihybrid crosses. The research of the past fifty years has elucidated a number of mechanisms which, while they in no way negate the basic principles of inheritance, certainly obscure them. Little purpose would be served by exploring all of these variations in complete detail. However, anyone who considers working seriously in the field of cytogenetics should at least realize that some of these complexities exist.

Association vs. Linkage

A distinction must be drawn between *association, stratification* and true *linkage*. The term *linkage* is applied to genes which occupy the same chromosome. A constant relationship between several phenotypic features does not necessarily imply that there is linkage between two or more responsible genes. Such *association* of phenotypes may reflect the pleiotropic action of a single gene. Association, rather than implying gene linkage, more generally implies the presence of a common etiologic factor.

Conversely, linkage does not always produce association. The fact that two genes occupy the same chromosome does not, as has been pointed out, imply that they will travel together. The phenomena of *recombination* (crossing-over) usually have the effect of making association of phenotypes produced by linked genes a rarity. An obvious exception, of course, is seen in instances of complete linkage. An unusually high incidence of associated phenotypes may also be a consequence of *stratification* which is seen in inbreeding populations. Over generations, constant inbreeding in a population will tend to concentrate certain genes in that population.

Multiple Alleles

When a gene is the site of mutation, a two-allele system is produced consisting of the original gene (the "wild type" allele) and its mutant partner. There are several loci in the human genome where multiple mutations and/or minute structural alterations have produced a rather broad system of alleles, all affecting the same phenotype. Where mutation has produced only paired alleles with a dominant—recessive relationship, the inheritance pattern remains simple.

Unfortunately, however, many multi-allelic systems have alterations at different sites within the same locus and these may be expressed simultaneously in the same individual. Furthermore, alleles which are confined to exactly homologous loci do not always maintain the simple dominant-recessive relationship. Their effects may be additive, subtractive or completely independent. An excellent example of independent expression of alleles occupying the same locus is seen in the human blood groups.

Even further confusion may be introduced if the particular phenotypic feature under study (especially such general features as height, weight) is governed or even influenced by different sets of alleles at entirely separate loci.

Expressivity and Penetrance

The terms *expressivity* and *penetrance*, which are similar in implication though not identical in their formal definition, refer to the "strength" of genes. Repeated observations have been made which indicate that the phenotypic consequences of identical genotypes are not always identical as they would be expected to be. Such asynchrony between genetic constitution and phenotype has been attributed to differences in the "strength" of the gene.

Penetrance is an all or none reaction which is implicated in those instances in which a strictly dominant gene remains unaccountably unexpressed in a generation in which it is known to be present— "lack of penetrance." *Expressivity*, on the other hand, alludes to quantitative variations in the phenotypic expression of identical genotypes.

The recently developed concepts of operon activity and selective inhibition of genetic loci by other loci affords some insight into the actual mechanics of these phenomena. As the intricacies of site inactivation become better understood, these terms will undoubtedly be supplanted by terms with a somewhat less mystical connotation.

Position Effects

In addition to mediating the phenotype with which they are primarily concerned, some genes also modify the expression of other genes within the genetic complement. This type of modification not infrequently depends upon the spatial relationship which these genes bear to one another. Some such intergene activity occurs only when the interrelated genes are on the same chromosome ("cis" position), and do not occur when the genes are on different members of the homologous chromosome pair ("trans" position).

Position affects of this type are sometimes referred to as *pseudo-allelism* since they introduce variations in the development of a new allele at the affected locus. *Paramutation* is another term which has been coined recently to reflect position effects of the "cis" and "trans" type.

A more extreme type of position effect, known as a "V type" position effect, is noted in some structurally abnormal chromosomes. A small portion of a chromosome which is normally inactivated (heterochromatinized) in preference to its homologue may become attached to another chromosome which is not normally inactivated in the same fashion. The transplanted fragment may, when it undergoes its usual inactivation, inactivate the entire chromosome to which it has become attached. If, for example, the chromosome which is so inactivated happens to contain the dominant member of a pair of alleles, the anomaly of seeing expression of a recessive gene in heterozygote may completely obscure the true inheritance pattern of the affected alleles.

Affinity

A recent series of investigations suggests the segregation of chromosomes during meiosis is not always as random as has been generally assumed. Some evidence has accumulated which indicates that the centromere, rather than being a genetically inactive point of spindle attachment, has a genetic identity of its own. There is further evidence that centromeres of the same genetic composition (centrotype) tend to migrate to the same pole of the cell during first meiotic disjunction.

Gene Balance

Several references have been made to the effects which one gene may exert upon another. It is a generally accepted concept that the genetic complement of the normal individual represents a "balance" between all of the genes present. Such balance may be distorted by alterations in one or more genes which in turn induce reciprocal alteration in apparently unrelated genes. This alteration of balance may make Mendelian ratios difficult to discern, particularly if one is dealing with a series of multiple alleles which normally produce a spectrum of phenotypic activity.

One type of gene balance is *dosage compensation* which is exemplified in the effects of homozygosity, hemizygosity and heterozygosity on the expression of a given gene. The sex-linked blood group Xg, for example, reacts more strongly in the hemizygous than in the heterozygous state. The validity of the "balanced set" concept is also illustrated in the effects of abnormalities in chromosome number. Defects which affects entire chromosome sets (triploidy, for example) not uncommonly have less profound effects on development than do abnormalities of a single chromosome.

Structural Chromosome Abnormalities

Although this subject is discussed at much greater length in later portions of the monograph, it is useful to point out that structurally abnormal chromosomes do not necessarily imply an abnormal gene complement in the affected individual. Such anomalies do, however, exert profound effects on the phenotypic ratios of succeeding generations and are thus another source of variation in normal Mendelian inheritance patterns.

Gene Effects on Gametes

Most discussions of genetic inheritance patterns assume that the gametes function as more or less passive carriers of chromosomes from generation to generation. It is also rather generally assumed that if the genes are distributed to the gametes in a given proportion, this proportional distribution will be reflected in the offspring. Such is not necessarily the case.

Examples have been found in mice and in other animals (possibly also in man) of genes which impart to the sperms bearing them a selective advantage or disadvantage in their ability to fertilize ova. Thus, a series of matings will yield a preponderance of genes which are advantageous to the activity of the sperm and do not reflect the typical Mendelian inheritance pattern.

Gene Control of Segregation

It would be most surprising if such a complex activity as cell division and segregation was not itself under the control of specific genes. Evidence of such gene control of cell division is found in the activity of such genes as the "segregation distorter" (S.D.) gene of *Drosophila*. This gene will alter segregation in such a manner that preferential recovery of the S.D. allele results. The effects on linked genes, which may be the very ones under investigation, is not hard to imagine.

Environmental Factors

Many phenotypic expressions of gene activity are modified by environmental factors. This seemingly self-evident observation has great pertinence to the human geneticist. The environmental variation of the human population can, and does, modify phenotype sufficiently to make inheritance patterns of some genes very difficult to determine.

THE PEDIGREE CHART

With the recently increasing interest in human genetics, it is an unusual medical periodical which does not have at least one example of the ubiquitous pedigree chart tucked away somewhere in an annual accumulation. These charts are virtually the trademark of the geneticist. They represent an extremely convenient form of genetic shorthand which can be highly informative when examined with comprehension.

Pedigree charts are constructed in a conventional fashion and employ conventional symbols. However, a key to these symbols is not always provided for the convenience of the non-geneticist (particularly in the more highly specialized publications). A brief exposition of these standard symbols and an example of standard pedigree chart construction may prove useful to those who have occasion to deal with them in the medical literature. (*See figure below and figure on the next page.*)

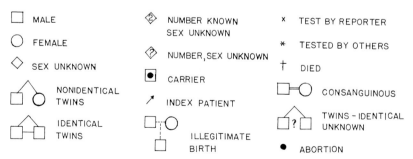

Figure 11. Conventional Symbols Used in Pedigree Charts.

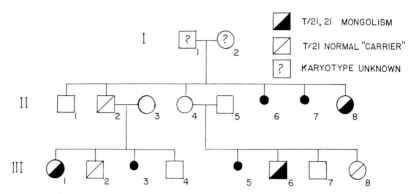

Figure 12. A Model Pedigree Chart. The chart depicts the pedigree of a hypothetical instance of familial mongolism.

CHAPTER IV

SEX DIFFERENTIATION AND THE CHROMATIN TEST

Cytogenetics may be defined as "the study of microscopically visible alterations in the chromosome complement (or its counterpart in the interphase nucleus) in relation to associated genetic changes." Within the scope of this rather broad definition, falls the *sex chromatin test.* Sex chromatin studies have the distinction of being the first of the human cytogenetic techniques to attain stature as clinically valuable laboratory tests. It is therefore most appropriate that sex chromatin receives our early attention.

SEX DIFFERENTIATION IN MAN

Since interpretation of the sex chromatin test involves many implications in respect to the genetic sex of the patient, a survey of the normal mechanisms of sex determination in man will help clarify some of the problems in interpretation. This basic knowledge is also invaluable in sorting out some of the complex chromosomal and non-chromosomal aberrations of sex determination.

In man, as in other mammals, sex is determined by genes which are borne on specific sex chromosomes. These chromosomes may be either homologous (*homogametic*) or non-homologous (*heterogametic*). In man and other mammals, the male (XY) is heterogametic and the female is homogametic (XX). This method of sex determination does not obtain in all bisexual organisms. In some, the female is heterogametic and in some insects, including *Drosophila*, sex is determined by the number of X chromosomes which are present and is modified only slightly by the Y chromosome.

63

The X and Y chromosomes of man were first convincingly demonstrated by Wieman (1917).

In man, the X chromosome is one of the medium sized submetacentric chromosomes. It is one of a group of fifteen (in males) or sixteen (in females) very similar chromosomes and cannot be identified with certainty within this group. The Y chromosome in man is one of the smallest members of the complement and is composed entirely of heterochromatin.

The behavior of the sex chromosome in the male and female differs both in mitosis and meiosis. In meiosis, the paired X chromosomes of the female undergo synapsis, and presumably crossing-over, much as do the other members of the complement. In the male, on the other hand, the X and Y chromosomes do not act as homologous chromosomes. In some animals, such as the rat, there appears to be limited pairing between the X and Y chromosomes suggesting that there is some homology between parts of these chromosomes. In man, the association between the X and Y chromosomes is almost always of an end-to-end type and there is little evidence that any homology exists between the human X and Y chromosomes. In addition, the DNA of the XY complex in the human male is replicated *asynchronously* with the DNA of the rest of the complement. The imperfect pairing and asynchronous duplication of these chromosomes has an important influence on the chromosomal abnormalities of sex (see Chapter VII).

During mitosis also, there is a difference between the behavior of the sex chromosomes in males and females. In males, the X and Y chromosomes replicate their DNA and divide in synchrony with the remainder of the chromosomes. In females, however, DNA replication is much slower in one X chromosome than it is in the remainder of the complement.

Differentiation of the Sex Organs

The mechanism of the differentiation of the internal and external genitalia, particularly as it relates to gonadal function, was most explicitly revealed by the classical experiments of Jost. In a most ingenious series of investigations, Jost castrated fetal rabbits *in utero*, returned them to the uterus, and allowed the pregnancies to proceed to term. The contrasts between genital development in the castrated and non-castrated animals elucidated the gonadal role in sex differentiation with great clarity. These studies have contributed immeasurably to our understanding of the human intersex states.

Recognizable development of the sex organs begins with the differentiation of the ambivalent primordial gonadal ridge into histologically distinguishable testes and ovaries. In man, the sexes can usually be distinguished on a histologic basis at about the fourteen millimeter stage of fetal development. Gonadal differentiation is followed by "somatic sexual differentiation" during which the double genital duct system (Wolffian and Mullerian) differentiates into appropriate male and female structures. The changes which occur at puberty are also mediated by the gonads, but these need not concern us at this point.

In the fetus, both the Mullerian and Wolffian duct systems develop during sexual morphogenesis. Under the influence of the normal fetal ovary, the Mullerian system persists and forms the fallopian tubes, uterus and upper portion of the vagina. The Wolffian duct in the female undergoes almost total retrogression. Under the influence of the normal fetal testis, the Mullerian anlage retrogresses and the Wolffian duct forms the seminal vesicles, the prostate and the vasa deferentia.

Castration of female fetuses is followed by comparatively little alteration in the usual pattern of differentiation of the Mullerian derivatives and involution of the Wolffian system. Castration induces only hypoplasia of the developing genital tract. The severity of the hypoplasia so induced is dependent upon the stage of development at the time of castration. There is no tendency to masculinization.

The effects of castration in male fetuses are variable and depend upon the stage at which castration is carried out. If castration is performed after differentiation of the gonadal primordium but before the onset of "somatic differentiation," the net result is similar to that induced by castration of a female fetus at the same stage. The Wolffian duct involutes completely and the Mullerian system forms hypoplastic tubes, uterus and cervix. Performed at later stages, castration will arrest the development of the Wolffian system and an admixture of masculinization and feminization ensues. These effects are unilateral. Unilateral excision of the testis is followed by Mullerian development on the affected side while the ducts on the side with an intact testis differentiate into male structures. The external genitalia undergo imperfect male differentiation in unilateral testicular castrates.

The activity of the fetal testis cannot be wholly duplicated by androgen administration. Androgen, though it promotes Wolffian development, fails to inhibit Mullerian development. The fetal testicular "evocator" is therefore in part an active Mullerian inhibitor. Mullerian development is not estrogen dependent (Mullerian explants *in vitro* continue to develop in the absence of estrogen) and maternal estrogen does not, therefore, bear the responsibility for Mullerian development in castrates.

In summary, Jost's experiments show that:

1) In the absence of gonadal activity, either ovarian or testicular, Mullerian (female) differentiation predominates.

2) The fetal testis governs male differentiation *via* two distinct factors, Wolffian stimulating (androgen ?) and Mullerian inhibiting.

3) The activity of the fetal testis is unilateral.

Many parallels with these experimental findings can be recognized in the various forms of human intersex (see Chapter XII).

Function of the Sex Chromosomes

In the light of the knowledge gleaned from the above cited experiments, the problem of sex differentiation in man would seem to be pretty well solved. It would be delightfully simple to assume that the Y chromosome governs testicular development and hence the male phenotype. Biologic phenomena being what they are, however, one might well anticipate that so neat and uncluttered an explanation would be deficient in some respect. It is deficient, in fact, in many respects.

Using the generally accepted statement that "the Y chromosome in man is male determining" as a point of reference, a catalogue of some exceptions to the apparently logical corollary "Y makes testes and testes make males" leaves one wondering just what the Y chromosome *does* do.

The Y chromosome is obviously not essential to the evolution of male secondary sex characteristics such as deep voice, hirsutism and muscular development. These are well developed in genetic females with adrenal virilism and some of the masculinizing ovarian tumors. The Y chromosome is not even mandatory, at least as far as present knowledge would indicate, to the development of testicular tissue. Recognizable testicular derivatives are present in true hermaphrodites with an XX genetic constitution. Furthermore, the presence of a Y chromosome does not ensure development of a male phenotype even if testes are produced. Some XY individuals with testicular feminization are virtually perfect phenotypic females.

To the credit of the Y chromosome is the fact that it can withstand the effects of extra X chromosomes in rather formidable numbers. Klinefelter's syndrome has an XXY chromosome complement, yet these individuals are unquestionably males. So are patients with XXXY and even with XXXXY chromosome complements. Obviously, the Y chromosomes in such instances is a potent masculinizer. Also to the credit of the Y chromosome is the fact that a virtually perfect male phenotype (scrotal gonads, male phallus, penile urethra, intact perineum and obliteration of the Mullerian system) has not yet been reported in its absence.

Evidence that the human sex-determining system is not analogous to that in *Drosophila* (controlled by the number of X chromosomes) is derived from study of a variety of developmental abnormalities in man. Many instances of XO chromosome constitution have been reported in humans. All of these have been phenotypic females. In *Drosophila*, such individuals are males. Such cases afford very strong evidence of the function of the Y chromosome in man. In this same vein, one cannot help but be impressed by the close parallels which exist between the experimental findings of Jost and some of the developmental anomalies in man.

Present knowledge of the role of the sex chromosomes in man can be rather easily, albeit unsatisfactorily, summarized. There is an inherent tendency for the human fetus to differentiate as a female. This tendency is enhanced by the X chromosome and is opposed by the activity of the Y chromosome. Whether the Y chromosome functions alone or in concert with some autosomal loci has not yet been determined.

THE CHROMATIN TEST

Since disorders of sex development have long excited the interest of both the lay public and the medical profession, it is not surprising that a simple test for determining genetic sex would arouse considerable interest. The sex chromatin tests have certainly done so.

A morphologic difference between the chromatin patterns in male and female nuclei was first reported by Barr and Bertram in 1949. In the course of research on cats, these authors noted a predictable difference in the chromatin patterns of neurones. In these cells, female cats have an extra distinctive chromatin mass which is absent from the nuclei of males. Further investigation revealed that this same difference is demonstrable in humans and a clinical technique was devised which was based on the examination of skin biopsies.

In 1954, Davidson and Smith reported that polymorphonuclear neutrophil nuclei also bore the distinctive imprints of their genetic sex. This test, and the introduction of a buccal smear technique for detecting the sex chromatin in epithelial cells (Moore and Barr, 1955) provided cheap, rapid and convenient methods of determining "genetic sex" in man. The techniques became readily accepted and were soon applied to the investigation of every conceivable disorder of sex development in man.

Recognition of Sex Chromatin

Nuclear sex chromatin (or the *Barr body*) is a distinctive mass of chromatin which is seen in the nuclei of genetically normal (XX) females. Like other nuclear chromatin, the sex chromatin is derived from chromosomal material and stains with the usual nuclear dyes. (For a discussion of methods see Appendix II.) It generally appears as a plano-convex mass of dark staining chromatin tightly applied to the nuclear membrane. The mass has average dimensions of 1.2 x 0.7 micra and the nuclear membrane is not infrequently indented at the point of attachment to the mass. Usually, the chromatin mass appears solid although more detailed attention will often reveal an apparent bipartite configuration or a suggestion of some internal structure.

Most morphologic variants of the chromatin mass have little clinical significance and should be recognized as normal features.

or a time, these morphologic variants were thought to reflect an origin from both chromosomes (*vide infra*). The most common variant (which may even be the commonest form) consists of two roughly hemispherical masses lying attached to one another in very close apposition. Other morphologic variants include areas of central pallor or a distinctly pyramidal or inverted "V" configuration. The latter may assume the configuration of two distinct bars forming a pyramid with its base on the nuclear membrane. Studies of the X chromosomes during prophase reveal that it is often sharply folded—this undoubtedly accounts for the morphologic variations described.

Frequently, the sex chromatin has either a visible or an apparent close relationship with a nucleolus. Actual fine chromatin strands may extend from the sex chromatin mass to a nearby nucleolus. Similar strands at times appear to link the sex chromatin with other masses of chromatin in the nucleus. Whether or not these connecting strands represent true communications between the chromatin and nucleoli is not yet certain. It is quite possible that they may be artefacts in view of the many random chromatin strands which are present in the interphase nucleus.

> This occasional association between sex chromatin and nucleolus indicates that the sex chromatin is not invariably associated with the nuclear membrane. The original description of the sex chromatin by Bertram and Barr was, in fact, related to an intranuclear chromatin mass closely associated with a nucleolus. An association of sex chromatin with the nuclear membrane was not emphasized until later publications.
>
> While it is certainly true that the sex chromatin may occupy a position removed from the nuclear membrane, this possibility is seldom mentioned in descriptions of the appearance of the Barr body. There is a sound practical reason for not emphasizing this possibility. The interphase nucleus contains many chromatin masses of varying size which might be confused with a sex chromatin mass. This, in fact, is one pertinent objection to techniques which depend upon differential staining as a method of identifying sex chromatin.

The description of sex chromatin to this point has been confined to the findings in the normal female nucleus. Is there a counterpart in the male nucleus? Opinion seems almost equally divided.

Using special staining techniques, some authors have obtained preparations which have led them to conclude that the male nucleus may contain a chromatin mass. This is usually described as a very minute body, less than half the size of that present in the female. For all practical purposes, the male of normal genetic constitution (XY) may be regarded as chromatin negative.

Origin of the Sex Chromatin - The Lyon Hypothesis

Barr's original observations of the chromatin body, particularly of its morphology, led him to conclude that the sex chromatin body is derived in equal parts from the heterochromatic areas of each of the two X chromosomes of the normal female. One defect in such an hypothesis is the absence (or very minute size) of the chromatin mass in male nuclei. Equal derivation of the sex chromatin from each X chromosome would imply that the male should have a nuclear chromatin mass half the size of that present in chromatin positive nuclei from normal females.

Following the introduction of direct chromosome studies, other defects in this theory became apparent. Why does a patient with three X chromosomes possess two Barr bodies of equal size? Why do patients with Turner's syndrome (XO chromosome constitution) not express their single X as a chromatin mass of half normal size? Such nagging questions as these obviously require an explanation at variance with that originally proposed by Barr.

The currently accepted theory of origin of the Barr body was elaborated by Mary Lyon. Although other authors had predicted that the Barr body would be found to be the product of a single X chromosome (e.g., Stewart, 1960) and some authors devised moderately detailed explanations, the most comprehensive and lucid exposition is that of Lyon. Another group, including Grumbach and Morishima, preferring to regard the X chromosome changes leading to sex chromatin formation as differentiation rather than "inactivation," have advanced much the same hypothesis under the name of the *"fixed differentiation hypothesis."* The more euphonious nomenclature, *"Lyon hypothesis,"* seems to have garnered more popular acceptance.

The Lyon hypothesis is a synthesis of two seemingly unrelated series of observations. The first of these are the observations made by Ohno and co-workers who have studied the origin of the sex chromatin in great detail. Their studies provide almost incontrovertible proof of the single X nature of the Barr body. (The earliest published support of their findings came from Barr himself.)

In brief, Ohno noted that in the female rat, the somatic cells contain a sex chromatin body. In these same cells, one of the X chromosomes is always heteropyknotic during cell division. The other remains isopyknotic with the autosomes. Similar attention was then directed to the oocytes of the rat. In these cells, there is no sex chromatin body though their chromosome complement includes the XX pair. During meiosis, the X chromosomes are isopyknotic both with one another and with the autosomes.

These observations make the conclusion that the heteropyknotic somatic X chromosome forms the chromatin body inescapable. Confirmatory evidence is derived from studies of the germ cells and somatic cells in males. In both instances, no Barr body is present and, in both instances, the X chromosome is isopyknotic.

A second series of observations of importance in the derivation of the Lyon hypothesis are related to the genetic effects of X chromosome inactivation (heterochromatinization) in mice. In these animals, sex-linked coat color genes are expressed in a mosaic (patchy) fashion when they are heterozygous. This is attributed to a selective inactivation of one or other of the X chromosomes in the cells of the skin. Since the same X chromosome is not inactivated in all cells, the heterochromatinization must occur after the first mitotic (cleavage) division in the enbryo and must affect the X chromosomes in a random fashion. Similar mosaicism is present in the erythrocytes (glucose-6-phosphate dehydrogenase activity) of heterozygous human females.

The Lyon hypothesis holds that the sex chromatin mass (Barr body) present in the interphase nuclei of normal females is derived wholly from a single inactivated (heterochromatinized) X chromosome. This inactivation of the X chromosome occurs early in embryonic life, probably about the twelfth day, and does not affect the same X chromosome in all cells. In some, the maternally derived X is inactivated and in others it is the paternally derived X chromosome which is inactivated. This is confirmed by the variations which may occur in X-borne heterozygous genes in man, such as those which govern erythrocyte glucose-6-phosphate dehydrogenase activity. The inactivation of the X chromosome

XO	XX	XXX	XXXX	ISO-X	DELETED X
XY	XXY	XXXY	XXXXY		

Figure 13. Nuclear Sex-Chromatin Patterns. Shows the sex chromosome complement which may be associated with various nuclear chromatin patterns.

affects all but one of the X chromosomes in any given cell. After the X chromosome becomes inactivated, any X chromosomes which are derived from the inactive X by subsequent mitosis are also heteropyknotic.

This hypothesis is in full accord with the observed relationships between X chromosomes and chromatin bodies. Studies of DNA synthesis using autoradiographic methods have shown repeatedly that one of the X chromosomes in human cells is heterochromatic. In the abnormal sex chromosome patterns so far observed, the number of Barr bodies present has unfailingly been of the order $n - 1$ where n is the number of X chromosomes present.

Inactivation (or differentiation) of the X chromosome seems to occur about the twelfth to fourteenth day of gestation since sex chromatin is not detectable until this time. It could be expected that inactivation would occur fairly late in fetal development since both X chromosomes are essential to proper sex differentiation (the XO state produces sterile females).

Preferential heterochromatinization of one segment of one of a pair of homologous chromosomes with expression of the genes borne on the same segment of the other homologue does not appear to be unique to the sex chromosomes. Heterochromatic segments are present in the autosomes as well. There is probably a well established system which promotes segmental or even chromosomal differentiation. This system is reflected morphologically by heterochromatin formation.

In the X chromosome, heterochromatin formation seems to be an inducable system much like that described in the operon of Jacob and Monod. This may be initiated at some special locus on the chromosome which ultimately affects all of the loci in the *cis* position (*i.e.*, on the same chromosome). Functionally, this produces a dosage compensation mechanism which "balances" each set of autosomes with a single X chromosome.

There is also a tendency for heterochromatinization to affect an abnormal chromosome such as a deleted X (which has a missing segment) or an isochromosome X (which has an extra segment). Thus the normal homologue remains the "active" member of the pair. This might be a consequence of some selective disadvantage which affects those cells in which the abnormal chromosome is the functional member of the pair. Alternatively, the formation of the abnormal X may deprive the chromosome of some (hypothetical) locus which inhibits heterochromatinization.

Interpretation of Barr Chromatin Tests

Chromatin studies may be conducted on any cell which produces a suitably vesicular, open chromatin pattern (see Appendix II). One of the early errors made in interpretation of the chromatin test is one which is still being made with unnecessary frequency. This is the unwarranted assumption that the chromatin test can be used to determine true genetic sex. It cannot. If one accepts the definition of "male" as being an individual who possesses a Y chromosome and a "female" as one who has no Y chromosome, it is obvious that **the chromatin test does not reflect true genetic sex** since it has nothing whatever to do with the Y chromosome.

The salient feature to proper interpretation of the chromatin test is that the number of Barr bodies, with only the rarest reported exception, is always one less than the number of X chromosomes present. It is therefore an error, and sometimes a serious one, to report smears as "male" or "female." They are best reported as "chromatin positive" or "chromatin negative" with some explanatory comment as to the possible genetic constitutions which may be represented. As a point of emphasis, it should be noted that chromatin negative individuals can very well be females (XO Turner's syndrome) and that chromatin positive individuals may be males (XXY Klinefelter's syndrome).

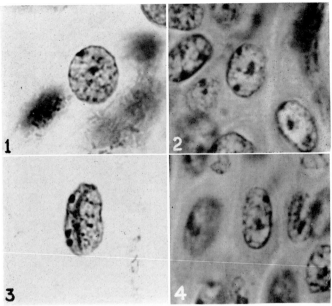

Figure 14. Epithelial Sex-Chromatin Patterns. (*1*) Chromatin-positive nucleus, smear preparation. (*2*) Double-positive nucleus, tissue section. (*3*) Triple-positive nucleus, smear preparation. (*4*) Chromatin-positive nucleus, tissue section. (These photomicrographs were furnished through the kindness of Dr. M. L. Barr and originally appeared in Carr, D. H., Barr, M. L., and Plunkett, E. R.: *Canad. M.A.J.*, *54:*131-137, 1961.)

Abnormalities of chromatin pattern may be either numerical or morphologic. Chromatin bodies may be present in increased numbers—double positive or even triple positive. Again, the known correlation with the number of X chromosomes provides reliable evidence as to the possible sex chromosome constitution of the individual under study. There may also be variations in the percentage of cells which are chromatin positive. The usual range of chromatin positive cells in smears and skin biopsy specimens will vary from laboratory to laboratory and should be established by each laboratory doing these tests. In general, skin biopsy material contains a higher percentage (about eighty per cent) of chromatin positive nuclei than do smears (sixty to sixty-five per cent) from the same individual. Only vesicular nuclei should be counted in calculating such percentages.

Variations from such percentage figures must be interpreted with considerable reservation. Elevations of the percentage of chromatin positive cells in a given smear are rare and have no special significance. Reductions of significant magnitude (to half the usually observed levels or less) *may* be clinically meaningful. Such reductions in the percentage of chromatin positive cells may reflect an underlying sex chromosome mosaic (*q.v.*).

A reduced incidence of chromatin positive cells smear may also reflect variations in the hormonal status of the patient and bear no relation to the sex chromosome constitution. Immediately following parturition, and for about three days thereafter, there is a precipitous drop in the percentage of chromatin positive cells encountered in buccal smears. Although a buccal chromatin test would rarely be indicated immediately after pregnancy, similar hormonally induced decreases may accompany estrogen and corticosteroid therapy. Under such conditions, conclusion-jumping can yield diagnostic errors.

The most important of the artefactual diminutions in the incidence of chromatin positive cells is that which occurs in *newborns*. In newborn female infants, the percentage of chromatin positive cells (four to twenty per cent) rather closely parallels that of the mother. In fact, in the immediate postpartum period, genetically normal female infants may appear to be chromatin negative. Thus, even if there is clinical evidence of intersex, buccal chromatin examinations should be deferred until at least the third day of life and preferably until the end of the first week. Although the properly investigated intersex patient should have actual chromosome analysis confirming the Barr test findings, much confusion can be avoided if the above precaution is kept firmly in mind.

Normal variations in the morphology of the Barr body are fairly common. Pathologic variations are confined largely to alterations in size. Isochromosomes of X (which have extra segments), and deleted X chromosomes (which have missing segments) are associated with unusually large and unusually small chromatin masses respectively. Size alterations may be rather subtle and must be interpreted with great reservation. Diminution in size, particularly, may be without pathologic basis.

Among the non-chromosomal alterations in chromatin size which may be encountered are those inherent in the epithelial cells from various body areas. The chromatin body in buccal smears, for instance, is appreciably smaller than the normal chromatin body in vaginal preparations from the same individual. Drug ingestion, especially the oral ingestions of antibiotics and the sulfonamides has been associated with measurable reduction in Barr body size. Size alterations should be interpreted only after a thorough review of the clinical history.

The Neutrophil Appendages

In 1954, Davidson and Smith first described a sex difference in the nuclei of polymorphonuclear leukocytes. The comparative simplicity of the technique which they described has made it a rival of the Barr test in popularity. Properly employed, the two tests are more aptly regarded as complementary rather than competitive. Examination of a blood smear is a most useful technique in cytogenetic investigation.

Differences in the nuclear configuration of the polymorphonuclear leukocytes in males and females are readily detected using routine blood staining methods. The female nucleus is characterized by the presence of distinctive nuclear appendages, the most striking of which are the "drumsticks." The usual features of these and other types of neutrophil appendages are summarized below:

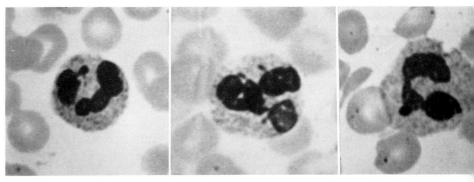

Figure 15. Polymorphonuclear Leukocyte Nuclear Appendages. (*Left*) A "drumstick." (*Center*) A nucleus bearing three "small clubs." (*Right*) A "balloon."

"*Small clubs*"—these appendages occur with equal frequency in males and females, and must be distinguished from "drumsticks." They are comparatively small (one micron or less) weakly basophilic appendages which are attached to a nuclear lobe by a narrow stalk. They may be multiple. Their configuration is quite similar to that of the "drumsticks" and the distinction may be quite difficult to make in some preparations.

"*Drumsticks*"—these appendages are characteristically found in the neutrophil nuclei of females. They are large, round and deeply basophilic structures which are attached to the polymorphonuclear nucleus by fine, basophilic stalks. Drumsticks have a diameter of about one and one-half micra. They are found most readily in mature cells (two lobes or more) and are more frequent in smears in which high lobe counts are noted. They occur singly.

"*Sessile nodules*," "*balloons*" and "*racquets*"—these are all morphologic variants of drumsticks. Some authors feel that racquets are not characteristic of the female nucleus and are reportedly equally common in males. More recently, there is a tendency for investigators to include them in the enumeration of "female" appendages. They differ from drumsticks only in that they show an area of central pallor. Sessile nodules and balloons have a "drumstick" configuration but lack stalks. Balloons are closely applied to the nucleus; sessile nodules have a more bud-like configuration.

In enumerating these appendages, it is common practice to include drumsticks, sessile nodules and balloons. Since the status of the racquet is still somewhat doubtful, it is our practice to ignore them. They are not especially numerous in most smears and their exclusion has little effect on the validity of most counts.

Small clubs are frequently confused with drumsticks, especially when the observer has had limited experience. Occasionally, small accessory nuclear lobes which lie in the isthmus between two normal sized nuclear lobes may cause confusion. These can be readily identified as true nuclear lobes by the presence of two "stalks" uniting them with two nuclear lobes.

The usual incidence of drumsticks in smears from normal females is about 6/500 polymorphonuclear leukocytes. As a rule, none are encountered in normal males. These generalizations are not amenable to such broad application as are the criteria for identification of the Barr body. Some phenotypically normal females (as many as twenty-five per cent according to some authors) have less then 4/500 polymorphonuclear leukocytes. As many as ten per cent of normal males may have one or two drumsticks in five hundred neutrophils.

The origin of the polymorphonuclear appendages is obscure. Though some authors equate them with the Barr body, there are several observations which tend to negate this view. Most pertinent, perhaps, is the vastly lower incidence of these appendages in normal females and their occasional presence in the cells of ostensibly normal males. Studies in mice, in fact, have shown that drumsticks are equally frequent in the nuclei of males and females in this species (whose sex determining mechanism is similar to that of man). Neither of these findings is consistent with the behavior of sex chromatin in other cells.

Additionally, there is poor correlation between the number of appendages present on the neutrophils and the number of X chromosomes in the complement. Multiple drumsticks are encountered infrequently. Double appendages have been encountered only occasionally. Even in polysomy of the XXXXY type, we have not found any report in which more than two drumsticks have been observed. Some authors state that they have demonstrated both Barr bodies and nuclear appendages in the same cell. The concept that drumsticks may be secondary sex characteristics may not be entirely unrealistic.

The vagaries of these interesting little appendages makes their interpretation difficult. At present, the wisest course would seem to be the adoption of a rather noncommittal attitude. We regard these tests as useful adjuncts to buccal smear examinations. The occasional wide discrepancy between buccal smears and drumstick incidence can be most useful in pointing out possible mosaicism. In general the correlation between the tests is good and some authors feel that any marked asynchrony is significant. If this test is reported alone, a report of the incidence of the appendages is about all that one may offer. Interpretation of these tests alone, without the additional information derived from the buccal smear, is not particularly informative in the majority of cases.

It is only fair to point out that there are other authors who are much more enthusiastic about drumstick analysis. Particularly, drumstick analysis has received endorsement as a very valuable tool in detecting morphologic abnormalities of the X chromosome. Investigators who have had access to larger series of such cases feel that variations in size of the drumstick are much more readily apparent then are alterations in size of the Barr body. Maclean has introduced the D/N ratio as an aid in assessing the size of the drumstick. The ratio is calculated according to the formula $\frac{\text{area of the drumstick} \times 100}{\text{area of the nucleus excluding the drumstick}}$. The normal D/N ratio is 2.93 $\pm$ 0.44. In instances of deleted X, where the Barr body is also reduced in size, the D/N ratio is in the range 2.39 $\pm$ 0.39. Values in instances of X isochromosome formation have been in the range 3.37 $\pm$ 0.40. These variations reflect visible changes which are usually readily detectable.

CHAPTER V

IDENTIFICATION OF
HUMAN CHROMOSOMES

W<small>HEN</small> consideration is given the immense volume of research which has been directed to the chromosomal complement of innumerable plants and animals, one cannot help but be startled by the virtual absence of such information in respect to man until the last decade or so. In the early phases of chromosome investigation, Arnold (1879) made what are probably the first published drawings of human chromosomes. An attempt to enumerate the human chromosomes was made as early as 1891 (Hansemann). Results obtained by such early investigators produced such a variety of reports that the human chromosome number was not established to anyone's satisfaction until 1912.

In 1912, DeWiniwarter turned his attention to dividing spermatocytes and concluded that the human chromosome number was forty-seven. Painter, in 1921 and 1923, produced more convincing evidence that the human chromosome number was forty-eight (though he vacillated for a time between forty-six and forty-eight). Extensive work by Koller (1937) led him to conclude that Painter's estimate of forty-eight was, indeed, correct and the human chromosome number thus became "officially" established as forty-eight. With this signal accomplishment, interest in human cytogenetics languished and little work of importance is to be found relating to the human chromosomes between 1937 and the most recent advances.

There are two factors which contributed to this apparent lack of interest, one technical and one philosophical. It is difficult to say which provided the most significant encumbrance to research in the field, though the technical impediments were, until recently, truly formidable. During cell division, human chromosomes are entangled in the sticky web of the spindle body and piled haphazardly upon one another. Since these bodies are quite minute and are split longitudinally in the bargain, the technical difficulty becomes such that even the establishment of an "official" chromosome number (even though it was wrong) by Painter and Koller is no little triumph.

The philosophical impediment lay in the rather general assumptions that visible defects probably did not occur in human chromosomes. Even those who were willing to concede the possibility of error in human mitosis and meiosis assumed that if such errors did occur, they would almost certainly be lethal. Interestingly enough, the technical and the philosophical impediments to human chromosome research were swept away almost simultaneously.

In 1956, Tjio and Levan modified the techniques available for the study of human metaphase chromosomes and showed that the human diploid number is *forty-six*. These findings were rapidly confirmed by other workers taking advantage of the new techniques (e.g., Ford and Hamerton) and met with surprisingly little contradiction. With the technical difficulties surmounted, any residual attitude of "interesting but probably useless" was dispelled with no little certainty by Lejeune and others in 1959 with their description of the chromosomal defect associated with mongolism.

TECHNICAL METHODS

The details of a variety of technical methods are presented in Appendix II. The principles which underlie these methods deserve considerable attention. With these principles in mind, individual investigators will be able to devise modifications which may be more appropriate to their needs.

Generally speaking, human chromosome analysis is dependent upon the techniques of tissue culture. Two important modifications, the use of colchicine and the use of hypotonic solutions, hold the key to successful chromosome analysis (*karyotyping*). Formally defined, a *karyotype* is a systematized array of the chromosomes of a single cell prepared either by direct photography or camera lucida drawings. Such an array may serve to typify the chromosome complement of all of the cells of an organism or even of a species.

In brief, karyotyping is accomplished by taking body cells which are capable of dividing, culturing them and examining them in metaphase. In metaphase, chromosomes are split longitudinally into chromatids united at the centromere. The outlines of the chromosomes are most sharply defined at this stage of cell division.

Collection of Samples

Any tissue which has cells which are capable of dividing in culture media is amenable to use in chromosome analysis. By far the most widely used tissue is peripheral blood which, in routine studies, is unquestionably the most satisfactory source of material. It is easy to obtain, easy to resample, simple to culture and requires the least time (with the exception of bone marrow) to obtain satisfactory preparations. When blood is cultured, the cells which divide are the lymphocytes—these revert to large mononuclear cells and begin to divide. Polymorphonuclear leukocytes are, apparently, incapable of such reversion.

Other sources of culture material include bone marrow, skin, fascia, effusions and tumor tissue. Each of these, when used appropriately, has its own peculiar advantages. In bone marrow, two (at least) types of cells will divide, the erythroblasts and the myeloblasts. Possession of two such distinct cell populations may prove advantageous in the diagnosis of mosaicism (*q.v.*). Similar advantages derive from the simultaneous use of blood and bone marrow cultures since a diversity of cell types is obtained. The sole disadvantage to the routine use of marrow in chromosome analysis is its comparative inconvenience of sampling. Techniques have been devised for ultra short term cultures of marrow. The rapidity with which a karyotyping may be obtained is not infrequently a great advantage.

Skin and fascia have been used as cell sources with great success by many investigators. They have several significant drawbacks which, in our opinion, preclude the use of these tissues as routine sources of cells for karyotyping. The tissues are inconvenient to obtain and they are hard to culture. Culture time for solid tissue is measured in weeks rather than in days and, aside from the delay in obtaining a karyotype, makes these cultures more susceptible to a variety of viscissitudes (especially infection) which are less prominent using blood or bone marrow. Prolonged culture of cells also tends to increase the incidence of aneuploid mitoses obtained. These facts do not obviate the value of skin and fascia as cell sources in those special instances in which a comprehensive survey of karyotypes in various body cells is of diagnostic import.

Although it is much more desirable to inoculate tissues obtained into media as soon as possible, some delay can be tolerated. The tolerance of lymphocytes is such that mail-in methods have been used successfully. Even more interesting are reports of successful cultures of lymph node material obtained at autopsy as long as forty-eight hours after death.

Karyotype analysis of cells cultured directly from tumors or from effusions is more comprehensively discussed in Chapter XIV. Suffice it to say at this point that tumor tissue is handled as are solid tissues in general and that effusions respond well to the culture methods used for peripheral blood. While such techniques are more or less experimental at this stage, it is not improbable that karyotype analysis in this field may ultimately offer much of clinical value.

Culture Media

In essence, the nutrient media used for tissue culture have been utilized in human cytogenetics with only minor modifications. Basically, all of these media consist of a balanced and buffered saline solution to which a variety of carbohydrate and sometimes protein nutrients have been added. The patient's own serum is a creditable protein source.

Cultures, especially those requiring weeks for completion, are sensitive to alterations in the pH of the medium, electrolyte imbalance and bacterial and viral infections. Culture of solid tissue, particularly, can be a series of compound frustrations for the novice approaching these techniques for the first time.

Commercial preparations have been devised with a view to minimizing as many of these variables as possible. One of the more popular of these supplies a medium with an indicator and antibiotics as standard components. Such media can be invaluable to laboratories in which karyotyping is being used as a diagnostic tool rather than as a research procedure. If these media are com-

bined with the patient's own serum as a protein source, a medium
is obtained which is as nearly trouble free as a medium for tissue
culture can become.

Some workers have used pooled human sera as a protein source.
We use the patient's own serum in preference to any other protein
source. The optimum protein concentration is in the range of ten
to twenty per cent. By using the patient's own serum the complexities of antibody-antigen reactions between the cultured cells
and the protein of the medium can be minimized. Despite all
precautions, about twenty to twenty-five per cent of the cultures
will fail to produce satisfactory preparations.

Phytohemagglutinin

A panhemagglutinin of plant origin (*phytohemagglutinin*), ex-
tracted from red kidney beans (*Phaseolus vulgaris*), was used originally as a convenient agent for separating leukocytes from the
erythrocytes in peripheral blood preparations. As familiarity with
the agent increased, a valuable side effect was noted, namely that
the agent stimulated mitotic activity in peripheral blood cultures.
The side effect is now more valuable than the action for which
the agent was originally employed. The nature of the mitosis-
stimulating (*mitogenic*) component is not well defined. Though it
is unrelated to the agglutinating factor, it is unquestionably an
inherent property of phytohemagglutinin (a polysaccharide ?)
rather than a contaminant.

A number of explanations for the mitogenic action have been
advanced. There is a distinct difference in the cell population of
blood cultures to which phytohemagglutinin has been added when
compared with untreated cultures. In the former instance, the
lymphocytes revert to "blast" forms in greater number than is the
case in the untreated samples. This bespeaks some direct cellular
effect of phytohemagglutinin.

Concomitant with the effect on the lymphocytes, there is an ac-
celeration of the degenerative changes which affect the polymorphonuclear leukocytes. The effects on the lymphocytes may,
in some way, be related to the degenerative changes in the poly-
morphs (release of a "growth factor?") or may reflect some alteration in the surface membrane of the lymphocytes. The most widely
held view seems to be that the action of phytohemagglutinin is one
which enhances the reversion of the lymphocytes to primitive forms

and thus makes them more amenable to mitosis, rather than a direct effect on mitosis *per se*.

Phytohemagglutinin has two major chemical fractions, a mucopolysaccharide and a protein. The latter fraction seems to possess the bulk of the agglutinating activity and, presumably, the mucopolysaccharide is the mitogenic component. Commercial preparations, some of which have been very highly purified, are very potent agglutinators but have minimal mitogenic activity. For this reason, many workers prefer to prepare their own reagent directly from beans. The extraction is not unduly complex.

Phytohemagglutinin will agglutinate the red cells from all of the mammalian species in which it has been tried. It is also capable of precipitating protein in some media. It has been suggested that this latter action, by precipitating some mitosis-inhibiting factor, may account for its mitogenic action. This explanation seems less likely than those outlined above.

Mitogenic activity has also been attributed to the chelating agent ethylenediaminetetracetic acid (EDTA). Since this is also a useful anticoagulant, some workers have substituted EDTA for heparin as an anticoagulant and have not bothered to add phytohemagglutinin as a mitogenic agent. Although our experience with this technique is admittedly narrow, we have not been especially enthusiastic with the results we have obtained. Since the medium which is usually used has considerable calcium, clotting is occasionally troublesome. Cells in culture also have considerable sensitivity to hypocalcemia which may produce a variety of secondary constrictions (this is not necessarily a disadvantage—see: Chromosome Identification) or even death of the culture. EDTA is more generally available and somewhat cheaper than heparin and this reagent probably deserves more attention than we have given it to date.

Colchicine

Colchicine is the magic ingredient of human cytogenetics. This old and widely used drug had one of its well known properties rediscovered and applied in a new context by Tjio and Levan in their classical investigations on the human chromosomes. Colchicine is a spindle poison and arrests cell division at metaphase. Addition of a weak solution of colchicine to a tissue culture thus promotes an accumulation of metaphase figures.

Colchicine also tends to contract the chromatids making them shorter, darker and more sharply defined. There is considerable evidence that the degree of contraction is variable in different members of the chromosome complement with the longer members being more strongly contracted than the shorter members. Whether this is statistically significant in karyotype analysis is a moot point.

Destruction of the spindle body makes the chromosomes infinitely more amenable to examination. Released from the entangling web of the spindle body, the chromosomes can be dispersed in a single optical plane and photographed, counted and otherwise examined with much increased facility. Rediscovery of colchicine, more than any other single factor, has brought human karyotyping from the realm of the near-impossible to that of the almost-simple and has thereby launched the science of human cytogenetics.

Other Steps

After the tissue under investigation has been collected, cultured and "arrested" with colchicine, all that remains is to stain, count and identify the chromosomes. Since human chromosomes are very small bodies, the longest being about eight micra, all examinations must be conducted under oil immersion. Success in obtaining good preparations demands that the chromosomes be separated from one another and placed, as nearly as possible, in a single optical plane where they can be photographed.

Chromosome separation is encouraged by treating the arrested cells with hypotonic solutions which swell the cells and disperse the chromosomes. The cells can then be flattened by either physical pressure ("squash" technique) or by air drying. Either method is satisfactory. The chromosomes from cells which have been squashed tend to have somewhat more sharply defined outlines but more of the cells are ruptured and rendered unsuitable for counting. While air dried chromosome preparations may have slightly "fuzzy" chromosome outlines, cells are rarely ruptured.

Any of the basic stains with an affinity for DNA may be used. The stains in most common use are orcein, Fuelgen and Giemsa stains. The chromosomes in as many intact and well spread metaphase plates as possible are counted. Usually, the majority of cells will have the same chromosome number—the *modal number*.

The normal modal number in man is forty-six. In any series of cells, a rare cell will be seen with a hypermodal count and a number of cells will be encountered with hypomodal counts. In good preparations, deviations from the modal number are seldom in excess of five per cent.

In part, non-modal counts are attributable to technical accidents which affect the cells. However, a certain proportion of non-modal counts are not of technical origin. Hypomodal counts become proportionately more frequent in patients of increasing age, reaching an incidence of nearly nine per cent in the older age groups. Most of these non-modal cells reflect abnormalities of the sex chromosomes in the affected cells rather than abnormalities of the autosomes.

Pathologic variations from the modal number of forty-six (aneuploidy) may affect all of the cells studied or may affect only a portion of them (in mosaicism). In some pathologic states, bimodal, or even trimodal counts may be obtained.

Karyotyping is completed by photographing one or several representative metaphase figures, enlarging the photographs to a magnification of about 3000X and cutting out the individual chromosomes. These are then arranged in homologous pairs (within the limits discussed below) in descending order of length.

CHROMOSOME IDENTIFICATION

One of the most fortunate occurrences in human cytogenetics was the early establishment of a standard system of nomenclature for the human mitotic chromosomes. Any reader who has struggled through the literature relating to some of the newer fields (and some not so new) in which standardization has yet to be achieved will fully appreciate the foresightedness of the conferees of the Denver Conference of 1960. The conference, participated in by the major research groups in the infant field of human cytogenetics, produced a workable, logical system of nomenclature to which all of the participants have since adhered with gratifying fidelity. It is indeed a rare article subsequent to 1960 in which a personal system is used in preference to the Denver system. A "conversion table" correlating the personal designations in use prior to the conference is included in Appendix IV.

Unfortunately, this uniformity of terminology seems to have engendered in many authors a false sense of security. Many of the case reports and articles relating to the human chromosomes are typified by diagrams and photographs which show the full human chromosome complement neatly arranged in "homologous" pairs and carefully "identified" by number. The implication left by this practice, namely that human chromosomes can be and are being identified with precision by most laboratories, is entirely false. More recently, this pernicious practice appears to be becoming somewhat less common and the great difficulties of chromosome identification are becoming more widely publicized and recognized.

The Denver Nomenclature

The standard nomenclature devised at the Denver Conference (1960) has a very simple basis. The chromosomes are arranged in homologous pairs in order of descending length and are numbered consecutively 1 through 22. The sex chromosomes are set apart from the remainder of the chromosomes (autosomes) and are designated in the classical fashion as X and Y.

When the human chromosomes are arranged in this manner, they fall rather naturally into seven major groups which have quite distinctive physical characteristics. The Denver group elected to identify the groups by the numbers of the chromosomes which they contain. More recently, individual authors have elected to identify the groups either by Roman numerals or by letter designations for convenience. The major chromosome groups are:

Group A (or Group I)—chromosome pairs 1 to 3—these are the largest chromosomes. They have median or almost median centromeres.

Group B (or Group II)—chromosome pairs 4 and 5—these are large submetacentric chromosomes which have well defined long and short arms.

Group C (or Group III)—chromosome pairs 6 to 12 and the X chromosome—these are medium sized chromosomes of almost equal size which have submetacentric centromeres.

Group D (or Group IV)—chromosome pairs 13 to 15—these are medium sized acrocentric chromosomes which may or may not have satellites on their short arms.

Group E (or Group V)—chromosome pairs 16 to 18—these are rather short chromosomes with nearly median centromeres.

Group F (or Group VI)—chromosome pairs 19 and 20—these are short chromosomes with median centromeres.

Group G (or Group VII)—chromosome pairs 21 and 22 and the Y chromosome—these are very short acrocentric chromosomes which (with the exception of the Y chromosome) may bear satellites on their short arms.

Identification of Individual Chromosomes

Assigning the human chromosomes to one or the other of the major Denver groups presents no undue difficulty in average preparations. Identification of individual chromosome pairs within these groups may be exceedingly difficult and, as often as not, is completely impossible regardless of the diligence with which identifying criteria are applied.

The principal criteria used in chromosome identification are the relative chromosome length, the long arm:short arm ratio and the centromeric index. A carefully drawn table of these values was appended to the report of the Denver conference and is reproduced in full on the following page. There is considerable overlapping of the values obtained by the various investigators.

The relative chromosome length is expressed as the individual chromosome length as a percentage of the total length of the entire chromosome complement excluding the sex chromosomes. The centromeric index is obtained by determining the ratio of the length of the short arm to the length of the whole chromosome.

Other features which have been used with varying success in chromosome identification are satellites, secondary constrictions, and, as a more specialized technique, autoradiography. At the time of the Denver conference, the presence or absence of satellites on the acrocentric chromosomes was thought to be of aid in identifying the various members of these groups. Since then, however, satellites have been demonstrated on all of the acrocentric chromosomes at one time or another and their usefulness as an identifying chromosome characteristic is minimal.

Secondary constrictions are areas of negative heteropyknosis which occur in chromosomes at points other than the centromere.

TABLE II

CHROMOSOME MEASUREMENTS (DENVER CONVENTION, 1960)

Chromosome	Tjio and Puck			Chu and Giles			Levan and Hsu			Fraccaro and Lindsten			Lejeune and Turpin			Buckton Jacobs and Harnden			Range			Group
	A	B	C	A	B	C	A	B	C	A	B	C	A	B	C	A	B	C	A	B	C	
1	90	1.1	48	90	1.1	48	85	1.1	48	82	1.1	48	87	1.1	48	83	1.1	48	82 - 90	1.1	48 - 49	A
2	82	1.6	39	83	1.5	40	79	1.6	38	77	1.5	40	84	1.5	40	79	1.6	38	77 - 84	1.5 - 1.6	38 - 40	
3	70	1.2	45	72	1.2	46	69	1.2	45	65	1.2	45	67	1.2	46	63	1.2	46	63 - 72	1.2	45 - 46	
4	64	2.9	26	63	2.9	26	63	2.7	27	62	2.6	28	62	2.6	25	60	2.6	28	60 - 64	2.6 - 2.9	25 - 29	B
5	58	3.2	24	58	3.2	24	59	2.6	28	60	2.4	29	57	2.4	30	57	2.4	30	57 - 60	2.4 - 3.2	24 - 30	
X	59	1.9	34	57	2.8	38	52	1.6	38	54	1.6	38	58	2.2	32	51	1.7	37	51 - 59	1.6 - 2.8	32 - 38	C
6	55	1.7	37	56	1.8	36	56	1.7	37	54	1.6	38	56	1.7	37	56	1.6	38	54 - 56	1.6 - 1.8	36 - 38	
7	47	1.3	43	52	1.9	35	51	1.9	35	50	1.7	37	51	1.8	36	50	1.7	37	47 - 52	1.3 - 1.9	35 - 43	
8	44	1.5	29	46	1.7	29	48	1.6	33	47	1.7	37	48	2.4	29	46	1.5	40	44 - 48	1.5 - 2.4	29 - 40	
9	44	1.9	40	46	2.4	38	47	1.8	36	45	2.0	33	47	1.9	35	44	2.1	32	44 - 47	1.8 - 2.4	32 - 40	
10	43	2.4	27	45	2.3	30	45	2.0	33	45	2.6	34	45	2.6	27	44	1.9	35	43 - 45	1.9 - 2.6	27 - 35	
11	43	2.8	34	44	2.1	32	44	2.2	31	43	2.2	31	44	1.6	39	43	1.5	40	43 - 44	1.5 - 2.8	31 - 40	
12	42	3.1	24	43	2.1	24	42	1.7	32	43	1.7	37	42	2.8	27	42	2.1	32	42 - 43	1.7 - 3.1	24 - 37	
13	35	8.0	11	32	9.7	10	32	5.0	16	34	4.8	17	33	6.8	14	36	4.9	17	32 - 36	4.8 - 9.7	10 - 17	D
14	32	7.3	12	34	9.5	9	37	4.0	18	35	4.5	19	32	7.0	13	34	4.3	19	32 - 37	4.3 - 9.5	9 - 19	
15	29	10.5	9	31	11.9	8	35	4.7	17	33	4.6	22	31	10.0	9	34	3.8	22	29 - 35	3.8-11.9	8 - 22	
16	32	1.8	36	27	1.6	38	30	1.4	42	31	1.4	42	29	1.4	41	33	1.4	41	27 - 33	1.4 - 1.8	36 - 42	E
17	29	2.8	26	30	2.1	33	29	2.4	30	30	1.9	35	29	3.1	23	30	1.8	36	29 - 30	1.8 - 3.1	23 - 36	
18	24	3.8	21	25	3.8	22	25	2.6	28	27	2.5	29	26	4.2	21	27	2.4	29	24 - 27	2.4 - 4.2	21 - 29	
19	22	1.4	41	22	1.9	34	24	1.2	40	25	1.3	43	22	1.4	42	26	1.2	45	22 - 26	1.2 - 1.9	34 - 45	F
20	21	1.3	44	19	1.3	44	21	1.2	40	23	1.3	43	20	1.2	43	25	1.2	46	19 - 25	1.2 - 1.3	40 - 46	
21	18	3.7	21	15	6.8	13	13	2.5	28	19	2.5	29	15	2.3	31	20	2.5	29	13 - 20	2.3 - 6.8	13 - 31	G
22	17	3.3	23	12	6.0	14	16	2.0	33	17	2.3	30	13	4.0	20	18	2.7	27	12 - 18	2.0 - 6.0	14 - 33	
Y	19		0	11		0	18	4.9	17	22	2.9	26	18		0	18	4.9	17	11 - 22	2.9 -	0 - 26	

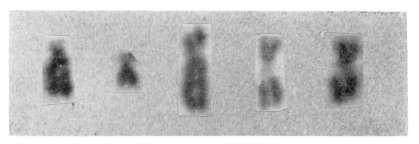

Figure 16. Morphology of Satellites and Secondary Constrictions. (*From left*) Positively heteropyknotic satellite, group G. Negatively heteropyknotic satellite, group D. Short arm constriction, group B. Long arm constriction, both chromatids, group C. "Achromatic gap," group C.

These have proven to be extremely useful identifying features in other organisms (especially in plants) and appear to offer considerable potential as useful identifying features in human material. They may present a number of morphologic variants and may appear as areas of pale "puffing," as areas of sharp narrowing of a chromatid, as areas of pallor or, more uncommonly, as completely achromatic gaps.

The appearance and the incidence of secondary constrictions may be accentuated by culturing cells in media which are slightly deficient in calcium. They may also be enhanced by using modified fixation techniques. Investigation of secondary constrictions using modified media and fixation is in its early stages and the reproducibility of the findings so far reported has yet to be confirmed. Even at this relatively early stage of development, the investigation of secondary constrictions seems to offer considerable potential as a means of identifying human chromosomes with more facility. Some constrictions have been reported by several different authors as occurring in the same chromosomes. These constrictions are indicated in the ideogram despite the reservation which must be entered in respect to their ultimate validity.

Autoradiographic studies, in which dividing cells are tagged with radioactive tritium (^{3}H) incorporated into the thymidine molecules added to the culture medium, have been used extensively by several groups of investigators. As cells divide, the DNA of the chromatin in certain portions of the chromosome will replicate either earlier or later than the remainder of the DNA in the chromosome. The later replicating portions retain their induced radioactivity longer than other areas and are still "hot" in metaphase preparations. The replication times for various parts of the individual chromosomes seem to be fairly reproducible. Autoradiography is a technique which is too cumbersome for the average diagnostic laboratory and hence it seems unlikely that the method will gain wide use as a means of identifying chromosomes within the forseeable future.

An even more specialized technique which is being applied to human chromosome identification is the study of the chromosomes in prophase. At this stage of the mitotic cycle, the chromosomes are represented by the threadlike chromonemata along which are strung the chromomeres. The chromosomes are intricately tangled together at this stage and the techniques which have been used for their separation are very vigorous and result in cell loss and loss of chromosomes. Despite these deficiencies, the preliminary investigations reported suggest that chromomere distribution is fairly characteristic and may ultimately be of value in chromosome identification and mapping.

Even when all of these techniques are employed, chromosome identification in man remains imperfect. One of the most experienced investigators in this field, Klaus Patau, has expressed the opinion that only chromosome pairs 1, 2 and 3 and pairs 16, 17 and 18 can be identified with reasonable certainty in average preparations. In superior preparations, if the chromosomes can be paired accurately, then chromosome pairs 4 and 5 and chromosome pairs 19 and 20 can often be identified with confidence. The individual members of Group C (pairs 6 to 12 and X) are virtually impossible to identify accurately. The difference in size between adjacent pairs is, not infrequently, less than the normal variation in size (about 5 per cent) which occurs between the homologues within a pair.

It is interesting to note that animal cytologists working with other organisms such as *Ellobius lutescens* which have very simple chromosome complements also comment upon the difficulty in identifying individual chromosomes with accuracy. Some, in fact, have attempted to apply the criteria of the Denver group to these animal chromosomes. These criteria do not enhance the accuracy with which the chromosomes of other mammalian forms can be identified.

There are no satisfactory criteria for the identification of the sex chromosomes, X and Y. The X chromosome is very similar in size and appearance to the remainder of the chromosomes in group C. Its position within the group is uncertain although the preponderance of opinion places it somewhere in the size range of pair 6 or 7. Similar difficulty attends the identification of the Y chromosome. This has been regarded as the largest, the smallest or about the same size as the other chromosomes in group G. Most generally, it is regarded as the largest member of the group.

Both of the sex chromosomes tend to be heteropyknotic and to reproduce slightly out of phase with the remainder of the chromosome complement. This *allocycly* may influence the relative length of these chromosomes within the complement. Depending upon the stage of metaphase in which the cells are arrested, and upon some technical factors (such as colchicine concentration), the total complement length (the sum of the lengths of all of the autosomes) may vary considerably. The ratio of the length of the X chromosome (X) to that of the total complement (TCL) may vary considerably between long complements and short complements. This difference is measurable in such organisms as the *Diptera*, and, if it also occurs in man, may account for some of the difference of opinion as to the position of the X chromosome relative to other members of the human chromosome complement.

The X/TCL ratio also shows demonstrable differences in complements with isopyknotic X chromosomes when these are compared with complements with heteropyknotic X chromosomex. Since one of the X chromosomes of the human female is heteropyknotic this phenomenon may also influence the identification of the X chromosome.

Among the various factors which make *accurate* karyotyping difficult or impossible in man are the hereditary variations in size and morphology which are known to occur in chromosomes. Such hereditary variations, which are not necessarily related to any alteration in phenotype, have been most extensively reported in respect to satellite size and the size of the Y chromosome. Some of these variations are, in fact, inherited in a Mendelian fashion and may serve as useful markers in chromosome mapping. It seems improbable that such size variations are confined to the Y chromosome.

Variations in the apparent size of chromosomes may be a consequence of technical factors. Chromosomes which are in early metaphase are longer and less strongly contracted than those in late metaphase. There is also reason to presume that chromosome contraction is not equal in all chromosomes, particularly when colchicine is being used. There are many examples of morphologic dissimilarity between homologues. Heteropyknosis of one X chromosome in females is an example of such non-homology. Other examples are the presence of a satellite on only one member of a chromosome pair or the presence of a secondary constriction in only one member of a chromosome pair. Again, it seems unrealistic to assume that such variations would not also be apparent in chromosome length.

When these many sources of potential error are considered, it is somewhat difficult to share the confidence of some investigators who feel that, with high quality preparations, accurate karyotyping can be accomplished in all instances. Very experienced investigators may be able to achieve this goal without uncertainty. However, the average laboratory had best adopt a more conservative view of their capabilities. This is particularly true when reports of new chromosome abnormalities are being published. Specific chromosomes should not be implicated unless their identity has been established beyond equivocation.

As a practical matter, exact identification of the sex chromosomes as individual entities is rarely essential when cytogenetic techniques are employed as a diagnostic procedure. Numerical variations in chromosomes are detected readily enough. The affected chromosome group can also be readily identified. Clinical criteria usually provide reliable evidence as to the chromosome involved when this cannot be established on purely morphologic grounds. Abnormalities of chromosome morphology can usually be diagnosed by similar correlation of the clinical and cytogenetic findings. These generalizations do not, of course, apply to the investigation of previously unreported or uncommon chromosomal abnormalities.

The accompanying diagram is an ideogram (idealized drawing) which incorporates the morphologic features which are most commonly used for chromosomes identification at present. Although

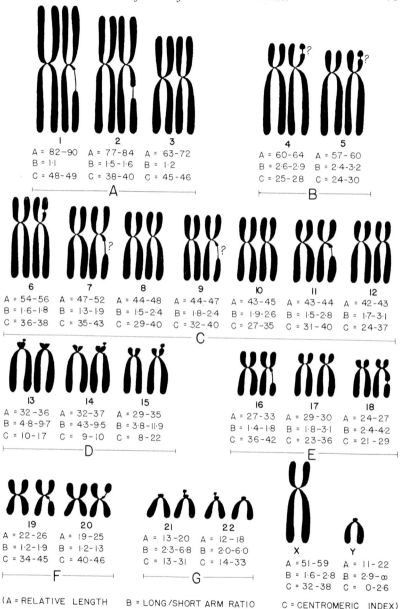

Figure 17. Ideogram of Human Chromosomes (Male).

some reservation must yet be attached to their validity, the most commonly reported secondary constrictions are also shown in the right hand member of each chromosome pair. The photographs

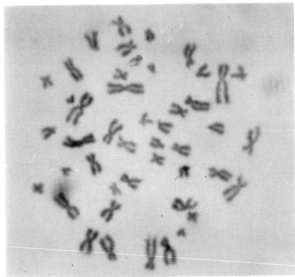

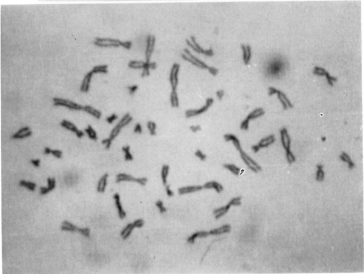

Figure 18. Human Metaphase Chromosomes. (*Above*) Normal female. (*Below*) Normal male.

are those of a normal female and normal male complement both as they appear in a squash preparation and as they appear after karyotyping. Karyotyping has been carried out only within the limits which we feel that we can attain without uncertainty.

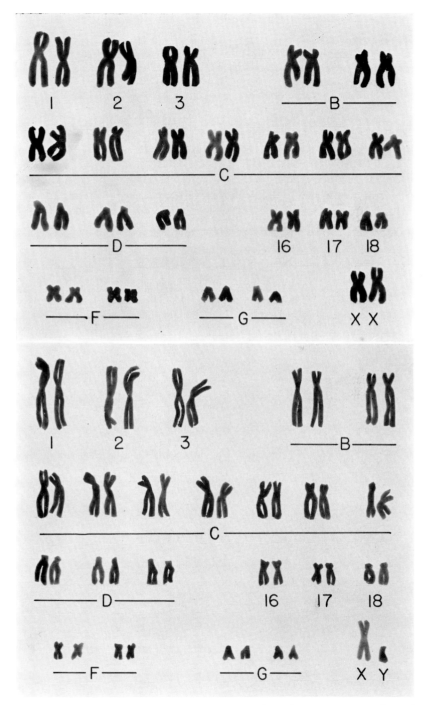

Figure 19. Typical Normal Human Karyotypes. (*Upper*) Normal female. (*Lower*)
Normal male. Note the difference in chromosome configuration in long and short
complements (same magnification).

There will be occasions in the experience of an active laboratory where an attempt to identify individual chromosomes with certainty will be desirable. The following criteria represent a synthesis of many isolated bits of information gleaned from the literature. For the most part, criteria have been tabulated on a "majority rule" basis and reflect preponderant opinion as it exists at the time of writing. If opinion as to the identification of any given chromosome is about equally divided, the fact is noted.

It must be emphasized that these criteria do _not_ purport to be absolute and should not be utilized as though they are. For almost any of the criteria listed, a dissent made by some very competent observer could be recorded.

Group A

These chromosomes are the largest and show appreciable differences in length. As a rule, they present little difficulty in identification even in average preparations.

Chromosome 1—The largest pair of the group, these chromosomes have virtually metacentric centromeres. In both routine and special preparations, the long arm of one or of both of the members of the pair will occasionally bear a narrow secondary constriction about one-third of the length of the long arm from the centromere. Autoradiography will reveal a heavily labelled segment in the midportion of the long arm.

Chromosome 2—This pair of chromosomes is appreciably shorter than pair 1 and their centromeres are slightly eccentric. In low-calcium preparations, an occasional narrow gap will be seen in the long arm. ^3H labelling increases progressively from the end of the long arm to the centromere.

Chromosome 3—The shortest pair of the group, these have almost metacentric centromeres. Secondary constrictions are only occasional. Autoradiography is not very informative.

Group B

Chromosomes 4 and 5 are very difficult to differentiate even when the various special techniques are used. There is little difference in length. Identification should be made with reservation.

Chromosome 4—Slightly the longer pair in the group, these chromosomes have short arms which are usually somewhat longer than the short arms of chromosome pair 5. A secondary constriction is sometimes noted in the long arm of 4 (or 5?) in routine preparations and is accentuated in low-calcium cultures. The group is the most heavily labelled when autoradiographic techniques are used—the labelling of each pair is much the same.

Chromosome 5—The smaller pair, these chromosomes have somewhat shorter short arms than those of pair 4. In low-calcium cultures, the short arm of one of pair 5 (or 4?) may have a narrow constriction in its midportion.

Group C

The members of this group are exceptionally difficult to differentiate. They are all about the same size and have submedian centromeres. Relative length and arm ratio measurements have limited value. Although the longest members (pair 6) and the shortest (pair 12) can be isolated fairly readily, differentiating pair 6 from pair 7, or pair 12 from pair 11 may be impossible. Secondary constructions and autoradiography have very limited value. Using special techniques, two members of the group can be (tentatively) isolated.

Chromosome 6—As the largest pair, this pair can usually be identified with some confidence.

Chromosome 9—One of the larger members of the group, identified as chromosome 9 in the majority of reports (and as 7 in a significant minority), bears a rather striking secondary constriction in its long arm which extends from near the centromere almost to the middle of the long arm. Autoradiographic studies show that this same (?) chromosome shows a striking difference in the labelling of its long and its short arms.

Chromosome 11—One of the smaller pairs in this group, tentatively identified as pair 11, bears an occasional long arm constriction occupying one-fifth to one-third of the long arm. It is accentuated by low-calcium techniques.

Chromosome 12—The shortest pair—two homologous pairs are frequently very difficult to isolate from the four smallest members of the group.

The X Chromosome

In most karyotypes, this chromosome is categorized as a member of Group C, which it most closely resembles. There are no reliable criteria which allow its unequivocal separation from the other members of group C. Most observers regard the X chromosome having a size similar to pair 6 or pair 7. The chromosome may be somewhat easier to identify in females than in males. In females, where the chromosome is paired, one member of the pair often has a peculiarly "fuzzy" appearance (heterochromatic) which is rather strikingly accentuated by special techniques. This change may be more prominent in the short arm of the affected X chromosome. Similarly, in females, one of the X chromosomes is much more heavily labelled ("hot X") in autoradiographic studies than other group C chromosomes. In females (and in males where only one X is present) the other X chromosome presents no characteristic features and appears as a large member of group C.

Group D

Only in very good quality preparations can the members of this group be identified with fair certainty. Accurate identification is usually impossible in average preparations. It is usually easiest to identify pairs 13 and 15 and isolate pair 14 by elimination. Secondary constrictions have been seen on the long arms of the members of the group. They appear only sporadically and seem to vary in position. It is uncertain as to whether these varying positions of the secondary constriction represent constrictions in different positions on different chromosomes or whether they represent variations of a secondary constriction which occurs in only one of pairs.

Chromosome 13—This is the largest pair of the group and has the longest centomere-satellite distance. The long arm labels heavily during autoradiography.

Chromosome 15—The shortest pair, these have the most well defined short arms of the group. This pair labels somewhat more strongly than pair 14 which is the "coldest" of the group D chromosomes by autoradiography.

Group E

Chromosome pairs 16, 17 and 18 are readily identifiable in good quality preparations without resorting to specialized techniques.

Chromosome 16—The largest pair, these have submedian centromeres. Not infrequently, routine preparations reveal a long arm constriction near the centromere which is accentuated with special techniques. There is a striking difference in the intensity of labelling of the long and the short arms of autoradiography.

Chromosome 17—A pair of intermediate size, these have subterminal centromeres with a well defined short arm readily seen. No secondary constrictions have been described.

Chromosome 18—This is the shortest pair in the group and has its centromere inserted so eccentrically as to almost resemble an acrocentric chromosome. A narrow secondary constriction in the long arm is an infrequent feature.

Group F

Chromosome pairs 19 and 20 can be identified in superior preparations which permit accurate pairing of homologues.

Chromosome 19—In the larger pair of the group, a narrow secondary constriction may be seen in very good low-calcium preparations.

Chromosome 20—In the smaller pair of the group, a narrow secondary constriction is occasionally seen in the short arm near the centomere in very good low-calcium preparations.

Group G

The members of this group are very short chromosomes whose morphologic features defy the resolving power of the microscope in all but very superior preparations. Their differentiation is very difficult.

Chromosome 21—The longer pair of Group G chromosomes will frequently bear a satellite on one or both members of the pair. Even when a satellite is absent, an area of pallor at the end of the short arm (so-called SAT zone) may be a useful differential feature. This pair is much less heavily labelled than pair 22 using autoradiographic techniques.

Chromosome 22—The shorter pair of the group, these chromosomes label very heavily with ^{3}H thymidine.

The Y Chromosome

Categorized as a member of Group G in most karyotypes, this chromosome is regarded by most investigators as the largest of the group, somewhere between group F and group G in size (the opinion is not unanimous). The long arms of the Y chromosome generally tend to lie parallel to one another. A most helpful morphologic feature is the presence of a zone of pallid "fuzziness" in the middle of the long arm. This can be recognized in as many as 91 per cent of cells in routine preparations according to some authors. It is accentuated by special techniques. Of all the chromosomes, the Y chromosome seems to be subject to the widest variation in size in normal individuals (though its size in cells from the same individual is fairly constant).

CHROMOSOME MAPPING IN MAN

Chromosome mapping, identifying the chromosomal regions which bear the genes controlling given phenotypic features, is barely commencing in man. At the present state of the art, the only features which have been assigned to a specific chromosome with any certainty are the sex-linked genes which are borne on the X chromosome. To date, the relative positions of even these genes on the X chromosome have not been determined in any more than a most speculative fashion. The majority of the techniques which have been used to great advantage in the study of other organisms have most limited application to the study of human material.

The technique which seems to be most applicable to man is the correlation of observed chromosomal abnormalities with variations in phenotype. Since major alterations in chromosome morphology in viable humans are comparatively infrequent and technical advances which allow detection of minor alterations have yet to be made, even this technique affords only sporadic insights into the gene sequence of man. One of the phenotypic variations which has received attention in mice is that which occurs in antigens and antibodies. Some antibodies can be produced by cells in culture and correlation between chromosome alteration and antigenic variations has been useful.

Transducing systems, useful in other organisms (especially in bacteria) have only extremely limited application to man. These systems are based upon viral infection of cells which results in an association of the virus with the chromosomal material of the host cell. If the chromosome attachment of the virus can be identified, and the virus then induced to infect another cell, the virus may carry with it a fragment of the chromosome of the first host cell. The genetic changes induced in the second host cell as a consequence of this addition of genetic material from another cell may provide an insight into the genetic composition of the fragment so transferred.

Linkage studies in man have been somewhat more useful and have indicated a number of associations between varying genes which indicates that they are probably carried on the same chromosome (although the chromosomes involved have yet to be identified). The most useful mating, at least in respect to linkage studies, is one in which one of the parents is heterozygous at two loci which are under study (double backcross). Linkage studies in man are increased in complexity by the randomness of human matings and by the comparatively small numbers of progeny which each mating produces. Detection of linkage between genes and its differentiation from associations of a chance nature require some very intricate mathematical manipulations.

Chromosome mapping in man within the limits of present techniques is many years away. Accumulation of useful mapping information depends upon the persistent cooperation of all investigators. When reports of chromosomal abnormalities are published, very meticulous reporting of phenotypic abnormalities should be included (or at least recorded by the investigator). In at least one specialty publication, reporters have been encouraged to include a table outlining as extensive an antigen (blood group, haptoglobulin, etc.) survey as possible. A gradual accumulation of information of this sort seems to offer the greatest potential for eventual mapping of the human chromosomes.

CHAPTER VI

ANEUPLOIDY AND NONDISJUNCTION

ABNORMALITIES in the human chromosome complement are divisible into two main classes—abnormalities of number (aneuploidy) and abnormalities of structure. Of the two, the numerical abnormalities are by far more frequently reported. Morphologic abnormalities are discussed in Chapter VII.

Numerical abnormalities of karyotype are collectively referred to as *aneuploidy*. Several classes of aneuploidy can be recognized:

A) Abnormalities affecting entire chromosome "sets" producing cells whose chromosome complement is some multiple of the basic chromosome number (n).

   1) Haploidy—cells with twenty-three chromosomes (n) are seen in normal gametes. Haploidy may occur as an abnormality in some (?) parthenogenetic pregnancies.

   2) Diploid—cells with forty-six ($2n$) chromosomes are present in normal human tissues but may occur in abnormal diploid gametes.

   3) Triploidy—cells with sixty-nine ($3n$) chromosomes.

   4) Polyploidy—cells with ninety-two or more ($4n$ or more) chromosomes.

B) Abnormalities affecting one (or more) individual chromosome(s). These numerical alterations may affect the cells of the body as a whole (*heteroploidy*) or only a proportion of body cells (*mosaicism*).

   1) Monosomy—a specific chromosome is present in an unpaired state ($2n = 45$).

   2) Trisomy—a specific chromosome is present in triplicate ($2n = 47$).

3) Polysomy—a specific chromosome is represented four (or more) times within the complement ($2n = 48$ or more).

4) Complex aneuploidy—two or more specific chromosomes are present in abnormal numbers e.g., monosomy-trisomy ($2n = 46$), double trisomy ($2n = 48$), etc.

C) Supernumerary Chromosomes—extra chromosomes which occasionally appear in the complement either as normal variations of the basic diploid ($2n$) complement, or, more rarely, as pathologic alterations of karyotype.

NONDISJUNCTION

Disjunction, strictly defined, refers to the separation and migration of chromosomes which follows synapsis in the first meiotic division. The term has been broadened to encompass the division of the centromere and the migration of chromatids which occurs in the second meiotic division and in normal mitosis. By far the bulk of the numerical abnormalities of chromosomes are a consequence of failure of this separation-migration mechansim—*nondisjunction.*

The intracellular factors which predispose to nondisjunction are only poorly understood. Either abnormal spindle activity or failure of a normal spindle to handle an abnormal chromosome may be implicated. A significant majority of the aneuploidies in man affect the sex chromosomes. While this fact undoubtedly reflects the more serious consequences which attend abnormalities of the autosomes, the sex chromosomes themselves exhibit some peculiarities during cell division which may predispose them to nondisjunction.

During mitosis, there is some tendency for the sex chromosomes to replicate their DNA complement more slowly than the remainder of the chromosome complement. This asynchrony, if exaggerated, may make the sex chromosomes less readily available for incorporation into the spindle body. As a consequence, they may become attached to only one pole of the spindle and migrate only to that pole, with a resulting inequal distribution of chromosomes to the daughter cells produced.

During meiosis, this tendency to late DNA replication is also present. In males, where the sex chromosomes are non-homologous (XY), the usual side-by-side association which characterizes synapsis in the autosomes is absent. Most often, the X-Y association is a more tenuous end-to-end one which is more prone to accidental dissociation. Should dissociation occur before the formation of the spindle (premature disjunction), one or other of the chromosomes may fail to gain a spindle attachment and wander undirected to the same pole as its "homologue." As a corollary, both of the sex chromosomes may become attached to the same pole of the spindle.

The X-Y complex also replicates noticeably later than the remainder of the complement during spermatogenesis. While this phenomenon virtually ensures that no interchange of material will occur between the X and Y chromosome, it enhances the propensity for these chromosomes to associate in rather a loose fashion. Though evidence as yet is hardly conclusive, there is reason to believe that nondisjunction during spermatogenesis may be the more common accident producing sex chromosome aneuploidy.

Aneuploidy also affects the autosomes, though seemingly with somewhat lesser frequency. The autosomes show no striking differences in behavior which provide a convenient explanation for failure of these chromosomes to migrate normally. Only the most indirect evidence exists to support some of the theories which have been advanced. One of the most plausible of these is that such anomalies are a consequence of gene action. There are several well known instances of direct gene influence upon cell division (e.g., the segregation-distorter gene of *Drosophila*). There is ample reason to suppose that some similar gene-directed mechanism may be instrumental in human nondisjunction. The tendency for chromosomal abnormalities to show a familial predisposition has been noted repeatedly.

The presence of chromosomal structural abnormalities predisposes the affected chromosomes to nondisjunction. Whether such structural abnormalities also influence the rate of nondisjunction of unaffected members of the complement is uncertain. There is some evidence that structural abnormalities in any chromosome can affect the disjunctive mechanisms of the complement as a whole.

There is a correlation between the incidence of some chromosomal defects and advancing maternal age. This suggests that ageing may exert some deleterious effect upon the meiotic activity of germ cells. Primary oocytes in man cease their mitotic activity in the intrauterine life of the female. They then enter the extremely long resting (dictyotene) stage which persists until ovulation. Spermatocytes, on the other hand, continue mitotic and meiotic activity throughout the life of the adult male and spermatozoa are hence much "younger" cells than are ova. Little correlation has been demonstrated between paternal age and chromosomal abnormalities. These implications are embodied in the observation "old women have old eggs, but old men have young spermatozoa."

Meiotic Nondisjunction

Meiotic nondisjunction produces abnormal gametes and consequently, after fertilization, abnormal zygotes in whom all of the body cells are affected. Meiotic nondisjunction may occur during either the first or second meiotic division (or both) and may affect either parent (or both). This offers the potential for some rather striking complexity in chromosomal patterns. Many of these hypothetical patterns have been observed in man. The bulk of the highly complex aneuploidies affecting individual chromosomes are those which affect the sex chromosomes. This reflects both the relatively innocuous sequelae of sex chromosome abnormalities and, probably, an inherent predisposition of these chromosomes to such accidents. Similar degrees of aneuploidy have not been reported affecting the autosomes.

Throughout the subsequent discussions, the sex chromosomes will be used as model chromosomes for convenience. The mechanisms discussed are equally relevant in respect to autosomal aneuploidy and the use of the sex chromosomes as examples is not intended to infer that the mechansisms discussed are peculiar to the sex chromosomes in any sense.

Normal first meiotic division (meiosis I) produces two haploid daughter cells (pregametes - primary oocytes or primary spermatocytes) from a diploid parent germ cell. Nondisjunction in meiosis I produces two dissimilar aneuploid pregametes:

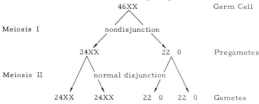

Fertilization of these gametes by a normal gamete (23X or 23Y) will produce 47XXX (or 47XXY) and 45 XO (or 45YO) zygotes in equal numbers.

In the above, and in subsequent examples, one of the conventional modes of expressing chromosomal constitution is used. In this form of shorthand, the number of chromosomes in the complement is shown numerically and the complement in respect to the chromosome or chromosomes in question by the letter or numerical designations of the chromosome (e.g., 46 XX is the shorthand used to designate the chromosome complement of a normal female with 46 chromosomes and two X chromosomes).

Nondisjunction may affect meiosis II as an isolated event. In this instance, each germ cell will ultimately produce two normal and two abnormal gametes. Using an autosome as an example:

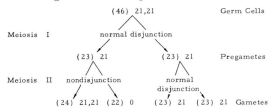

Fertilization of such a group of gametes will produce offspring in the approximate ratio of two normal: one trisomic (21,21,21): one monsomic (–,21).

Thus, if sufficient offspring result from a mating in which meiotic nondisjunction has occurred, the meiotic stage affected may be ascertained fairly readily:

Nondisjunction in meiosis I produces only abnormal offspring, one half trisomic (**XXX** or **XXY** in the example cited) and one half monosomic (**XO** or **YO** in the example used).

Nondisjunction in meiosis II produces normal and abnormal offspring in equal proportions. Of the abnormal offspring, half will be trisomic (21,21,21 in the example cited) and half will be monosomic (–,21 in the example cited).

Examples of nondisjunction in meiosis I and meiosis II and their possible offspring are also shown in the accompanying diagrams.

MEIOSIS I

MEIOSIS II

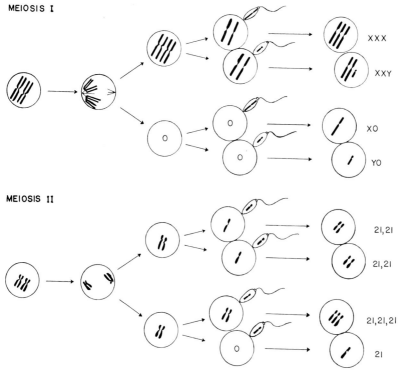

Figure 20. Sequelae of Meiotic Nondisjunction.

The foregoing mechanisms are those of *simple nondisjunction*. The nondisjunctive mechanisms which may occur in meiosis have been classified as:

1) *Simple nondisjunction*—nondisjunction which occurs during either the first or second meiotic division of a germ cell.

2) *Double nondisjunction*—simple meiotic nondisjunction which occurs simultaneously in both parents.

3) *Successive nondisjunction*—meiotic nondisjunction which occurs successively in both meiotic divisions of a parental germ cell.

Viable examples of double nondisjunction or successive nondisjunction have not been encountered affecting the autosomes in man. Many of the hypothetical products of both of these mechanisms have, however, been encountered in the sex chromosome abnormalities (see Chapter XII).

Double nondisjunction may produce any one of a rather broad array of chromosomal patterns in affected offspring:

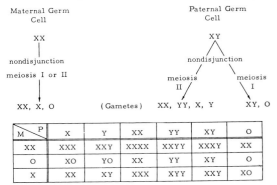

M \ P	X	Y	XX	YY	XY	O
XX	XXX	XXY	XXXX	XXYY	XXXY	XX
O	XO	YO	XX	YY	XY	O
X	XX	XY	XXX	XYY	XXY	XO

All of the hypothetical offspring tabulated, with the exception of the presumably lethal YO, O and YY have been reported in humans.

Successive nondisjunction yields an equally complex array of hypothetical offspring:

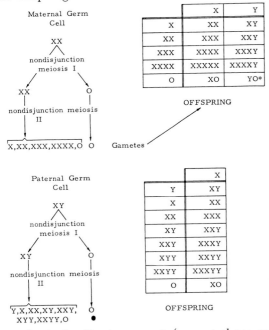

	X	Y
X	XX	XY
XX	XXX	XXY
XXX	XXXX	XXXY
XXXX	XXXXX	XXXXY
O	XO	YO*

OFFSPRING

	X
Y	XY
X	XX
XX	XXX
XY	XXY
XXY	XXXY
XYY	XXYY
XXYY	XXXYY
O	XO

OFFSPRING

Of these hypothetical offspring, most (except those marked with an asterisk) have been reported in man.

In surveying the various nondisjunctive mechanisms which may occur, it becomes apparent that the ratio of offspring will rarely conform to the hypothetical values indicated. Many of the zygotes which are hypothetically possible are undoubtedly nonviable (especially if they affect the autosomes). In addition, of course, the likelihood that nondisjunction will affect gametogenesis with predictable frequency is remote. Nondisjunction is a sporadic phenomenon even in those families in which it occurs with some frequency.

Determining the Source of Nondisjunction Gametes

There are many abnormal chromosome complements which may arise as a consequence of any one of a number of mechanisms. For example, an individual with a chromosome complement of XXX or XXY may, in theory at any rate, be derived as a consequence of simple, double or successive nondisjunction in the parental germ cells. It is sometimes of consequence, particularly if the nondisjunction has a familial pattern, to determine which of the parents contributes the nondisjunctive gametes.

Since marker loci have not yet been assigned to specific autosomes, determining the source of autosomal nondisjunction lies beyond present capabilities in most instances. The situation in respect to the sex chromosomes is less disheartening. Numerical anomalies affecting the Y chromosome are, obviously, always paternal. The X chromosome bears a sufficient number of marker loci that the parental source of nondisjunction involving the X chromosome may be assessed fairly frequently.

The color blindness loci have been of considerable value in this regard. A single example will suffice to illustrate the type of investigations which are being used to elucidate the source of faulty gametes. Color blindness is a typical X-linked abnormality which is carried by, but not expressed in, females (unless they are homozygous—a rare eventuality) and is always expressed in males when it is present. Color blind fathers do not transmit the character to any of their sons. In the example below, these facts are applied to the investigation of Turner's syndrome (45 XO).

An XO individual arises from the fertilization of a normal X-bearing gamete (of either maternal or paternal origin) by a nullo-X nondisjunctive gamete (again of either maternal or paternal origin). If the father is color blind and the mother is normal and

1) The XO daughter is normal, the X must be of maternal origin (*matroclinous*) and the nondisjunctive gamete is therefore of paternal origin.

2) The XO daughter is color blind, the X is of paternal origin (*patroclinous*) and the nondisjunctive gamete is therefore of maternal origin (*unless* the mother is a carrier).

If the mother in the above example also happens to be a carrier of the color blindness gene, the source of the nondisjunctive gamete in the color blind XO daughter is not so easily assessed. The family history and an analysis of other family members should reveal the carrier state if it is present. If the mother is a carrier, some other X-borne locus must be selected for investigation. Diagrammatically,

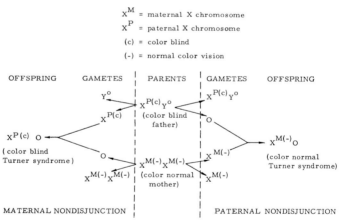

Studies of this type, as well as studies of the incidence of the various classes of offspring, suggest that paternal nondisjunction is a more common cause of sex-chromosome aneuploidy than maternal nondisjunction. The overall frequency of nondisjunction in man has not been determined. The frequency differs among the various chromosomes. The rate of nondisjunction is fairly low—in *Drosophila*, for instance, nondisjunction affecting the X chromosome occurs with a frequency of about $1/2,500$.

Mitotic Nondisjunction

Errors of mitotic disjunction undoubtedly occur with a frequency at least equal that of meiotic nondisjunction. The sequelae of mitotic nondisjunction are similar to those of meiotic nondisjunction. The principal difference lies in the resultant chromosomal constitution of the affected individual. Meiotic errors produce abnormal gametes which, after fertilization, yield zygotes in whom all of the cells reflect the disjunctive error and have the same chromosomal complement.

Mitotic errors, on the other hand, produce at least two distinct cell populations in the affected individual. This is the mechanism by which *mosaicism* arises. The complexity of the mosaicism produced by mitotic nondisjunction varies, and depends upon the stage of development at which it occurs, the viability of the nondisjunctive cells and the number of times nondisjunction occurs.

Nondisjunction in the first mitotic division of the zygote (first cleavage division) produces two cell populations distributed through all tissues in approximately equal proportions. If the chromosomal complement of the zygote is normal, both of the disjunctive lines will be abnormal. Mitotic nondisjunction in the first cleavage in an **XX** individual, for example, will produce a mosaic of the 47 **XXX**/45 **XO** type. That is, about one-half of the body cells will be triplo-**X** with forty-seven chromosomes and the remainder **XO** with forty-five.

Nondisjunction which occurs during the second cleavage division produces a mosaic in whom half of the cells are normal (normally disjunctive) and half the cells are abnormal (the nondisjunctive line). The abnormal cells, in turn, have two different chromosomal constitutions. Thus, nondisjunction in second cleavage division produces *triple stem line mosaicism*.

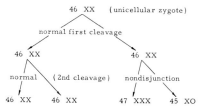

From this point on, assuming equal viability of all the cell lines and no further nondisjunctive mitoses, this individual will have a chromosomal constitution of 47 XXX/46 XX/45 XO in an approximate ratio of 1:2:1.

Many examples of mosaicism have chromosomal patterns which cannot be the result of nondisjunctive mechanisms as simple as these. In general, zygotes arising from the union of nondisjunctive gametes have a tendency to undergo mitotic nondisjunction more readily than those derived from normal gametes. This mechanism is most probably responsible for such mosaic patterns as the 45/46 type:

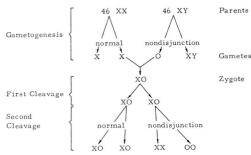

Since the OO form is lethal, the above sequence of events results in an individual who is a mosaic of the 45 XO/46 XX type.

While it is true that mosaicism is a consequence of an error of mitosis, the converse is not necessarily true. Mitotic nondisjunction does not invariably produce mosaicism since one of the cell lines produced may be nonviable. In fact, if the zygote is abnormal at the outset (e.g., 45 XO), nondisjunction in the first cleavage division may return the chromosome complement to normal. In the example cited (45 XO) nondisjunction in first cleavage will produce a viable 46 XX cell line and a nonviable 44 OO cell line and result in a uniform 46 XX (normal) constitution.

Mosaicism in man may be diagnosed by careful karyotyping. Chromosome counts made upon cultured cells will reveal a bimodal chromosome count with two (or more) distinct cell lines, each with its own characteristic chromosome number. True mosaicism may be differentiated from sporadic artefactual changes in chromosome number if the following criteria are satisfied:

1) Chromosome counts which are nonmodal must be too frequent to be attributed to chance alone.

2) The nonmodal cells must themselves have a constant chromosome number.

3) The bimodal count must be reproducible in successive cultures and, preferably, should be demonstrated in two or more tissues.

The fact that the incidence of nonmodal cells does not fit any of the hypothetical ratios shown does not militate against a diagnosis of mosaicism. Aneuploid cells reproduce at varying rates and one cell line may predominate because of a more favorable mitotic rate.

Chimerism

A condition which may also produce a mosaic karyotype is the comparatively rare phenomenon of *chimerism*. A chimera is an individual in whom a genetically distinct line of cells exists which has been introduced as a result of grafting. This phenomenon will occasionally be encountered in peripheral blood cultures made from one member of a pair of fraternal twins. During intrauterine life, blood cells may be exchanged between twin fetuses by transplacental transmission and such cells may be capable of survival and proliferation in the twin to whom they were transfused (grafted).

Several blood cell chimeras have been demonstrated in man. Erythrocytes with blood group antigens completely at variance with those of the host individual have been demonstrated. At least one instance of sex chromosome difference has been proven in chimerical lymphocytes cultured from male and female twins. An almost unbelievable instance of mosaicism resulting from whole body chimerism has been reported. This amazing individual, in effect a fused twin pregnancy, resulted from the fusion of two separately fertilized ova at the one- or two-cell stage of embryogenesis, judging from the evidence accumulated. This fascinating example of chimerism is further discussed in Chapter XII.

An effect of chimerism which has not been demonstrated in man, but is known to occur in animals, is "runt disease." Chimerical lymphocytes which survive and proliferate in the host animal may begin to produce antibodies to the host tissues. The constant outpouring of anti-host antibodies by the interloping lymphocytes produces a constant, low level anaphylactic reaction within the host which may severely impair normal development. Affected animals may succumb to intercurrent infection of degrees which would leave normal individuals unscathed.

Secondary Nondisjunction

The term *secondary nondisjunction* is applied to the unequal distribution of chromosomes to gametes which are derived from an aneuploid parent. In the uncommon event that such an aneuploid individual remains fertile and reproduces, the production of aneuploid progeny is a familial phenomenon. This mechanism, though uncommon, has occasionally been encountered in man:

```
Aneuploid Parent      47 XXX        46 XY     Normal Parent
                        /\            /\
                    secondary        /  \
                                    /    \
                  nondisjunction   normal
                   /       \       /  /    \
                  X         XX    X  /      Y    Gametes
                             \    /
                              47 XXX              Aneuploid Zygote
```

OTHER CAUSES OF ANEUPLOIDY

Nondisjunction is the commonest cause of aneuploidy. There are other less frequent causes of aneuploidy. These are a consequence of abnormal chromosome migration during cell division which most commonly eventuates in chromosomal loss.

One such mechanism is *premature disjunction*. This phenomenon is thought to be the basis for some forms of sex chromosome aneuploidy. As the term implies, chromosomes may separate prematurely during meiosis I, lose their normal orientation at the equatorial plate and both become attached to the same pole of the spindle. Conversely, the loss of normal orientation may eventuate in one of the chromosomes failing to gain any attachment to the spindle body thus becoming isolated from the remainder of the chromosome complement.

Premature disjunction is less commonly invoked as a possible source of autosomal aneuploidy. The propensity of the sex chromosomes to premature disjunction relates to their unique behavior during meiosis. The tenuous end-to-end association which passes for synapsis in the sex chromosomes seems much more prone to dissociation than the intimate side-by-side pairing of the autosomes at this same stage. The non-homology of the sex chromosomes in males (XY) makes them especially susceptible to this accident.

Premature disjunction in meiosis II or during mitosis is a less common event. Premature disjunction in these instances implies early division of the centromere uniting paired chromatids. By inference, it would seem reasonable to assume that this variant of premature disjunction would be less common than would synaptic failures.

Anaphase Lagging

An error which has been seen during cell division in some other organisms has been tentatively implicated in some instances of human aneuploidy. *Anaphase lagging* implies failure of migration of a chromatid after splitting of the centromere. This in turn may reflect a failure of spindle attachment. In consequence, the affected chromatid lies inert at the equatorial plate or meanders aimlessly through the cytoplasm and is eventually lost.

Population studies conducted on mice with various aneuploid chromosome complements indicate that chromosome loss is a very significant factor in the genesis of aneuploidy in this species. These same studies indicate that meiotic nondisjunction, especially in the first meiotic division, is a comparatively rare event whose incidence is far exceeded by that of chromosome loss. Whether the high incidence of matroclinous X chromosomes in human XO aneuploids has a similar implication is uncertain. Nondisjunction during spermatogenesis is an equally likely probability.

SUPERNUMERARY CHROMOSOMES

There are some organisms, both plant and animal, in which the normal diploid number may vary without apparent phenotypic alterations. In these forms, occasional extra chromosomes appear as normal variants of the chromosome complement. These occasional extra chromosomes are called *supernumerary chromosomes* and apparently are nonfunctional. For a short time in the early history of human cytogenetics, some authors (notably Kodani) felt that the normal human complement could include cells with forty-six, forty-seven or forty-eight chromosomes with forty-six being the basic diploid number. Variants of the basic number were attributed to the presence of occasional supernumerary chromosomes. The consensus is that supernumerary chromosomes are not a feature of the normal human complement.

Though most investigators are of the opinion that supernumerary chromosomes do not occur in normal humans, it seems premature to regard the issue as closed. There are two reasons for keeping in mind the fact that "majority rule" is not invariably a sound criterion of scientific validity.

In the first place, much of the study upon which Kodani based his opinions was performed on spermatocytes. These cells have not been widely studied in man and most articles pertaining to the normal human chromosome complement relate to studies of somatic tissues. There are several animals in which asynchrony between somatic and germ cell chromosome complement is a regular finding. Further studies of human testicular material are needed.

Secondly, an appreciable number of case reports have been published which allude to "trisomy of a small acrocentric chromosome." Many of the patients have been asymptomatic or have had such minimal findings that the implication of the "extra" chromosome in their genesis is very tenuous. Many of the authors of these reports concede that a supernumerary chromosome is a possible explanation of the findings.

CLONES

By formal definition, a *clone* is a population of cells which has been derived from one and the same progenitor exclusively by non-sexual (mitotic) reproduction. Thus, by definition, each of the cell lines in a mosaic is a clone. A somewhat more restrictive implication has evolved by common usage in which the term is applied to cell populations within tissues or within organs which differ from the remainder of the cells of the tissue or organ either phenotypically, chromosomally or both. These cells also tend to propagate as an independent population. Either implication is entirely acceptable. As a matter of convenience, we use the term in its more restrictive sense in the classification of chromosomal abnormalities (Chapter VIII) as a handy means of differentiating whole body clones (mosaics) from individual tissue clones.

CHAPTER VII

STRUCTURAL ABNORMALITIES OF CHROMOSOMES

NUMERICAL aberrations in the chromosome complement are dramatic and easy to detect with rather unsophisticated technical methods. They have, therefore, received what is probably a disproportionate share of attention in these early stages of cytogenetic study. There is ample direct and indirect evidence which indicates that chromosomal structural abnormalities will ultimately have the far greater significance in relation to human disease. Doctor M. J. D. White, in fact, presents very convincing arguments to support his view that structural alterations of chromosomes are the ultimate physical basis of evolution.

The import of structural variations in chromosomes may be surmised from the very extensive research which has been done on the large, banded salivary gland chromosomes of the Diptera where the structural alterations are imprinted with great clarity. In man, on the other hand, technical advances have not yet reached the point at which any but the very most gross structural changes can be detected. It seems reasonable to assume, however, that with increasingly sophisticated techniques, more and more of the subtle structural changes will come to light.

GENESIS OF STRUCTURAL ALTERATIONS

Structural alterations are a consequence of chromosome breakage. Broken chromosome ends are "sticky" and will unite very readily with one another. In this respect, broken chromosome ends differ significantly from normal free chromosome ends (telomeres) which will neither unite with one another nor with broken chromosome ends. Intact chromosome ends are regarded as being in-

119

capable of assuming an interstitial position in a chromosome. Thus, any chromosomal abnormality which results in an interchange of material between two chromosomes is the consequence of breakage of *both* involved chromosomes. Simple chromosome fusion without fracture probably does not occur.

Another general principle which should be borne in mind in respect to chromosome breakage and reunion is the fact that fragments which lack a centromere ultimately become lost. This failure of acentric fragments to survive cell division accounts for the absence of some of the chromosome parts which should in theory be present after a structural rearrangement involving two chromosomes. In this situation, it is common for only the larger, centromere-bearing product of the exchange to survive.

Spontaneous and induced chromosome breaks are of several types:

1) *Single chromatid breaks*—these occur after replication and separation of the chromosome into two chromatids has been completed.

2) *Chromosome breaks*—these occur prior to (visible) replication and affect both chromatids at the same locus.

3) *Isochromatid breaks*—these are breaks which occur after replication and chromatid formation but nevertheless affect both of the chromatids at the same locus.

Chromosome breaks may also be classified on the basis of the number of chromosomes affected:

HOMOSOMAL BREAKS—affect only one chromosome.

HETEROSOMAL BREAKS—affect two or more chromosomes.

Chromosome breaks may occur in one of two positions in respect to the centromere:

PARACENTRIC (*homobranchial*) BREAKS—affect only one chromosome arm.

PERICENTRIC (*heterobranchial*) BREAKS—affect both arms of the same chromosome and are thus situated on both sides of the centromere.

Each of the above named types of breaks has its own peculiar consequences.

Truly spontaneous chromosome breakage is probably a rare event. The incidence of spontaneous breakage in leukocyte cultures does not usually exceed 0.0023 breaks per cell. There are many extracellular environmental factors which may induce chromosome breakage (see Chapter VIII) and these are probably involved in the majority of structural rearrangements which affect chromosomes. There are, however, a number of intracellular and intrinsically chromosomal factors which predispose certain chromosomes to a higher incidence of fracturing.

In general, chromosome breaks tend to occur near the chromosome ends or near the centromere, i.e., at euchromatin-heterochromatin junctions. There appears to be an inherent instability at these areas which predisposes them to fractures. Induced (irradiation) fractures occur at random in the euchromatin component of chromosomes. The induced fractures which occur in heterochromatic regions are more orderly and tend to occur in an incidence proportional to the length of the heterochromatic segment. This may also be the case in spontaneous rearrangements.

Of all of the human chromosomes, the satellited acrocentric chromosomes seem most prone to structural alterations. This relates to the specialized function of these chromosomes. In man, as in other organisms, the acrocentric chromosomes are instrumental in the development of the nucleoli of dividing cells. In the course of cell division, chromosomes which serve as *nucleolus organizers* are very intimately associated with the nucleoli and are much stretched and elongated as a consequence of this relationship. The intense distortion to which they are subjected makes them very susceptible to accidental fracturing.

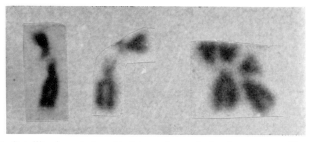

Figure 21. Satellite Association. End-to-end association between satellited chromosomes is common. An extreme example is shown on the right.

In man, there is also evidence that the centromeric region of chromosome 1 and possibly the sex chromosomes also serve as nucleolus organizers. It is true that, aside from the acrocentrics, these chromosomes are among the ones more commonly subject to structural alterations than are other chromosomes of similar size. Preliminary reports indicate the incidence of end-to-end association between satellited chromosomes (satellite association) is significantly higher in patients with chromosome anomalies than in normal individuals.

While the mechanical stresses of nucleolus organization unquestionably play a significant role in producing the high incidence of structural alteration in the acrocentric group, this incidence is also accentuated by other factors. There is some possibility that the high incidence of structural change seen in the acrocentrics may, in fact, be more apparent than real. There are some authors who are not impressed that the acrocentrics are particularly important in nucleolus organization in man.

Defects which affect the acrocentric chromosomes often produce deletions of the minute short arm-satellite portions of their complement. Since these short arms bear only a minute proportion of the genetic material, it is not surprising that their loss would still be compatible with life (since they are mostly heterochromatin anyway). Similar loss of an entire short arm in one of the metacentrics of similar size would be expected to produce considerably more genetic derangement in view of the much larger quantity of functional chromosomal material borne. The very magnitude of such defects would be expected to keep them from clinical attention by producing lethal zygotes or nonfunctional gametes.

Chromosome labeling experiments have produced results which have led some authors to suggest still another explanation for the preponderance of structural rearrangements in some chromosomes. During the course of such investigations, it has been noted that some chromosomal areas complete their DNA synthesis much in advance of other areas. Interestingly enough, the areas which complete DNA replication earliest are the very ones at which structural anomalies seem most common.

This has led some investigators to suggest a "healing time" concept to explain the propensity of these areas to exhibit structural

changes. According to this concept, viable structural rearrangements are more likely to occur if there is ample time for a firm
union of the reattached ends to occur prior to spindle formation.
Fractures which occur at the early replicating areas would thus
have more time to "heal," produce a strong union and therefore
yield viable products. In late replicating areas, then, union would
be less firm and fragments could become lost during cell division.

There are reported examples, in other organisms, of structural
alterations occurring under the influence of direct gene control.
One such gene whose existence has been well established is the
"mutator" gene of *Drosophila*. So far, this mechanism has not been
implicated in man in other than a speculative manner.

SINGLE CHROMOSOME BREAKS

A break which occurs in a single chromosome will not produce
a viable *re*arrangement. When a fracture occurs in a single chromosome, one of two sequelae is possible. In *restitution*, the fracture
reunites immediately and there is no consequent alteration in
chromosome structure. This is probably the more usual consequence of single chromosome breaks. When broken chromosome
ends are present, there is a distinct tendency for those which lie
closest together to fuse (*propinquity effect*).

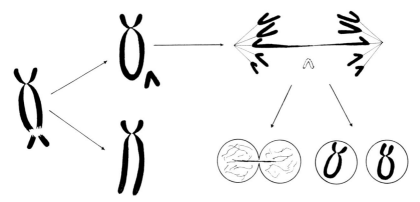

Figure 22. Single Chromosome Break. Single-chromosome breaks may be followed by either restitution ("healing"), *below*, or sister strand reunion and
dicentric formation, *above*.

When a break occurs in a single chromosome, it affects both of the chromatids of the chromosome. If the fractured ends of the sister strands (chromatids) are in closer proximity to one another than to their respective telomere ends, *sister strand reunion* may follow. This produces two abnormal and usually nonviable chromosomes—an acentric (from the fused telomere ends) and a dicentric (from fusion of the two chromatids still attached to the centromere). The acentric is lost. The dicentric fragment forms anaphase bridges which either prevent successful telophase or fracture once again. The latter event initiates a breakage-fusion-bridge-breakage cycle which eventually results in loss of the affected chromosome. Anaphase bridges are rather common following irradiation.

DELETIONS

As the name implies, *deletion* is a loss of chromosomal material. Deletions may arise from single chromosome breaks by the mechanism just described. Loss of the acentric fragment leaves behind a chromosome from which material has been lost—a deleted chromosome. A deletion of the one-break type usually results in loss of the affected chromosome because it produces a dicentric.

Two-break deletions can persist through many cell divisions if their genetic effects are not lethal. Two fractures which occur in the same arm of a chromosome may be followed by reunion of the telomere end with the centromere end of the arm and isolation of the interstitial segment. This type of deletion leaves no free broken ends and is therefore not mechanically unfit for survival during cell division.

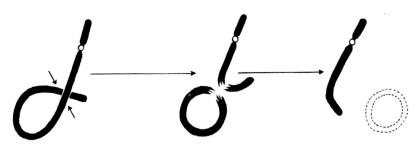

Figure 23. Deletion.

There may be some question in mind as to why broken ends do not merely reunite with their fellows in all instances. Most often, chromosomes are studied in the relatively rigid, rod-like configurations of metaphase. However, throughout prophase, chromosomes are long tangled threads with many loops and coils and are intimately associated with the other chromosomes in the nucleus. The ultimate consequences of breaks depend upon the associations of the moment and these are constantly changing. Microcinematography reveals that the chromosomes during cell division undergo a rather surprisingly vigorous thrashing about which can readily displace fractured ends from their appropriate fellows. In some of the accompanying diagrams, we have tried to illustrate chromosomes in their more elongated form, replete with loops and coils, so that the image of chromosomes as orderly, rigid little rods does not become so firmly implanted that their other morphologic variants are forgotten.

TRANSLOCATIONS

A *translocation* (reciprocal or mutual interchange) may be defined as an exchange of genetic material between two non-homologous chromosomes. Translocation is a consequence of simultaneous or nearly simultaneous breaks in each of the affected chromosomes with union of the fragments with the "wrong" chromosome. While the formal definition of translocation is usually quoted as "removal of a segment of a chromosome to a new location," the term is very rarely used in the formal sense (which embraces nearly all two- or three-break rearrangements). For all practical purposes, the terms "translocation" and "reciprocal translocation" may be regarded as synonymous.

Functionally competent translocation chromosomes are derived from *symmetrical translocations* in which each of the translocation chromosomes receives a centromere. *Asymmetrical translocations* are those in which a dicentric and an acentric chromosome are produced, both of which are functionally incompetent; the dicentric produces anaphase bridges and the acentric is lost.

Translocations are among the commonest of the structural abnormalities reported so far in man. Not all translocations are

ASYMMETRICAL

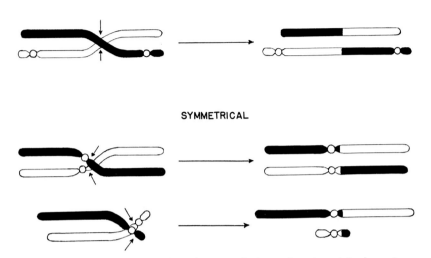

SYMMETRICAL

Figure 24. Types of Translocation. Asymmetrical translocations (*above*) produce non-viable acentric and dicentric forms. Of the symmetrical exchanges (*below*), only the "centric fusion" type (*bottom figure*) can be easily detected in man.

readily detectable, since they may involve segments of nearly equal length. Because symmetrical reciprocal interchanges yield two functionally competent chromosomes without loss of chromosomal material, there may be no resultant phenotypic changes unless position effects are induced. Such interchanges, however, produce complex synaptic figures in meiosis (*vide infra*) which may impair meiosis to such an extent that the translocation carrier (*translocation heterozygote*) is rendered functionally sterile. Probably many nondisjunctive meioses have underlying structural defects.

Chromosome breaks are most prone to occur at euchromatin-heterochromatin junctions. The area near the centromere of most chromosomes is heterochromatic and a considerable proportion of chromosome breaks occur near the centromere. Should two such breaks occur simultaneously, large translocations called *whole-arm interchanges* may occur. Their net effect depends upon the types of chromosomes involved. If two metacentrics exchange arms, or a metacentric and an acrocentric exchange arms, there is usually little morphologic alteration in the complement (especially in man).

However, if whole arm translocations affect two acrocentric chromosomes, both long arms may unite to form one large metacentric chromosome and a minute chromosome composed of the two very tiny short arms of the acrocentrics.

A whole arm translocation between two acrocentrics as described above is referred to by some as a *centric fusion*. The minute short arm chromosome is composed almost entirely of "nonfunctional" heterochromatin and is therefore rather readily lost from the complement. When this occurs, the complement remains functionally unaltered while the number of centromeres is reduced by one (thus, "centric fusion"). This is thought to represent an evolutionary mechanism whereby chromosome complements composed almost entirely of acrocentric chromosomes gradually evolve into mostly metacentric complements with fewer chromosomes.

Since translocations are not accompanied by loss of chromosomal material, something more than their evolutionary implications must commend them to our attention. This is their profound effect upon meiosis. Mitosis is little affected by a translocation chromosome which, unless it is a dicentric, proceeds happily through mitosis like any other chromosome. Meiosis is an entirely different story.

One of the most significant phenomena of meiosis is synapsis and this is where the trouble starts. As has been emphasized before, the pairing which occurs in normal synapsis is extremely exact (probably to the nucleotide level) and chromosomes will spare no effort to pair all of their homologous segments. Thus, a reciprocal exchange is followed by synapsis of *four*, rather than the usual two chromosomes in meiotic prophase. The *tetravalent* which forms is composed of the homologues of the two chromosomes between which the reciprocal exchange occurred and the two translocation chromosomes, all of which are arranged to pair homologous segments. Such tetravalents form a characteristic configuration called a "pachytene cross" which, during diakinesis, is converted to either a "ring" or a "zigzag" figure. The ring forms produce nondisjunctive gametes and the zigzag forms yield balanced chromosome sets in the gametes to which they are distributed (see diagrams).

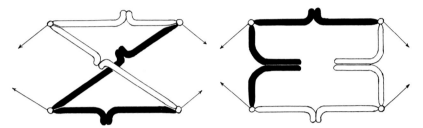

Figure 25. Tetravalents at Meiotic Anaphase. Varying spindle attachment to the centromere may produce either "zigzag" (*left*) or "ring" (*right*) anaphase figures in translocation heterozygotes. These produce balanced and unbalanced gametes respectively.

The results of meiosis are most favorable in some of the whole arm translocations, especially that type which yields a single large metacentric chromosome from a reciprocal translocation between acrocentric chromosomes (centric fusion). This type of whole arm interchange produces *trivalents* rather than tetravalents since the short arm fragments are usually lost. Depending upon the manner in which the centromeres become attached to the spindle, one of two types of segregation of the chromosomes may follow:

ALTERNATE SEGREGATION in which the translocated chromosome and the two homologues move to opposite poles of the cell.

ADJACENT SEGREGATION in which the translocated chromosome and one of the homologues travel to the same cell pole and the other homologous chromosome travels alone to the opposite pole— gametes produced by adjacent segregation are unbalanced.

Should adjacent segregation occur, the resultant gamete is, in effect, the recipient of two homologous chromosomes since the translocated long arm in a centric fusion translocation bears the bulk of the functional portion of the acrocentric chromosome from which it was derived. Fertilization of a gamete which bears the products of adjacent segregation produces a zygote which is functionally trisomic for one of the acrocentric chromosomes. This is the mechanism involved in the carrier state in familial mongolism (*q.v.*).

The least favorable meiotic consequences are those which follow the smaller, segmental reciprocal interchanges. Such small seg-

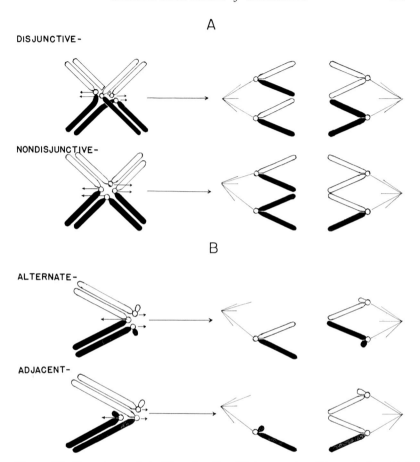

Figure 26. Gametogenesis in Translocation Heterozygotes. The pole to which the spindle thread is attached is indicated by the arrows. Disjunctive anaphase migration produces balanced gametes. In trivalents formed by "centric fusion" translocation chromosomes (*B*), alternate segregation produces balanced gametes and adjacent segregation produces unbalanced gametes.

ments not infrequently fail to undergo synaptic pairing and a random segregation of translocated and normal homologous chromosomes follows. This results in the formation of gametes which bear a variety of deletions and duplications, many of which are lethal. In such a situation, balanced gametes are produced only by chance.

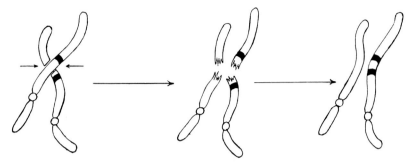

Figure 27. Duplication. Unequal reciprocal exchanges between homologous chromosomes produce chromosome pairs in which affected loci (black bar) are duplicated in one member and deleted from the other member of the pair.

DUPLICATIONS

In essence, a *duplication* produces a chromosome in which one segment is present in duplicate. There are several mechanisms by which a duplication may arise. Probably the most common, particularly where very short segments are affected, is unequal crossing-over. This produces one duplicated and one deleted chromatid and thus, by the time meiosis is complete, two abnormal chromosomes, one bearing a duplication, the other a deletion. Other possible mechanisms are unequal reciprocal translocations between homologous chromosomes and minute insertions which involve homologous chromosomes. A zygote which bears a duplicated chromosome is functionally trisomic for whatever loci are borne on the affected segment (see "Partial Trisomy").

ISOCHROMOSOMES

An *isochromosome* is a chromosome in which the arms on either side of the centromere are physically identical and bear the same gene loci. A true isochromosome is exactly metacentric. There are two possible mechanisms by which an isochromosome may be formed. If two homologous acrocentric chromosomes fracture at their centromeres and the long arms reunite, an isochromosome is produced which consists of two homologous long arms. This mechanism is called "centric fusion" and is similar to an exchange between non-homologous acrocentric chromosomes. An isochromo-

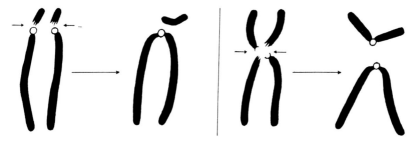

Figure 28. Isochromosome Formation. Isochromosomes may form either as a result of a "centric fusion" between two homologous chromosomes (*left*) or following sister strand reunion in a single chromosome if transverse fission of a centromere occurs after chromatids have formed (*right*).

some may also follow a "centric fusion" involving two metacentric chromosomes. In theory, such an exchange between homologous metacentric chromosomes should produce two isochromosomes but not infrequently two of the fragments produced are acentric and become lost.

A second mechanism by which an isochromosome may arise is transverse fission through the centromere of a chromosome in which the chromatid strands have already formed. If the fractured chromatids reunite with their adjacent (sister) strands, one or sometimes two isochromosomes are produced. This is called *sister strand reunion*.

In general, isochromosomes exert minimal effects upon meiosis. It is only in the uncommon event that either of the above mechanisms produces two isochromosomes and both are transmitted to the same zygote that meiotic abnormalities might follow. The meiotic abnormality would then occur during meiosis in the zygote and result in trivalent formation between the two isochromosomes and their normal homologue. This must indeed be an extremely rare event for it implies gametogenesis in a trisomic individual (whose complement contains three long arms and three short arms—two in each isochromosome plus one in the normal homologous chromosome). To our knowledge, such an instance has never been reported in man.

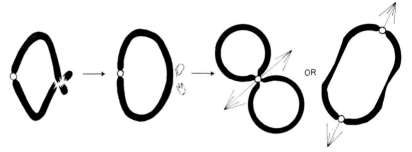

Figure 29. Formation and Meiotic Behavior of Ring Chromosomes.

RING CHROMOSOMES

Ring chromosomes are two-break structural rearrangements which may occur when breaks occur near both ends of the same chromosome simultaneously. The two "raw ends" of the large, centromere-bearing central fragment may unite with one another and form a complete ring. Such forms have been encountered rarely as spontaneous aberrations in man. More commonly, they are discovered in irradiated cells.

The mitotic and meiotic behavior of a ring chromosome depends upon the configuration which it assumes as the chromosome affected splits longitudinally into chromatids. If two small rings are formed, united at the centromere, chromosomal division may be unimpaired. On the other hand, a single large ring may form which is dicentric. This configuration will lead to anaphase bridging and initiates the bridge-break-fusion cycle which is common to dicentric chromosomes.

INVERSIONS

An *inversion* is a two-break structural anomaly which affects a single chromosome. The segment between the two breaks becomes rotated through 180° and reattaches to the chromosome ends. There is a resultant rearrangement of chromosome loci in the fashion:

A-B-C-D-E-F-G ⟶ A-B-E-D-C-F-G

The underlined segment has undergone an inversion.

Inversions are classified on the basis of their relationship to the centromere:

PARACENTRIC INVERSIONS do not include the centromere in the inverted segment.

PERICENTRIC INVERSIONS incorporate the centromere in the inverted segment.

Since there is no loss of genetic material, the phenotypic effects of inversions are often inconsequential.

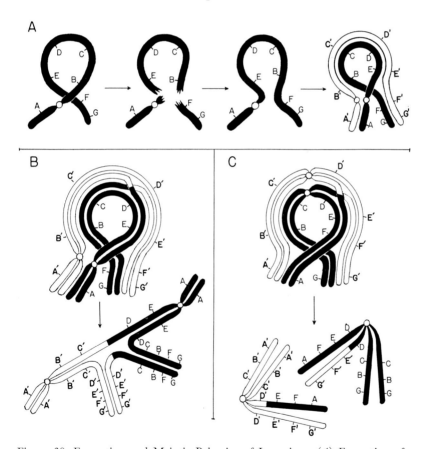

Figure 30. Formation and Meiotic Behavior of Inversions. (*A*) Formation of a paracentric inversion. Synapsis requires loop formation. (*B*) Crossing-over in a paracentric inversion will produce non-viable forms. (*C*) Crossing-over in a pericentric inversion.

Three break inversions are also described in which two segments are formed and each is rotated through 180°. These are called *tandem inversions* and may be of two types:

Direct tandem inversions—the segments are inverted but retain their normal relationship to one another:

A-B-C-D-E-F-G-H ————> A-B-D-C-F-E-G-H

Reversed tandem inversions are those in which the segments, in addition to being inverted, are altered in sequence:

A-B-C-D-E-F-G-H ————> A-B-F-E-D-C-G-H

Again, it is the effect which these rearrangements have upon meiosis which makes them of importance. During synapsis, inversions are characterized by loop formation (*inversion loops*). It is only by formation of such loop configurations that pairing can occur accurately. While the formation of loops alone is not an insurmountable mechanical problem, crossing-over between a normal and an inverted chromosome may produce dicentric configuration which lead to anaphase bridging and consequent cell loss during meiosis. Occasionally, such bizarre forms as loop chromosomes and acentrics result. Even when these severe morphologic abnormalities do not occur crossing-over may produce lethal duplications and deletions.

Inversions are only rarely implicated in chromosomal abnormalities in man. They are extremely difficult to detect unless one is fortunate enough to observe inversion loops in germ cells undergoing meiosis (testicular material is a valuable medium for such study). Cases of inversion with objective evidence of this type have yet to be reported in man. Some authors have expressed the opinion that inversions have not yet been convincingly demonstrated in any mammal.

INSERTIONS

Insertions are somewhat more complex structural rearrangements which require three chromosome fractures. As the term *insertion* implies, a segment of a chromosome is isolated by two breaks and the fragment so formed is inserted into the defect caused by a third fracture in another chromosome. An insertion

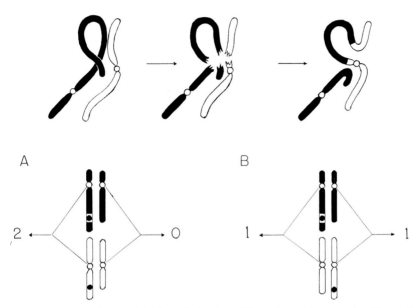

Figure 31. Formation and Meiotic Behavior of Insertions. The genetic effects of an insertion depend upon whether the inserted segment segregates with the intact homologue (*A*) or the donor chromosome (*B*).

cannot arise as a consequence of only two breaks since the inserted fragment would then have to bear a chromosome end (telomere) and these are generally regarded as being incapable of assuming an interstitial position. An insertion may be confined to a single chromosome in which instance it is known as a *shift*.

The phenotypic effect of an insertion which occurs during gametogenesis depends upon whether or not the inserted chromosome segregates with the donor chromosome or with its intact homologue. In the latter instance, the gamete will carry a double dose of the genes on the inserted segment and the zygote produced will be functionally trisomic for this segment. Other possible gametes include those with a normal (one-half the gametes) and those with a deleted (one-quarter of the gametes) gene complement (see diagram).

Occasionally, during synapsis, the inserted segment will pair with the homologous segment of the intact homologue of the donor chromosome. If crossing-over should occur under these circumstances, two entirely new chromosomes will form and will generally produce lethal defects. An insertion is formed:

A-B-C-D-E-F-G + H-I-J-$\underline{K}$-L-M-N————>A-B-C-D-$\underline{K}$-L-E-F-G

and pairs with the intact homologue of the donor chromosome:

$$\frac{\text{A-B-C-D}/\underline{\text{K-L}}\text{-E-F-G}}{\text{H-I-J}/\text{K-L-M-N}} \quad ———> \quad \frac{\text{A-B-C-D-K-L-M-N}}{\text{H-I-J-}\underline{\text{K-L}}\text{-E-F-G}}$$

Crossing-over between the loci indicated may produce the two new chromosomes shown on the right.

PARTIAL TRISOMY

A recently coined phrase with much to recommend it is the term *partial trisomy*. This term was first introduced into the literature on human cytogenetics by Patau in a discussion of duplication and has since been applied to other structural alterations whose clinical sequelae are far more striking than the morphologic alterations which they induce in the chromosome complement.

The term derives from the functional effect which small structural alterations have. This emphasis on functional implications is one of the most attractive features of the term. The introduction of the concept of partial trisomy has served to make cytogeneticists alert to the possibility that small structural alterations may underlie syndromes which are similar to, but less dramatic than, full-blown trisomy syndromes. With attention so focused, it may be anticipated that very careful karyotyping in such instances will uncover the smaller structural alterations which have so far escaped attention.

CHAPTER VIII

ETIOLOGY AND CLASSIFICATION OF HUMAN CHROMOSOME ABNORMALITIES

Occasional references have been made to some of the intracellular factors which contribute to errors in cell division. It is generally felt that environmental factors are of equal or even of greater significance in the genesis of chromosomal defects. A brief classification of these various factors will emphasize their interrelationships:

A) Intrinsic Factors—may induce chromosome abnormalities without environmental influence.

    1) General Factors.

        a) Age.

        b) Genetic complement.

    2) Chromosomal Factors.

        a) Nucleolus organizers.

        b) Sex chromosomes.

        c) Structural anomalies.

B) Extrinsic Factors—environmental factors which may induce anomalies in an otherwise normal complement.

    1) Radiation.

    2) Chemicals.

    3) Virus infections.

    4) Chronic disease, metabolic or infectious.

The role of many of these factors has not been assessed in a quantitative manner. In some cases, their role in human chromosomal abnormalities has been established only inferentially. These various factors will be discussed in the sequence that they have been assigned in the classification.

137

Age

A correlation between maternal age and the incidence of disease has been observed in many of the human chromosomal defects. The best documented correlation is that which exists in mongolism. In many other abnormalities, this relationship, while apparent, is less firmly established. There are some chromosomal anomalies which are unrelated to maternal age (e.g. Turner's syndrome). A correlation between paternal age and chromosomal defects has not yet been demonstrated.

The mechanisms of the deleterious effects of ageing are almost totally obscure. Some authors feel that the efficiency of synapsis and crossing-over is diminished with cell ageing. It seems reasonable to implicate ageing of the ovum as a source of many defects. The effects of ageing appear to operate at the germ cell level. Spermatogenesis is a continuing process in the male and the effects of ageing are certainly much less striking if they exist at all.

Some authors have suggested that the relationship between increasing age and an increasing incidence of chromosomal defects may be due in part to the steadily accumulating effects of background and other radiation to which man is subjected. It seems probable that this is a factor, albeit a minor one. More important, however, is the evidence that ageing *per se* is accompanied by increasing numbers of nonmodal cells. This implication has been stressed by authors who advance the view that rapidly dividing cells are "older" mitotically than those cells which divide slowly or not at all. The mitotic behavior of the sex chromosomes seems particularly prone to be altered by ageing.

Genetic Complement

Direct gene control of cell division is reasonably well established as a source of chromosomal derangements in other organisms. Such loci as the "segregation-distorter" and the "mutator" loci of *Drosophila* have been extensively investigated. Another such locus, the *claret* locus of *D. simulans* interferes with the proper organization and function of the spindle apparatus. There are many reports of unrelated chromosomal defects occurring in sibships and in successive generations in human families. The familial incidence of such defects suggests that similar loci are operative in at least some of the human chromosomal derangements.

Nucleolus Organizers

The role of the acrocentric chromosomes in the organization of the nucleolus in human cells and the mechanical consequences of this involvement have been discussed at some length in Chapter VII.

Sex Chromosomes

The sex chromosomes have two inherent qualities which make them susceptible to mitotic and meiotic accidents. These are late replication of DNA and non-homology of the sex chromosomes in the male (see Chapter VII).

Structural Anomalies

The mechanical impairment which various structural anomalies exerts upon subsequent cell division is discussed in detail in relation to each of these anomalies. Structural defects also exert a detectable influence upon the chromosome complement generally. Structural anomalies which impair chiasma formation in one chromosome pair are often accompanied by a compensatory increase in chiasma frequency in other members of the complement. There are probably other general effects on the complement as a whole which have yet to be elucidated.

Radiation

The effects of various types of radiant energy upon dividing cells has been investigated rather intensively. The major attention has been directed to x-irradiation. Exposure of cells in tissue culture to x-ray induces structural chromosomal changes in rough proportion to the dose of radiation given. Divided doses of radiation produce more striking changes than equal doses administered singly.

The precise physical and chemical changes induced by radiation are becoming known with increasing clarity. The principal mediator of x-ray effects appears to be "free radicals" of the $HO\cdot$ and $HO_2\cdot$ type. These particles are chemically hyper-reactive and unite with a variety of chemical groupings. Their chemical reactivity is of sufficient magnitude to induce cleavage of already established chemical bonds. These radicals, acting on the DNA helix, may rupture it and the entire chromatid. The validity of the "free radical" concept is reinforced by studies on cultures treated with ozone. Ozone releases free radicals of the type described and its effects on tissue culture mimic those of radiation rather precisely.

At the chromosome level, radiation injury is characterized by fractures of chromosome or chromatid arms. The fractures are distributed in a random fashion throughout the euchromatic segments of the chromosomes but affect heterochromatic segments in an incidence which is proportional to the length of the heterochromatic segment.

The consequences of radiation depend upon the stage of cell division at which the x-ray acts and upon the dose. Cells are much (about five times) more sensitive to radiation after chromatid duplication than are interphase cells. Low doses of radiation induce mitotic delay in irradiated cell cultures. Other early effects include increasing chromosome "stickiness" and anaphase lagging.

Higher doses of radiation produce actual structural defects. If irradiation occurs before the formation of the sister strands, both chromatids are fractured when they are formed. Irradiation after chromatid formation is complete may produce either single chromatid breaks or isochromatid breaks. Occasionally, a break in one chromatid is accompanied by formation of an achromatic gap in the other chromatid without actual fracture.

Any of the structural anomalies which are described in Chapter VII may be induced by x-irradiation. Dicentric and ring formations are very common in irradiated material, the former being a consequence of isochromatid breaks followed by sister strand reunion. Irradiation seems to have little influence on the incidence of aneuploidy—most of the defects produced are structural.

Studies on irradiated cultures reveal an increase in the number of deletions which bears a direct linear relation to the dose. Dicentrics ("two-hit" defects) increase roughly in proportion to the square of the dose. This numerical relationship is, according to some, sufficiently predictable that blood culture studies may be used as a sort of "biological dosimeter" to determine the amount of exposure to which an individual was subjected.

Though the effects of direct irradiation on cultures are well known, the effect of x-ray in producing clinical sequelae in irradiated humans or their offspring is not as well documented. There have been reports of chromosomal abnormalities appearing in peripheral blood cultures following diagnostic and therapeutic x-irradiation of the spine and following administration of therapeutic doses of radioactive I^{131}. In general, the anomalies reach their maximum intensity in three days to a week after irradiation and then gradually disappear. How long these effects persist is a moot point. Some authors feel that they may persist for as long as twenty years. Even such unstable forms as dicentrics reportedly have been found as long as five years after previous radiation.

In the case of irradiation directed to the spine, these findings are not unduly surprising. However, the effects of I^{131} suggest that irradiation has a more widespread effect than was at first suspected. With the evidence presently at hand, it would seem wise to avoid irradiation to as great an extent as possible during the reproductive era.

So far, there has been no report in which x-ray *per se* has been implicated directly in the genesis of heterosomal chromosomal abnormalities in the offspring of irradiated parents. There are several suggestive instances of chromosomal abnormalities in the children of parents with a history of exposure. One retrospective analysis of the effects of maternal irradiation in relation to the incidence of mongolism in the offspring is suggestive, but hardly conclusive.

Chemicals

Chemical induction of chromosomal abnormalities is a well known phenomenon which, in fact, is turned to advantage in the use of colchicine in cytogenetic studies. There are at least three possible mechanisms by which chemical compounds may induce abnormalities in cell division—radiomimetic, as a mitotic poison or acting as a nucleotide analog. In each instance, the mechanisms involved are somewhat different.

The group of drugs referred to as *radiomimetic* drugs are those which induce chromosomal changes similar to those induced by x-irradiation. Good examples of this type of drug action are seen in nitrogen mustard and Cytoxan (cyclophosphamide). These compounds induce chromosome fractures and structural anomalies which include dicentrics, rings and other defects very similar to those induced by x-ray. It seems improbable that the "free radicals" which are produced by x-ray are instrumental in the changes induced by the radiomimetic drugs.

Mitotic poisons, of which colchicine is an excellent example, act by impairing the normal mechanisms of cell division. Colchicine, for instance, inhibits formation of the spindle apparatus and results in an accumulation of metaphase figures (the so-called C-mitoses) which eventually degenerate. Other mitotic poisons increase the stickiness of chromosomes and may induce formation of pseudochiasmata. Late acting mitotic poisons may inhibit cell wall formation between daughter nuclei (statmodiaeresis). Extreme cytotoxic effects produce both nuclear and cytoplasmic degenerative changes.

The drugs which act as nucleotide analogs are capable of being incorporated into the DNA molecule but are incapable of functioning in the same fashion as the nucleotide which they replace. Bromouracil is an example of such a drug. When incorporated into the DNA helix, such a drug is incapable of functioning in the genetic coding system and may convert an otherwise meaningful segment to a nonsense region. In this fashion, the net effects are somewhat similar to chromosomal deletions. Other analogs, such as 6-azaguanidine which is a pyrimidine analog, interrupt the normal pathway for the synthesis of new nucleic acids.

Viral Infections

An allusion to the well known effects of the rubella virus in early pregnancy is sufficient to emphasize the demonstrable effects which viruses may have upon the genetic mechanisms of a human host. In theory, at least, one may envision four mechanisms through which a virus might influence the chromosomal behavior of the host. The role of some of these mechanisms in man is still speculative.

Viruses may induce chromosome breakage and structural anomalies in the chromosome complement of host cells. This mechanism has been only recently demonstrated in man. Peripheral blood

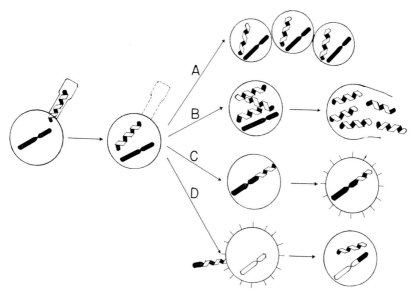

Figure 32. Cell-Virus Relationships. (*A*) A temperate phage. (*B*) A virulent phage. (*C*) Transformation. (*D*) Transduction. (*See text for discussion.*)

karyotypes performed at intervals after viral infections (measles was the first so investigated) have demonstrated increased numbers of deleted chromosomes, chromosome breaks and chromatid defects. That these defects are not inherent in the individuals under study is shown by their decreasing incidence over a period of time. The action is roughly analogous to the action of radiation and radiomimetic drugs which invoke similar chromosomal changes. Whether these fractures are a consequence of direct viral action upon the DNA helix or reflect some metabolic derangement induced by the virus is unknown.

A second mechanism which might account for viral modification of chromosome function is *lysogeny*. This is a mechanism which is well known in viral infections of bacteria. Bacteriophage viruses may infect bacteria, reside within them and duplicate their viral DNA (or RNA) in synchrony with that of the host. To all intents and purposes, a symbiotic existence becomes established which has no apparent effect upon the host bacterium. Such phages are called *temperate phages*.

Unfortunately for the affected bacterium, this amicable relationship between the virus and its host does not long endure. Sooner or later, under some metabolic or environmental stimulus as yet unknown, the virus begins to multiply within the host, completely commandeers the host's DNA-RNA synthesizing capabilities and produces eventual destruction of the host bacterium. This phenomenon, a peculiarity of the lysogenic strains of bacteriophage, is a reflection of the activity of a *virulent phage*. The virus SV40, which infects hamster tissues in culture, may "disappear" from infected cultures, be totally undetectable for several generations and then reappear "spontaneously" in some later generation. The similarity of this sequence to lysogeny in bacteria is striking. A similar mechanism has not been demonstrated in man although the activity of such viruses as the herpes simplex virus seem to us to be rather curiously reminiscent of lygogeny as well.

Another viral alteration of chromosomal function and probably of chromosome structure may result from incorporation of viral DNA into the genetic complement of the host cell. This mechanism, called *transformation*, is known to exist at the bacterial level. Viral transformation is responsible for the virulence of *Corynebacterium diphtheriae*, for instance. The relationship between viruses and such animal tumors as the Shope rabbit papilloma may be predicated upon such a mechanism resulting from incorporation of the viral DNA into the genome of the host epithelial cells.

The fourth possible way in which viral infection may alter the chromosomal pattern of a host cell is through the mechanism of *transduction*. Briefly, a virus which infects a cell may become attached to the host cell's DNA. When the host cell degenerates, the virus is released to infect another cell. In the process, the virus may carry with it a portion of the host cell's DNA complement and introduce it into the DNA complement of the second host cell. This is a well known mechanism at the bacterial level and has, in fact, been used as an experimental system in chromosome mapping.

Though only chromosome fracturing following viral infection is a mechanism which is known to occur in man, it seems probable that all of the four possible host cell-virus reactions will ultimately be discovered in human material. There is extensive research directed to the influence of viruses in human neoplasia. From such research many intriguing relationships will probably be elaborated.

Chronic Disease

Both metabolic and chronic infectious diseases produce widespread alterations of the cellular environment within which chromosome activity occurs. It might well be supposed that chronic disease would thus be responsible for at least some of the chromosomal abnormalities of man. An increased incidence of such abnormalities has been noted in experimental animals suffering chronic infectious and nutritional disease.

To date, the association between chronic disease and chromosomal defects is recorded only sporadically in man. For example, an instance of trisomy has been reported in the child of a hyperthyroid mother and the relationship between pregnancy losses and thyroid defects was emphasized by the authors of the report. No firm conclusions should be drawn from such occasional reports, though the fact that such reports do appear from time to time suggests that some such etiologic relationship does exist.

CLASSIFICATION OF HUMAN CHROMOSOME DEFECTS

It is generally useful to have an orderly framework within which to arrange a subject with as many complexities as the human chromosomal abnormalities. We have devised the classification published below principally as a convenient means of keeping the various disorders of chromosome structure and number catalogued in a comprehensive fashion. The chromosomal abnormalities described so far are classified on this basis in Appendix V.

From time to time, we have introduced minor modifications into our original classification as published elsewhere. Such modifications are necessitated by increasing familiarity with the field. The classification is offered as a useful starting point for the subsequent discussions of clinically significant aberrations.

I) Aneuploidy (abnormal chromosome number).

    I A) Heterosomy—aneuploidy affecting all body cells.

        1) Isolated monosomy—absence of one member of a chromosome pair without associated abnormalities. Diploid number (2n) = 45.

           a) Autosomal.

           b) Sex chromosomal.

        2) Isolated trisomy—one chromosome is present in triplicate without associated abnormalities. Diploid number = 47.

           a) Autosomal.

           b) Sex chromosomal.

        3) Isolated polysomy—four or more identical chromosomes present without associated abnormalities. Diploid number = 48 or more.

           a) Autosomal.

           b) Sex chromosomal.

        4) Complex aneuploidy—numerical abnormalities of two or more chromosomes without structural abnormalities. Diploid number varies.

           a) Autosomal.

           b) Combined autosomal—sex chromosomal.

        5) Triploidy.

    I B) Aneuploid Mosaics—aneuploidy affecting a proportion, rather than all, of the body cells.

    I C) Supernumerary Chromosomes.

II) Structural Anomalies.

    II A) Generalized.

        1) Translocations.

           a) Autosomal.

           b) Sex chromosomal.

        2) Duplications.

           a) Autosomal.

           b) Sex chromosomal.

        3) Deletions.

           a) Autosomal.

           b) Sex chromosomal.

       4) Isochromosomes.
          a) Autosomal.
          b) Sex chromosomal.
       5) Inversions.
          a) Autosomal.
          b) Sex chromosoml.
       6) Others (combined or unusual structural defects).

II B) Structurally Anomalous Mosaics.

III) Structurally anomalous aneuploids—combined aneuploidy of one chromosome and structural abnormality in another.

IV) Structurally anomalous aneuploid mosaics—individuals in whom one cell line is aneuploid, another structurally abnormal and with or without a normal cell line.

V) Clones—aneuploidy or structural abnormality of a cell line within an organ or tissue which (generally) yields distinct phenotypic differences between the normal cells and the anomalous clone.

The distinction is drawn between autosomal and sex chromosomal defects on the basis of their rather striking differences in clinical presentation. For the purposes of classification, the sex chromosomes are regarded as "homologues" e.g. sex chromosome trisomy may be the consequence of either extra X or extra Y chromosomes being present in the complement.

CHAPTER IX

INDICATIONS FOR CYTOGENETIC TESTING

In the preceding chapters, we have explored the basic principles upon which the new medical subscience of cytogenetics is based. In the following chapters, we will discuss the various clinical syndromes which are associated with chromosomal abnormalities. None of this discussion, however, provides a succinct answer to the questions, "What clinical value do these tests have?" and "How are these tests used?"

So far, the literature in cytogenetics has failed to provide an answer to these most pertinent queries except by indirection. Before already overburdened physicians can be expected to turn their attention to a field replete with a new and unfamiliar system of esoteric terminology, their efforts must be justified by the expectation of finding something in the field which will help them practice medicine.

Used with a definite intent, cytogenetic techniques can be of inestimable value to a practicing physician in almost any of the medical specialities. Not only do cytogenetic techniques offer an insight into the etiology of many abnormalities, they meet the ultimate test of practicality in that the information gained by their employment may modify the course of further investigation and treatment of the patient. In this chapter, we hope to show how to use these tests to their fullest advantage.

Cytogenetic techniques find their most concentrated applicability in two age groups—the newborn and the reproductive adult. One fairly common misconception seems to be that chromosome studies are concerned with sexual malformation and malfunctions almost exclusively. A list of clinical applications follows—its breadth will no doubt surprise many readers:

Differential diagnosis of congenital abnormalities.

Genetic counselling of parents with congenitally abnormal infants.

Differential diagnosis of intersex.

Investigation of primary amenorrhea.

Investigation of female infertility.

Investigation of male infertility.

Differential diagnosis of blood dyscrasias.

Differential diagnosis of dysproteinemia.

Medicolegal applications.

Antenatal sex determination.

The above list includes applications which have established clinical value. There are other applications which give every promise of having equal clinical value but are still in the investigative stages. In selected instances, and with recognition of their current limitations, cytogenetic examinations in the following instances can be of value:

"Biological dosimeter."

Detection of neoplastic cells in effusions and secretions.

Investigation of habitual abortion.

These applications will now be explored more fully.

Congenital Abnormalities

The presence of severe congenital abnormalities in the newborn is usually perfectly obvious. However, it is not always obvious whether these anomalies are chromosomal or metabolic. A case in point is the differentiation of mongolism from cretinism in the newborn. This is not always a simple differentiation but is one which must be *firmly* established as early as possible if the few cretins which do appear are to be salvaged.

Karyotyping in the newborn requires only that peripheral blood be obtained for tissue culture in most instances. This is neither unduly hazardous nor difficult. If karyotyping is done as a fairly routine procedure when abnormal newborns are encountered, the pediatrician and obstetrician will be much better equipped to cope with parental inquiries in respect to prognosis for the affected infant and, equally important, the prognosis for future pregnancies (see: Genetic counselling).

In addition, karyotyping performed on abnormal newborns may provide an insight into some of the possible visceral abnormalities which occur in infants with congenital abnormalities. As an example, the stigmata of trisomy-D syndrome are not invariably numerous enough to establish a diagnosis on purely clinical grounds. It is important to establish the presence of the syndrome so that associated visceral defects such as cardiac septal defects, intestinal diverticula, etc., may be considered before they present themselves as unanticipated emergencies.

While it must be admitted that the full blown trisomy syndromes —mongolism, trisomy-D and trisomy-E—are fairly characteristic clinically there are enough "shades of gray" to warrant energetic assessment of any case which presents suggestive stigmata. Adoption of cytogenetic techniques in the investigation of congenital anomalies will undoubtedly reveal a certain number of abnormalities heretofore undescribed.

Congenital malformations account for some fifteen to twenty per cent of infant deaths in advanced countries. Present knowledge has implicated chromosomal abnormalities in about ten per cent of these cases. Another thirty per cent are the result of gene mutations or of maternal virus infection. Some sixty per cent of congenital malformations are of unknown etiology. In this large, latter group there should reside a fruitful field for cytogenetic investigations.

Genetic Counselling

Until the advent of cytogenetic techniques, the physician faced with the distressing task of assessing the outcome of future pregnancies following the birth of a mongol or other congenitally deformed infant was wholly dependent upon statistical analysis. Cytogenetic techniques provide a method of obtaining objective evidence upon which to base such prognoses. To be sure, even with the objective findings of cytogenetic studies, one is still faced with the problem of issuing a prognosis in terms of "odds", but these can be cited with much increased precision and assurance.

Generally speaking, the inheritance patterns of defects associated with chromosomal abnormalities are of two types—sporadic or familial. Each of these is accompanied by a distinctive cytogenetic pattern. Numerical abnormalities of chromosomes such as tri-somy-21 (mongolism) and monosomy-X (Turner's syndrome) are sporadic occurrences. They are a consequence of nondisjunction and are generally nonrepetitive. If a congenital abnormality is on the basis of chromosomal aneuploidy, one may offer an optimistic prognosis. The possibility that two such defects will occur in successive pregnancies is rather remote.

On the other hand, a smaller proportion of congenital deform-ities can be attributed to transmissible chromosomal structural defects such as translocation. These defects have a familial pattern, tend to affect the offspring of younger parents and can readily occur in successive pregnancies. As an example, consider the inheritance pattern of familial (translocation) mongolism.

Familial mongolism is associated with a translocation of a long arm of chromosome 21 (an acrocentric chromosome), generally to another acrocentric chromosome of the 13-15 group or the 21-22 group. A phenotypically normal carrier has a translocated chromo-some plus one normal chromosome 21. Thus, a carrier may produce several classes of gametes depending on whether the normal and the translocated chromosomes are distributed to the same or to separate gametes. If these alternative distributions occur with equal frequency:

Twenty-five per cent of the gametes have no chromosome-21.

Twenty-five per cent of the gametes have both chromosome-21 and T/21.

Twenty-five per cent of the gametes have only T/21 (trans-location).

Twenty-five per cent of the gametes have a single chromosome-21 (normal).

If the above classes of gametes are fertilized by normal gametes with a single chromosome-21, the following distribution of offspring can be expected:

Twenty-five per cent of offspring are monosomic for chromo-some-21 (lethal).

Twenty-five per cent of offspring have two chromosomes-21 plus T/21 and are mongols.

Twenty-five per cent of offspring have one chromosome-21 and T/21—they appear normal but are carriers.

Twenty-five per cent of offspring are normal (two chromosomes-21).

From the above outline, one can discern the probabilities which attend congenital defects which have a chromosomal structural abnormality as their basis. In this situation, one can confidently predict that of the viable offspring (three out of four pregnancies), one out of three will be abnormal. Of the remainder, all of whom look normal, half will be carriers and will transmit the disease to their offspring in turn. This is a very significant difference from the rather optimistic prognosis which may be given following discovery of chromosomal aneuploidy. Aneuploidy and translocation are readily distinguishable using cytogenetic techniques.

Genetic counselling of prospective parents need not await the birth of a defective infant. If either parent has a mongol (or other abnormal) sibling or a family history of such a condition, karyotyping can establish the presence or absence of a familial (structural defect) pattern. Thus such parents may be intelligently apprised of the risk, if any, of this same condition appearing in their offspring.

Though findings are less well documented, karyotyping may offer insight into the etiology of some instances of habitual abortion (*q.v.*).

Differential Diagnosis of Intersex

Truly puzzling intersex states are most often encountered in early infancy when one confronts an infant with ambiguous external genitalia. It is of great consequence to establish genetic sex early and institute corrective procedures soon enough to provide the infant with an appropriate sexual identity. The present consensus is that these infants should be made as nearly functionally competent as is possible within the limits of present reconstructive ability. Many authorities are of the opinion that the gender role is firmly established by eighteen months of age—every effort should be directed to providing an appropriate role by that time.

It is difficult, if not completely impossible, to adopt a rational approach unless the genetic sex is known with certainty. Genetic sex in man is determined by the Y chromosome—Y-bearing individuals are genetic males and non-Y-bearing individuals are genetic females—the number of X chromosomes present does not alter this basic definition. With the means at hand to determine genetic sex unequivocally, it is possible to define "intersex" with precision.

An *intersex*, broadly defined, is an individual in whom the phenotypic sex differs from the true genetic sex. There are three major classes of intersex in man:

Male pseudohermaphrodites—true genetic (Y-bearing) males with varying degrees of female phenotypic differentiation.

Female pseudohermaphrodites—true genetic females with varying degrees of male phenotypic differentiation.

True hermaphrodites—may be either genetic males or genetic females but have *both* ovarian and testicular tissue which is histologically recognizable.

Some of these conditions will ultimately require laparotomy and gonadal biopsy for definite diagnosis. However, if an orderly investigative routine is adopted, laparotomy for diagnosis may be avoided in a significant number of cases.

It would be entirely unwarranted to try to compress the entire subject of human intersex into a few paragraphs and many of the subtleties must be completely ignored in this discussion. A few general guidelines can, however, be advanced for the investigation of such problems. The first facts which need emphasis are these:

Buccal and polymorphonuclear leukocyte chromatin tests do not reflect true genetic sex.

True genetic sex can be established unequivocally only by karyotyping.

Intersex in the newborn is characterized by ambiguous genitalia. In such an infant, cytogenic procedures will determine the category within which the infant should be placed. Genetic females (female pseudohermaphrodites) are masculinized in infancy almost exclusively as a consequence of adrenal virilism—this can be confirmed using 17-ketosteroid determinations. The few instances of sexual ambiguity in genetic female infants which are not examples of adrenal virilism are generally true hermaphrodites. True hermaphrodites are most commonly true genetic females (XX) and the diagnosis can be confirmed only by laparotomy.

Sexual ambiguity in a genetic male infant (XY) may reflect either testicular feminization or true hermaphroditism. Both of these conditions ultimately require gonadal biopsy for definitive diagnosis. The above comments indicate that only one type of infant intersex can be diagnosed without gonadal biopsy—adrenal virilism. This is not such a great disadvantage since the bulk of intersexes (well over half) which present as such *in infancy* are of this type.

Testicular feminization often produces such a perfect female phenotype that the condition remains unnoticed in infancy. The condition may, in fact, remain unnoticed until the time of puberty when these "females" may begin to masculinize or primary amenorrhea is noted. True hermaphroditism is a rare condition at any age.

Other sexual abnormalities do not usually present as clinical intersexes but as instances of amenorrhea (*q.v.*) or sterility (*q.v.*). In this regard, it must be emphasized that Turner's syndrome (chromatin negative gonadal dysgenesis) and Klinefelter's syndrome (chromatin positive testicular tubular dysgenesis) are *not* intersexes. Though they were so categorized briefly on the basis of their chromatin pattern, this basis for the classification of intersex has been discarded. Klinefelter's syndrome occurs in genetic males (XX*Y*) and Turner's syndrome in genetic females (XO— *no* Y) whose phenotype, though imperfect, is fully in accord with their genetic constitution.

Primary Amenorrhea

Failure of the menstrual cycle to commence, *primary amenorrhea*, is a comparatively uncommon condition in phenotypic females. When it is encountered, however, its investigation may become a tedious and expensive project. If an etiology is not discovered empirical cyclic hormonal therapy may be even more discouraging. Early karyotyping can circumvent both the tedium and expense of repeated hormone studies and futile courses of hormone therapy in somewhat over one-quarter of such cases. In this group, some defect of sex chromosomal complement can be found.

This high (twenty-seven per cent) incidence of chromosomal defects in primary amenorrheics was encountered in a comparatively large series of such patients, many of whom exhibited little or no phenotypic evidence of sex chromosome abnormality. Testicular feminization and true hermaphroditism may present as primary amenorrhea in "normal" females.

Female Infertility

An appreciable percentage of cases of female infertility have their basis in sex chromosome abnormalities. Buccal chromatin studies and karyotyping should be among the earliest diagnostic procedures employed in sterility studies. In addition to the chromosomal findings cited in primary amenorrhea, a significant percentage of patients with oligomenorrhea or even apparently normal menses may have chromosomal abnormalities.

While sex chromosome abnormalities do not militate against pregnancy altogether, their early discovery can obviate much unrewarding laboratory investigation. Sex chromosome mosaicism particularly, may yield infertility in otherwise normal-appearing females. Since karyotyping involves little more than obtaining a peripheral blood sample in many cases, there is little reason that this test should not be an early step in fertility studies.

Male Infertility

The majority of chromosomally induced instances of male infertility can be suspected on the basis of their clinical appearance. The principal type of chromosome defect inducing male infertility is Klinefelter's syndrome and its variants. A combination of testicular hypoplasia and chromatin positive buccal smears is diagnostic —even karyotyping is not essential to the diagnosis in clinically typical instances.

On occasion, male infertility may follow some less characteristic chromosomal abnormality such as mosaicism or XYY. Either of these conditions may be detected by karyotyping. Early karyotyping of the infertile male may obviate the need for more vigorous procedures such as testicular biopsy.

Blood Dyscrasias

In blood dyscrasias, the value of karyotyping as a differential diagnostic test is best established in the distinction between myeloid leukemoid reactions and true chronic myelocytic leukemia. In the latter instances, the Ph¹ chromosome may be found. In this instance, karyotyping is of value only in the presence of a positive finding (some instances of chronic myeloid leukemia may lack this characteristic chromosome defect).

In other forms of leukemia, the karyotypic findings are variable and much less well known. Karyotyping may provide confirmatory evidence that neoplasia is present. It can hardly be recommended as a routine procedure in any but the myeloproliferative disorders.

Dysproteinemia

Most of the dysproteinemias (e.g. hypogammaglobulinemia) can be readily diagnosed with such well known procedures as electrophoretic studies. Some of the less common dysproteinemias, such as Waldenstrom's macroglobulinemia, cannot be as readily diagnosed since they induce hard to detect qualitative rather than quantitative protein alterations. In the case of Waldenstrom's macroglobulinemia, for instance, definitive diagnosis has depended upon ultracentrifuge studies. Such tests are inaccessible to the average laboratory. A specific chromosome anomaly (an isochromosome in Group A) has been associated with Waldenstrom's macroglobulinemia. Karyotyping in this condition may thus circumvent the difficulty in obtaining a definitive diagnosis if ultracentrifuge studies are not readily available.

Medicolegal Applications

There are occasions during the practice of forensic medicine where cytogenetic techniques may be used to advantage. The use of skin biopsy material may help establish the sex of dismembered limbs. Fingernail scrapings taken from either accused assailants or from assault victims may be examined for epithelial sex chromatin (or chromatin in any vesicular nucleus) and aid in identifying the sex of the victim or the assailant respectively.

Examination of nuclear chromatin patterns in tissue adhering to curets or other instruments may forge another link in the chain of evidence in abortion cases, particularly where the nuclear sex of the tissue from the curet can be correlated with the sex of a found fetus. While none of these examinations of themselves are ever liable to solve a case or be the factor upon which a conviction hinges, they may form valuable additive bits of information in context with other findings.

The phenomenon of unequal crossing-over may have medico-legal implications. If an unequal crossover occurs *within* a gene locus, it may produce phenotypes which are, in theory, impossible on the basis of the genetic complement of the parents. This phenomenon has been implicated in some of the changes which occur in the haptoglobulin system.

Though unequal crossing-over has not been reported in the blood group systems or the hemoglobin systems, it probably will be eventually. The possibility must, at least, be recognized if a rare blood group or hemoglobin variant makes a sudden disconcerting appearance in the midst of a paternity study for instance.

Antenatal Sex Determination

Needle amniotomy in the intrapartum state may be used to obtain amniotic cells for chromatin examination and thereby permit antenatal sex determination. This is not a procedure about which we are at all enthusiastic and its role seems to be severely limited. It should most certainly *not* be employed to satisfy parental curiosity. The only excuse for performing such a procedure would arise where there is a family history of sex-linked fetal disease and local laws permit therapeutic abortion for suspected fetal abnormality. This method may, in such rare instances, offer some information of clinical value. Otherwise, it is not a very good test.

The "Biological Dosimeter"

With radiation sources becoming more commonplace, radiation accidents will undoubtedly become more frequent. There will be instances in which no accurate estimate as to the dose of radiation received by a victim can be made by on the scene investigations. In such instances, the victim himself may serve as a "biological dosimeter"—a term coined by Bender and Gooch. The severity of the exposure is reflected in the degree of damage sustained by the leukocytes. As we have noted in an earlier chapter, chromosomal aberrations occur in a predictable relationship to radiation dosage. This relationship has been expressed in mathematical terms as:

$$D = \sqrt{\frac{Y}{0.52 \times 10^{-5}}}$$

Where D is dose and Y is the number of rings and dicentrics seen per cell. The categories of chromosome damage used in the assessment are comparatively easy to identify.

Cytology of Effusions

Cytologic examination of nuclear and cellular morphology in vaginal and cervical smears, urine and pleural and peritoneal effusions is a well known diagnostic technique. The accuracy of these techniques in the examination of cervical and vaginal material exceeds ninety-five per cent. The results in urinary sediment and effusions are less satisfactory. Occasional attempts have been made to adapt cytogenetic techniques to the study of such material.

The reported results have not been encouraging. However, the techniques which have been used to date leave much to to desired. It is our opinion that these techniques have not yet been assessed fairly and that they probably offer much more potential than these early reports would suggest. To date, the techniques have been "short cut" methods which ignore full karyotyping. This is an area in which reports should be carefully scrutinized as they appear before the technique is arbitrarily discarded as unsatisfactory.

Habitual Abortion

This is another field in which only preliminary investigations are available for study. Karyotyping of parental blood cultures has revealed chromosomal abnormalities in some parents where habitual abortion has been a problem. This is another area of research well worth keeping an eye on.

Future Developments

"There is something fascinating about science. One gets such wholesale returns of conjecture out of such a trifling investment of fact."

MARK TWAIN—
from Life on the Mississippi.

We have touched upon two fields which we think offer much future potential for clinical applications of cytogenetic techniques—the study of effusions and the study of habitual abortion. Potential developments in cytogenetics depend largely upon the degree of acuity with which chromosomes and their individual segments can be identified in the future. Among the technical advances which may be anticipated are those directed to separation and identification of prophase chromosomes. These, as far as early research would indicate, are more distinctive in configuration than are metaphase chromosomes.

When chromosome identification becomes more satisfactory, many more chromosomal aberrations will be linked with disease states. As a corollary, chromosome mapping will develop and the infant science of cytogenetics will find very diverse clinical application, particularly in respect to genetic counselling.

As the genetic code becomes more perfectly understood and the code "words" for various enzymes discovered, attempts will probably be made to correct disease-producing coding errors, possibly by use of selective viral transducing systems. Though this seems like pretty wild speculation, it seems a distinct possibility within the next half century—particularly as applied to reversing whatever metabolic anomalies are responsible for carcinogenesis.

Even the truth of Mark Twain's observation is insufficient to keep one from predicting that some very fascinating developments are sure to derive from future cytogenetic research.

CHAPTER X

MONGOLISM AND OTHER AUTOSOMAL ANEUPLOIDY SYNDROMES

IN THIS and in the following chapters we will explore the clinical consequences which attend variations in the chromosome complement. The clinical syndromes discovered to date are a diverse group which defy classification on the basis of clinical findings. Therefore the discussion will follow the outline of the morphologic classification presented in a previous chapter.

There are a number of generalities which should be considered before we deal with the specific syndromes which attend chromosomal anomalies. The first of these is the pronounced difference between the clinical sequelae of autosomal aberrations and sex chromosome defects. Autosomal anomalies which affect all body cells are confined to trisomy or to some mosaic variant thereof. Monosomy and polysomy, frequent anomalies of the sex chromosomes, have yet to be described affecting the autosomes of viable individuals.

This reflects in part the paucity of vital genes carried by the sex chromosomes, especially the Y chromosome. This, however, is only a partial explanation. The X chromosome is known to bear loci which control very significant non-sex functions (hemophilia, glucose-6-dehydrogenase activity, etc.) and massive "overdoses" of such loci might be expected to have much more profound effects than have been observed. The phenomenon of "X-inactivation" alluded to earlier minimizes the effect of this excess of genetic material. Lack of such whole-chromosome inactivation mechanisms among the autosomes, on the other hand, allows any excess genetic material to function and therefore profoundly disturbs the metabolic pattern of the affected individual.

The concept of "gene balance" implies that the gene dosage in a normal chromosome complement is such that the metabolites controlled are in a state of functional equilibrium. Overdoses of single genes or of groups of genes disturbs this metabolic equilibrium and induces both metabolic and physical derangements. Generally speaking, the more genes that are affected, the more severe the anomaly will be. Correlations between clinical and cytogenetic findings bear this hypothesis out.

Whole-chromosome abnormalities, either trisomy or monosomy, have not yet been discovered in viable individuals in whom the defect affects one of the larger autosomes. The largest autosomes in which such defects have been compatible (briefly) with life are those of group D (13-15). The gene balance derangement induced by defects affecting the larger chromosomes (1-12) seems incompatible with life. The significance of "balance" is further emphasized by the finding of individuals in whom entire chromosome sets are present in excess (triploidy, 3n = 69). The *relative* proportions of genetic material in such individuals remains comparatively undisturbed and the attendant clinical sequelae have been comparatively minor.

Three well defined autosomal aneuploidy syndromes will be discussed at some length. These are sporadic mongolism (trisomy-21), the Group D trisomy syndrome (Patau's syndrome) and the Group E trisomy syndrome (Edwards' syndrome). Other autosomal defects have been infrequent.

SPORADIC MONGOLISM (TRISOMY-21)

Sporadic mongolism (Down's syndrome, Langdon Down anomaly) was the first anomaly of man in which an associated chromosomal defect was demonstrated. Gauthier, Lejeune and Turpin reported the association between mongolism and trisomy of chromosome-21 in 1959. It was this report which provided much of the impetus for the development of the field of human cytogenetics.

Etiology and Incidence

Mongolism is one of the more common chromosomal anomalies and occurs in about one of every eight hundred live births. Of this number, almost ninety per cent are instances of the sporadic (trisomy-21) variant. Sporadic mongolism is a consequence of nondisjunction of chromosome-21 during parental gametogenesis. There is a direct correlation between the incidence of mongolism and increasing maternal age. This suggests that the nondisjunctive accident occurs during oogenesis.

Characteristically, sporadic mongolism occurs in the child of an older (thirty-five years or so) mother who usually has had one or several previous normal pregnancies. Such mothers, while more prone to have another mongol child in a subsequent pregnancy than the population in general, are much less prone to bear successive mongol children than are those mothers who have delivered a 21-translocation (familial) mongol.

Preliminary investigations suggesting that trisomy-21 is associated with an excess of some enzyme in the tryptophane metabolic cycle remain unconfirmed. High levels of 5-hydroxyindolacetic acid which are sometimes seen in the urine of mongols do not appear to be consistent. This line of investigation should ultimately prove rewarding if the "one gene–one enzyme" hypothesis is correct.

Recent reports show that a "familial" form of trisomy-21 mongolism exists. A familial tendency to nondisjunction presumably is a consequence of some defect in the genetic control of meiosis. This possibility must be kept in mind when counselling the mothers in the younger age group (eighteen to twenty-five years) who have delivered a mongol child. An exhaustive family history is essential to intelligent prognosis. The incidence of recurrent mongolism in such young mothers, while not as high as that seen in the translocation type of familial mongolism, is appreciably greater than that seen with truly sporadic mongolism. The "non-disjunction gene," if such there be, is not selective in its activity; families are reported in which Klinefelter's syndrome and other. anomalies have occurred in the siblings of 21-trisomic mongols.

The least common etiologic variant of trisomy-21 mongolism is that which may occur in the offspring of a trisomy-21 mongol mother or father. Though the event is rare in humans, such instances of *secondary nondisjunction* are known to occur. The gametes produced by a trisomic individual may be either normal or abnormal (which receive two chromosomes from the trisomic set).

Fertilization of one of the abnormal gametes will yield another trisomic individual. A slightly more common form of secondary nondisjunction is that which affects the offspring of 46/47 mosaic parents. Several such instances have been described.

Etiologic factors other than maternal age and familial nondisjunction are not well established. One retrospective analysis attempted to correlate an increasing incidence of mongol offspring with increasing doses of radiation. Considerable issue has been taken with the results reported and the influence of radiation in the genesis of mongolism remains completely enigmatic.

Trisomy of chromosome-21 may also occur in mosaic patterns as a consequence of mitotic nondisjunction in the zygote. The implications of mosaicism are discussed later as are those of translocation (familial) mongolism and rarer structural defects.

Clinical Findings

The clinical manifestations of mongolism are well known and require only brief review. The most important consideration is the fact that mongolism, particularly in the newborn, cannot be diagnosed unequivocally on purely clinical grounds in all instances.

The most consistent clinical features which are associated with mongolism are epicanthic folds with tilted palpebral fissures; broad, flat nose; mental retardation; fissured tongue; high arched palate and anomalies of the dermal ridge pattern with a "simian crease" extending horizontally across the palm. Visceral defects are usually cardiac and a rather characteristic atrioventricular septal defect is most frequent.

Of the clinical features, the dermal ridge patterns are among the most helpful and may establish the diagnosis when other clinical criteria are equivocal. Dermatoglyphic studies, comparatively recently introduced, are not widely available. They are extremely useful in all three of the autosomal trisomy syndromes.

Mongolism is compatible with development to adult life. In this regard it differs significantly from the other autosomal trisomy syndromes. This again emphasizes the importance of the "dosage effect" of genes. The bigger the chromosome affected, the more severe the defect produced.

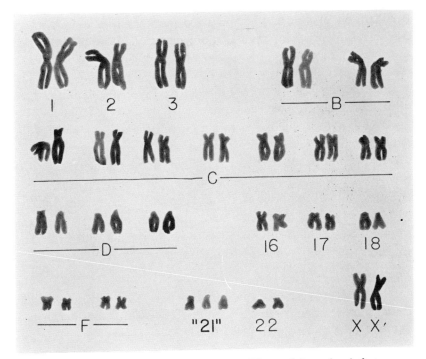

Figure 33. Karyotype in Trisomic Mongolism. The modal number is forty-seven and there is an extra autosome (?21) in group G.

Laboratory Findings

Mongolism *per se* produces no alteration in the nuclear chromatin or the polymorphonuclear leukocyte patterns. In the absence of an associated sex chromosome anomaly (not especially rare), there is no discrepancy between the apparent sex and that reflected in chromatin patterns.

There are several patterns which should be searched for in any patient suspected of having mongolism. These include trisomy, mosaicism (*q.v.*) and translocation (*q.v.*). There are at least two patients with clinical mongolism in whom no chromosome defects have been discovered despite diligent search. Increasing sophistication in the application of cytogenetic techniques may resolve these puzzling cases.

Sporadic mongolism can be unequivocally diagnosed by peripheral blood chromosome analysis. A modal number of forty-seven is characteristic and an additional small acrocentric chromosome is present in group G. Affected males will have six (normal—five) and affected females five (normal—four) such chromosomes.

It should be remembered that precise identification of the affected chromosome has still not been made. It is accepted convention to regard the involved chromosome as chromosome-21. More refined cytogenetic techniques may show this to be at variance with the criteria of the Denver classification.

GROUP D TRISOMY SYNDROME (PATAU'S SYNDROME)

The complex of congenital defects which comprises the D trisomy syndrome was first correlated with a chromosomal defect by Patau in 1960. Since that time, about twenty reports have been published and the syndrome has become fairly well delineated.

Etiology and Incidence

The D trisomy syndrome is a rare, or at least a very uncommon, congenital abnormality. This is due in part, no doubt, to the relative recency of its discovery. Even taking this into account, it is a less common condition by far than is mongolism.

The vast majority of patients who have presented the symptom complex of the D trisomy syndrome have had the trisomic form which is secondary to meiotic nondisjunction in one of the parents. There is sufficient correlation between the incidence of the disease and advancing maternal age to suggest that the defect is primarily one of oogenesis. Since afflicted individuals rarely survive the first year, secondary nondisjunction has not been reported. Mosaicism (*q.v.*) has been observed.

Clinical Features (See Table on Page 169)

The table summarizes the incidence of the clinical anomalies seen in the cases reviewed. The most common anomalies, present in over half of the reported cases, are apparent mental retardation; apparent deafness; eye defects; ear malformations; cardiac defects; polydactyly; cleft palate and/or harelip; multiple hemangiomas and horizontal palmar creases.

Mental retardation is somewhat difficult to assess in the age group affected. Infants who survive the first year do, however,

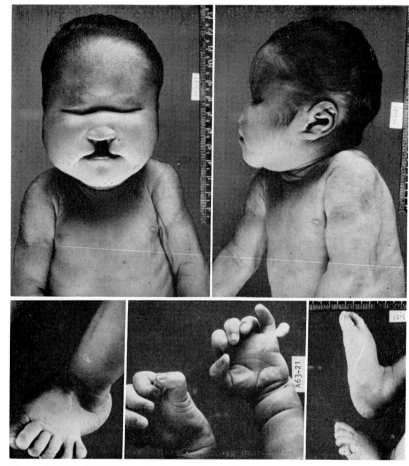

Figure 34. The D-Trisomy Syndrome. Most of the characteristic defects are seen in this infant including anophthalmia, hare-lip, low and deformed ears, downy hair, broad chest, polydactyly, transverse palmar creases, finger flexion deformities and "rocker-bottom" feet. (These photographs were furnished through the kindness of Dr. Fred W. Bauer, Boston, Mass.)

present impaired mental developmental patterns. Deafness is not an invariable finding but there is generally no startle reaction to loud or unusual noises.

Eye defects are almost invariably present and vary in severity from microphthalmia to complete anophthalmia. Irideal colobomata are very common. Less commonly, congenital cataracts are present.

The central nervous system defects encountered at autopsy have been fairly specific and are categorized as arrhinencephaly. Defects in the olfactory bulbs and the optic tracts are very common. Less often, midbrain and cerebellar anomalies are present either alone or in combination with arrhinencephaly.

The ears are low-set and show variable deformities of the pinna. Narrowing of the external auditory canal of variable severity has been reported.

Cardiac defects, which are very common, are characterized clinically by harsh systolic precordial murmurs which reflect underlying interventricular septal defects. Interatrial septal defects are less common.

Polydactyly, another almost universal finding, may affect either the hands or feet and seems to have a slight predilection to affect the left side. The digits vary in appearance from well developed digits with a bony skeleton to supernumerary fleshy tags.

Hemangiomata are extremely frequent and are characteristic in both appearance and in distribution. They appear as flat, red-purple capillary lesions which appear in the occipital region, the back of the neck and in the sacral area.

Palmar crease patterns are similar to those of mongolism with horizontal creases being the commonest finding. Dermatoglyphic studies (dermal ridges of both the fingerprints and the palm prints) present quite characteristic patterns and, if available, are extremely useful diagnostic tools.

Despite the specificity of the pattern of the anomalies in the well defined case of D trisomy syndrome, not all can be diagnosed with certainty using purely clinical criteria. The patients sometimes have clinical features which are commoner in the E trisomy syndrome (*vide infra*) such as finger flexion deformities and abnormalities of the foot. The E trisomy syndrome is associated with a hypertonic disorder whose convulsive episodes are often simulated by apneic episodes which may occur in the D trisomy syndrome.

The majority of the patients afflicted by the D trisomy syndrome have been females. This peculiar sex incidence is also noted in the E trisomy syndrome. Coincidence is one of the strongest probabilities in view of the comparatively few cases which are recorded. No satisfactory alternative explanation has been advanced.

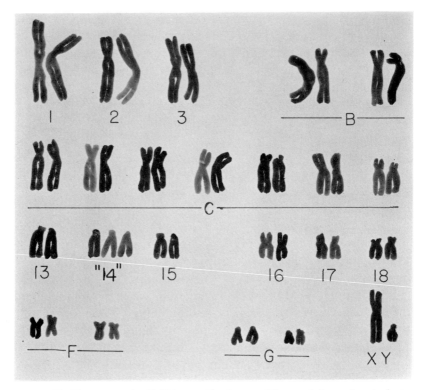

Figure 35. Karyotype in D-Trisomy Syndrome. The modal number is forty-seven and there is an extra autosome (?14) in group D.

Laboratory Findings

The D trisomy syndrome produces no alteration in the buccal chromatin or leukocyte patterns. Karyotyping reveals a modal number of forty-seven and there is an extra large acrocentric chromosome in the 13-15 group. The exact identity of the chromosome affected is uncertain though most investigators tentatively identify it as chromosome-14. It seems most improbable that the same syndrome results from trisomy of each of the three members of the group. The term "D trisomy syndrome" is to be preferred until definite identification of the affected member has been made.

Other chromosomal findings are less common. Rare instances of mosaicism (*q.v.*) have been reported. As far as we are aware, only a single instance of translocation has been reported.

TABLE III

CLINICAL FEATURES OF THE D-TRISOMY SYNDROME

CENTRAL NERVOUS SYSTEM	
Apparent mental retardation	100%
Apparent deafness	80%
Brain defects	(80)[a]
(Forebrain defect (arrhinencephaly), hydrocephalus, cerebellar defects, midbrain anomaly)	
Neuromuscular imbalance	65%
(Apnea, "seizures," hypertonicity, hypotonia)	
Spina bifida	—
Generalized congenital analgesia	(see text)
SKELETAL SYSTEM	
Skull defects	75%
(Sloping forehead, wide sutures, lacunar skull, thin temporal bones)	
Defects of nasal bones	—
Anomalies of cervical spine	—
Micrognathia	—
E.E.N.T.	
Ear anomalies	90%
(Low set, deformity of pinna)	
Eye defects	80%
(Microphthalmia, colobomata, anophthalmia, cataracts)	
Cleft palate	80%
Harelip	70%
EXTREMITIES	
Characteristic dermatoglyphic pattern	(100)[b]
Horizontal palmar creases	85%
Polydactyly hands (ulnar) and/or feet	80%
Prominent heel ("rocker-bottom" foot)	65%
Hyperconvex, narrow nails	65%
Retroflexible thumbs	50%
Flexion deformities of fingers	50%
Syndactyly toes	—
SKIN	
Capillary hemangiomata	85%
Umbilical hernia	65%

(Table Continues on Next Page)

Defects for which no percentages are cited occur only occasionally

a - percentage in patients examined by autopsy
b - percentage in patients so studied
c - percentage in males in whom genetalia were specifically alluded to
d - percentage in females examined by autopsy.

GENITOURINARY SYSTEM
Scrotal abnormality   (100)[c]
Cryptorchidism   (100)[c]
Renal anomalies (Double uretur, vascular anomalies)   (65)[a]
Septate uterus   (60)[d]
Hypospadias   —
Prostatic urethral defect   —

OTHER VISCERAL DEFECTS
Cardiac defects   (85)[a]
    (Interventricular septal defect, interatrial septal defect, patent ductus, overriding aorta)
Malrotation colon   (65)[a]
Accessory spleen   (60)[a]
Large gallbladder   (60)[a]
Achalasia esophagus   —
Anomalous lobulation lung   —

MISCELLANEOUS
Sex:
    Males   40%
    Females   60%
Mean maternal age –31 years
Abnormal umbilical vessels

GROUP E TRISOMY SYNDROME (EDWARDS' SYNDROME)

The first published description of the complex of congenital defects associated with trisomy of one of the group E chromosomes (16-18) is that of Edwards and his associates (1960). This syndrome seems somewhat more common than the D trisomy syndrome. About thirty cases have been reported.

Etiology and Incidence

Though this syndrome is somewhat more common than the group D trisomy syndrome, it is still less common than mongolism. The increasing frequency of reports has led some authors to speculate that its true incidence may approximate that of mongolism when its stigmata become as well known as those of mongolism. The peculiar sex incidence seen (twenty-two of thirty-one cases reviewed by one author were females) has not been adequately explained.

Etiologic factors are obscure. The ubiquitous effects of maternal age can once again be discerned in the etiology of this syndrome. Reports of parental exposure to irradiation are somewhat commoner in this than in other syndromes. A recent case report also suggests that a familial nondisjunctive variant may also exist.

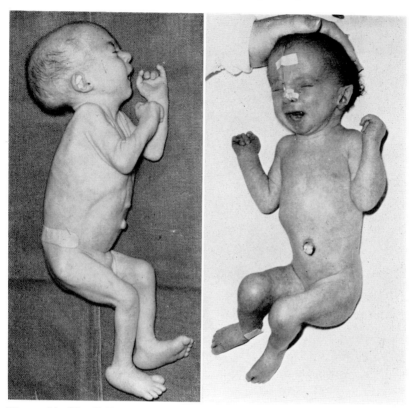

Figure 36. The E-Trisomy Syndrome. Note the characteristic micrognathia, prominent occiput, low-set ears, finger deformities, umbilical hernia and short dorsiflexed great toe. (These photographs were furnished through the kindness of Dr. Irene A. Uchida and originally appeared in: Uchida, I. A., *et al.*: *New England J. M., 288:*1198-1201, 1962.)

Far and away the most common chromosomal defect associated with the syndrome is autosomal trisomy. Occasional examples of mosaicism and translocation are reported. Trisomy of a deleted member of group E has been suspected a number of times. One of the few examples of ring chromosome formation in man has been associated with an incomplete variant of the E trisomy syndrome.

Clinical Features (See Table on Page 173)

The features which have been associated with the group E trisomy syndrome are summarized in the table. The most commonly encountered deformities, present in more than fifty per cent

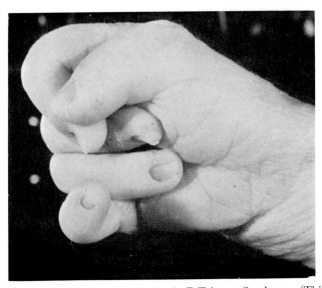

Figure 37. Characteristic Hand Deformity in E-Trisomy Syndrome. (This photograph was furnished through the kindness of Dr. Gerald Holman and originally appeared in: Holman, G. H., *et al.*: *New England J.M.*, *285*:982-988, 1963.)

of the cases reported, are apparent mental retardation; moderate hypertonicity; failure to thrive; prominent occiput; low-set and malformed ears; small mandible; finger flexion and overlapping; short sternum; inguinal and/or umbilical hernias; Meckel's diverticulum; cardiac defects; heterotopic pancreatic tissue and renal anomalies. The longest recorded survival has been twenty-three months.

The ears are mounted low on a moderately deformed head with a prominent occiput. Defects of the pinna, often described as "crumpling" are very common. These features, combined with the small and receding mandible, are quite reminiscent of the infant facies which are alluded to by Edith Potter in her description of infants afflicted with renal agenesis. It is not improbable that at least some of these patients have, in fact, been examples of the E trisomy syndrome.

Defects of the hands are so characteristic and frequent as to be virtually pathognomonic. They have been alluded to in almost every description of the syndrome. The fingers show a very characteristic flexion and overlapping of the index finger over the third

TABLE IV

CLINICAL FEATURES OF THE E-TRISOMY SYNDROME

CENTRAL NERVOUS SYSTEM	
Hypertonicity	85%
Mental retardation	80%
Spina bifida	—
Deafness	—
Atrophy optic nerve	—
7th cranial nerve palsy	—
SKELETAL SYSTEM	
Micrognathia	100%
Limited hip abduction	$(100)^a$
Nasal bone defects	$(100)^a$
(Prominent nose, anomaly of bridge)	
Skull defects	70%
(Prominent occiput, large fontanel)	
Deformity of sternum	65%
Small pelvis	40%
Shield chest	—
Short neck	—
E.E.N.T.	
Ear abnormalities	95%
(Low set, deformed pinna, narrow external auditory canal)	
Eye defects	35%
(Ptosis, epicanthus glaucoma, corneal opacity)	
Harelip and/or cleft palate	30%
High, arched palate	—
EXTREMITIES	
Finger overlapping	100%
(2nd over 3rd, 5th over 4th)	
Dorsiflexion great toe	100%
Characteristic dermatoglyphic pattern	$(100)^a$
Hypoplasia great toe	80%
Syndactyly toes	45%
Equinovarus deformity	35%
Prominent heel ("rocker-bottom" foot)	25%
Horizontal palmar crease	$(25)^a$
Hypermobility shoulders	—
Decrease muscle mass	—
Elongation 5th finger	—
SKIN	
Scanty subcutaneous tissue	$(100)^a$
Downy hair	$(75)^a$
Umbilical and/or inguinal hernia	60%
Loose skin folds	40%

(*Table Continues on Next Page*)

Defects for which no percentages are cited are encountered only occasionally
[a]Percentage in patients in whom this area is specifically alluded to

VISCERAL DEFECTS

Cardiac abnormalities	90%
(Interventricular septal defect, patent ductus, interatrial septal defect, bicuspid pulmonic valve)	
Meckel's diverticulum	80%
Renal defects	65%
(Hydrouretur, horseshoe kidney, double pelvis)	
Eventration diaphragm	45%
Heterotopic pancreatic tissue	45%
Malrotation colon	—
Cryptorchidism	—
Pyloric tumor	—

MISCELLANEOUS

Failure to thrive	100%
Low birth weight (under 6½ pounds)	95%
Sex:	
Male　　　35%	
Female　　65%	
Intrapartum anomalies:	
Small placenta	(100)[a]
Decreased intrauterine activity	(65)[a]
Polyhydramnios	(45)[a]
Mean maternal age - 33 years	

and, not infrequently, of the fourth and fifth fingers. Dermatoglyphic patterns are moderately characteristic.

Visceral defects are commonest in the digestive, cardiovascular and genito-urinary systems. Interventricular septal defects are almost invariably present and are often accompanied by interatrial septal defects. A substantial minority of patients also have a patent ductus arteriosus.

Abnormalities of the digestive system may not become apparent clinically but are useful diagnostic findings at autopsy. The most frequent are the hernias, Meckel's diverticulum and focal deposits of heterotopic pancreatic tissue. Renal defects are common and vary considerably. Renal vascular anomalies and renal hypoplasia are the commonest defects.

Mental deficiency becomes evident in those infants who survive for a year or more. There is a generalized increase in muscle tone. There are no specific brain defects which parallel those of the group D trisomy syndrome.

Other associated anomalies are sporadic in appearance and are of less diagnostic value than those alluded to. One of the less

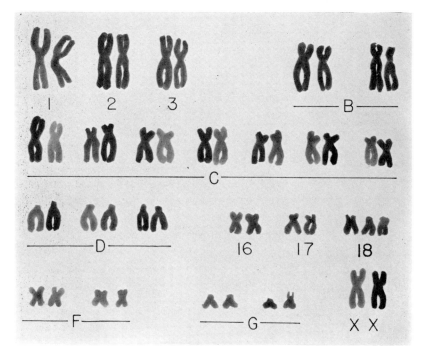

Figure 38. Karyotype in E-Trisomy Syndrome. The modal number is forty-seven and there is an extra autosome (?18) in group E.

common defects is a rather characteristic deformity of the foot which is referred to as a "rocker bottom" foot. This anomaly is a consequence of unusual prominence of the heel bone which imparts to the foot the curious appearance of having its ankle attachment in the middle of the arch.

Laboratory Findings

In common with the other autosomal trisomy syndromes, group E trisomy produces no alteration in the sex chromatin patterns. The modal number of chromosomes is 47 and the cells bear an extra member in group E.

The affected chromosome is generally regarded as being chromosome-18. There is still sufficient residual uncertainty about the identification that the less specific term "Group E trisomy" is to be preferred at this point.

Earlier reports were almost equally divided in opinion as to whether the affected chromosome was chromosome-17 or chromosome-18. One suggestion which helped to resolve this question was made by Muldal. He noted that unequal crossing-over was not infrequent in abnormal chromosome complements and that several reports had indicated that trisomy of a partly deleted chromosome-18 had produced the same syndrome. He suggested that those chromosomes which had been regarded as chromosome-17 were in actuality duplicated chromosome-18 (pseudo-17).

OCCASIONAL TRISOMY "SYNDROMES"

As is the case with many of the biological sciences, human cytogenetics is replete with an array of miscellaneous and sporadic phenomena whose precise significance is dubious. In not a few instances, new "syndromes" have found their way into the medical literature which reflect an anxiety to report something new rather more than they reflect exhaustive investigation. A most informative commentary on the problems of interpreting findings in this new field has been made by D. H. Carr. This article would be profitable reading for anyone entering the field of cytogenetics.

Group C Autosomal Trisomy

From time to time, reports appear which purport to be examples of trisomy of one of the Group C autosomes. Examination of these reports has not yet convinced us that a true instance of group C autosomal trisomy has been reported. All have had clinical features of comparatively minor degree and certainly not of the magnitude one might expect based upon the severity of the effects of trisomy of other autosomes.

At present, we have categorized all of these reports as examples of either the triplo-X syndrome or as variants of Klinefelter's syndrome. In several instances, the authors of the original report have arrived at similar conclusions.

Some of the reported cases have been so reported because they lack expected sex chromatin changes. In the absence of severe clinical anomalies, the absence of expected chromatin anomalies is not sufficient evidence that the defect reported is indeed autosomal. Not a few of these cases have mosaic patterns and it is entirely conceivable that the buccal or vaginal mucosa may contain a predominantly diploid cell line.

Group F Trisomy

Reported trisomy of chromosome-19 or -20 is rare. Of the two cases which we have reviewed, one was reported to have been seen in the asymptomatic father of a mongol child. Since the child had translocation mongolism, the distinct possibility exists that the "trisomy-19" is a consequence of translocation in the father as well.

The second example was alluded to in a study of chromosome patterns in congenital heart disease. In this instance, the "trisomy F" was seen in the mother of a child with "trisomy F" and "monosomy G." Again, translocation must be suspected.

Until translocation is convincingly ruled out in a reported case, one must reserve judgment as to whether true trisomy F has been encountered. The minimal defects associated with the two cases above cited are inconsistent with the behavior of autosomal trisomy so far reported.

Trisomy-22

Trisomy of one of the smallest acrocentrics may reflect either trisomy-22 or XYY (in males). Certainly no well defined syndrome characterizing trisomy-22 has emerged in spite of the fact that at least five reported instances can be found. This type of trisomy has been associated with Sturge-Weber syndrome, schizophrenia and benign congenital myotonia.

Sturge-Weber syndrome was the first of the clinical malformations in which this type of trisomy was seen. Many investigators studying other instances of Sturge-Weber syndrome have been unable to confirm this finding. This has led to the suggestion that Sturge-Weber syndrome might represent a form of partial trisomy of chromosome-22 (*vide infra*).

Trisomy of a group G chromosome has been reported in association with schizophrenia by several investigators but is far from a common feature of schizophrenia in general. One interesting instance was reported in monozygotic twin girls with mental deficiency and schizoid personality defects. Since neither girl exhibited any masculinization, a Y chromosome can be tentatively ruled out. The other alternative, that this small acrocentric represents a deleted chromosome, cannot be disproved.

The instance which was reported in association with benign congenital myotonia seems better reclassified as XYY (*q.v.*). One instance which was reported in association with a syndrome resembling either D or E trisomy has been classified as an example of trisomy of a deleted group E chromosome.

MONOSOMY AND POLYSOMY

Convincing examples of monosomy or polysomy of an autosome have not been reported. Monosomy of one autosome has sometimes been reported in association with trisomy of another autosome but not as an isolated autosomal defect (though it is fairly common in the sex chromosomes). The only instance in which polysomy was seen in peripheral blood karyotypes occurred in a mongol suffering from terminal leukemia. This patient's cells had a modal number of 49 and *five* chromosomes-21 were present. Earlier, karyotyping in this same patient had shown a modal number of 47 and classical trisomy-21. In this instance, the change is unquestionably a local alteration of the leukemic blood cells.

Complex Aneuploids

Within this category fall those patients in whom aneuploidy of one autosome is accompanied by simultaneous aneuploidy of another chromosome. Interpretation of karyotypes which suggest this constitution should be made with considerable caution. Several of the cases reported (especially those in the earlier literature) bear close re-examination. In some cases, revised reports have been issued by the original authors.

Several examples of concurrent monosomy and trisomy have been reported. Inspection of some of these reports indicates that they are more probably examples of translocation mongolism than monosomy-trisomy. Most of these reports were issued before the mechanism of familial mongolism was well known. Such cases are tabulated in Appendix V.

Two reported instances of double trisomy were instances of mongolism with associated Klinefelter's syndrome. The theoretical incidence of these deformities in combination is about one in five hundred and sixty thousand.

Combined autosomal trisomy is very rare. We are aware of only a single instance. This was a case of combined mongolism and trisomy-18 with stigmata of both syndromes and a modal number of 48 chromosomes. Chromosome analysis showed trisomy of both chromosome-21 and chromosome-18.

One example of "multiple trisomy," since revised by the original authors, is illustrative of the caution which must be applied to the interpretation of abnormal karyotypes. Originally, the case was reported as an instance of trisomy of chromosomes-8 and -11 combined with XXY. It has since been found to be an example of XXXXY. Caution in interpretation cannot be overemphasized.

Triploidy

One of the rarer anomalies of the human karyotype deserves special attention. Triploidy (three complete sets of chromosomes rather than the normal two) is an uncommon condition most often encountered in a mosaic pattern. In view of the severity of the anomalies induced by an extra single chromosome, one might expect the effects of a complete extra set to be profound indeed.

The clinical effects associated with triploidy have actually been comparatively mild. One of the viable patients had multiple lipomatosis, bony syndactyly and mental deficiency as predominating defects. In another patient, a six year old female, mental deficiency was mild and there was zygodactyly and hemiatrophy. Blood antigen studies revealed that the extra chromosome set was of maternal origin.

The comparative mildness of the clinical effects can be attributed to the fact that the relative genetic dosage remains more or less undisturbed when all of the genes are present in excess. In such defects as trisomy, selected groups of genes are present in excess and the clinical defects are more severe.

Partial Trisomy

The concept of partial trisomy was first introduced by K. Patau shortly after the reports of trisomy-22 in Sturge-Weber syndrome were published. The term was introduced as a convenient method of categorizing the clinical effects of small structural alterations which alter the dosage of small groups of genes. Such alterations are produced by duplications, small insertions and small translocations.

Among the defects which have been so categorized on the basis of either demonstrable or hypothetical structural alterations, are Sturge-Weber syndrome (duplication-22 ?), orofacialdigital (OFD) syndrome (insertion-1) and several instances of incomplete D or E trisomy syndrome which have been associated with an additional deleted D or E chromosome in the complement.

The usefulness of the concept of partial trisomy lies in its tendency to bring to mind chromosomal defects which have been associated with clinical syndromes where the chromosomal defects are only occasionally demonstrable. Initially nonproductive karyotyping should not discourage further karyotyping of individuals with similar anomalies. In any given congenital deformity, the majority of patients may be afflicted with "invisible" chromosome defects while a small minority bear the defects in somewhat larger, microscopically identifiable versions.

AUTOSOMAL MOSAICS

The discovery of mosaic chromosome patterns in patients who bear some of the stigmata of the full blown trisomy syndrome indicates that the clinical sequelae of chromosomal anomalies depends not only upon the chromosome affected but upon the proportion of body cells which are affected by the anomaly. With some exceptions, mosaic patterns have produced somewhat less severe anomalies than have their heteroploid counterparts. Clinically, the implication of these findings is self-evident. Mongolism, particularly, becomes ameliorated when present in mosaic patterns.

Autosomal mosaicism is a comparatively uncommon phenomenon, at least insofar as the number of reported examples would indicate. One suspects that mitotic nondisjunction is a phenomenon which would have an incidence at least equal that of meiotic nondisjunction. Why, then, are such cases so infrequently encountered? Two explanations may be advanced.

First, there is the ever-present possibility that mosaicism will go unnoticed if only a single tissue is used for culture. More probable an explanation is that karyotyping is not being done often enough in those patients in whom the clinical stigmata are only suggestive of a given syndrome and in whom normalcy is simulated closely enough that karyotyping is ignored.

Mosaicism in Mongolism

Mosaic variants of trisomy-21 mongolism are fairly frequent. At least fifteen examples can be cited (see Appendix V). The majority of these have been of the 46/47 type, though a few examples of more complex patterns are reported. There is considerable variability in the clinical stigmata encountered in such patients.

A feature which is common to such mosaics is the lesser severity of the stigmata of mongolism than is present in heterosomal trisomy-21. Some patients have, in fact, had almost no discernible stigmata of mongolism. The degree of mental deficiency is exceptionally variable and may be extremely severe—far out of proportion to the other clinical stigmata. In others, possibly a majority, the mental deficiency is of rather mild degree. One reviewer feels that the degree of mental impairment is roughly proportional to the percentage of trisomic cells in the body.

The clinical import of mosaic mongolism is twofold. First, and most important, one can sound a note of considerable optimism when counselling the parents of a child in whom mosaicism is detected, especially if the clinical stigmata have been equivocal. Secondly, since these patients may become almost fully functional adults, secondary nondisjunction is a very real possibility. Half of the children born of such a parent will be trisomic mongols.

Mosaicism in D-Trisomy Syndrome

There are several instances of mosaicism affecting the group D chromosomes. Rather a puzzling array of clinical sequelae has accompanied mosaicism of this type. Several examples have paralleled the clinical effects of mosaicism in mongolism in that the variants are incomplete counterparts of the fully developed trisomy syndrome. In at least one instance, however, the mosaicism had not moderated the clinical effects and the complex of anomalies produced paralleled those of the "standard" D-trisomy syndrome. Generally, the effects of mosaicism in this group are rather more severe than those of mosaic mongolism, probably reflecting the increasing genetic potency of the larger autosomes.

There are two unrelated patients in whom mosaicism has accompanied a syndrome at complete variance with that of the usual D-trisomy syndrome. Both have had 46/47-D-trisomy mosaicism associated with a sensory nervous system defect which has produced complete pain insensitivity unaccompanied by any of the usual findings in D-trisomy, with the exception of mental deficiency. Numerous areas of cutaneous ulceration and many deforming fractures reflect the lack of appreciation of painful stimuli. Both patients showed unusually large deposits of cutaneous melanin and both excreted what is called an "anomalous substance" in the urine. At the time of the report, the patients were three and seven years of age. Both were males.

Such a finding as that above defies explanation if one assumes that the usual chromosome of standard D-trisomy (usually regarded as chromosome-14) is affected in this syndrome. Quite probably, these particular patients are exhibiting mosaicism affecting one of the other group D autosomes (13 or 15). No other similar reports have come to our attention and the above comments are entirely speculative.

Other Autosomal Mosaics

Interestingly enough, we have been unable to find an instance of E trisomy mosaicism recorded.

A miscellaneous group of "occasional mosaics" can be found but none have been seen with sufficient frequency to warrant designation as specific syndromes.

One example of 46/47 mosaicism has been regarded by its reporters as being an example of group C autosomal mosaicism in a male. The principal clinical features were mental retardation and sexual hypoplasia. Since these same features are also the principal defects of Klinefelter's syndrome, a mosaic variant of this syndrome (46XY/47XXY) seems to be an equally probable interpretation. Certainly any case associated with sexual hypoplasia should be regarded with considerable reserve.

Mosaicism of the 46/47 type affecting a group G autosome has been reported in association with dystrophia myotonica. The report is so far unsupported.

Mosaicism has been the pattern encountered in most of the cases of triploidy reported. In one female adult, mental retardation and syndactyly were the prominent clinical features.

An interesting chromosome pattern noted in one mongol was 46XY/47 Tri-21 XY/48 Tri-21, Tri-F XY. The trisomy of the F chromosome in the 48 chromosome stemline apparently did not modify the basic mongol clinical pattern appreciably. This is another example of the effect which abnormality of one chromosome may have upon the mitotic behavior of another.

CHIMERAS

A chimera is an individual in whom two genetically dissimilar cell populations are present as a consequence of grafting. This condition is comparatively uncommon in man but has been described on several occasions in relation to blood cell populations. A blood cell chimera may arise in one of two ways—transplacental grafting of blood cells from infant to mother or transplacental grafting of blood cells between fraternal twins. In one example of the latter form of chimerism, cells could be found with normal male and normal female chromosomal patterns.

One extreme form of chimerism, which was responsible for an instance of hermaphroditism is almost unbelievable. In essence, the individual represented a chimera formed by the fusion of fraternal twins at the one-cell stage. The patient had both male and female cells in approximately equal numbers in skin and marrow preparations. The possibility of mosaicism was ruled out on the basis of blood antigen studies which showed that the male and the female cells were of different blood types.

SECONDARY NONDISJUNCTION

Secondary nondisjunction (the production of aneuploid gametes and children by aneuploid adults) though a theoretical possibility in any trisomic individual is uncommon in man. The reasons are not difficult to envision. Trisomy affecting the autosomes is rarely compatible with functional adult activity and trisomy of the sex chromosomes (*q.v.*) commonly produces sterility.

Nevertheless, occasional examples of secondary nondisjunction have been demonstrated in man. The most frequently encountered examples are those which occur in mosaic mongolism. A fertile adult with mosaicism of the 46/47-trisomy-21 type may have the germ cells of the gonads affected by the trisomic line. When these germ cells produce gametes, they produce them in an approximate ratio of one normal : one abnormal and offspring are produced in the same ratio.

A distinction must be made between the phenomenon of true secondary nondisjunction and that of familial nondisjunction. In the latter instance, there is some familial factor, presumably genetic, which encourages nondisjunction during gametogenesis. In such families, aneuploid parents may produce aneuploid offspring in whom an entirely different chromosome is affected. Such instances have been recorded in triplo-X females who have had mongol children. This same defect may affect the offspring of karyotypically normal parents. There are many families in which unrelated chromosomal defects are present in several children.

SUPERNUMERARY CHROMOSOMES

In plants, the presence of small and apparently nonfunctional chromosomes is not unusual. Often, such chromosomes are encountered in only a small proportion of the plant's cells. Such supernumerary chromosomes show a strong tendency to loss through mitotic nondisjunction.

In man, the existence of supernumerary chromosomes remains a moot point. In the earliest reports concerned with the normal karyotype of man, some investigators suggested that supernumerary chromosomes were not uncommon. One investigator in particular felt that while the normal modal number in man might well be 46, there were other human populations in whom a modal number of 47 or 48 might be normal due to the existence of small supernumerary chromosomes.

Though this suggestion has been largely discarded, the possibility that supernumerary chromosomes may exist is still alluded to from time to time as a possible explanation of the asymptomatic trisomies reported. The possibility that such chromosomes are supernumerary chromosomes cannot be entirely discarded. Certainly no well defined clinical syndrome accompanies such findings (particularly trisomy-22). Not uncommonly, a mosaic pattern is present which, too, is consistent with the behavior of true supernumerary chromosomes.

At present, the status of the supernumerary chromosome in man is that of "improbable but not impossible." Future reports will help to clarify the nature and the role of the extra small acrocentrics which are encountered from time to time in asymptomatic patients.

CHAPTER XI

CLINICAL EFFECTS OF AUTOSOMAL STRUTCURAL ANOMALIES

W ITH the exception of the translocations associated with the familial transmission of mongolism, the human chromosome structural anomalies form a diverse group within which few syndromes can be recognized with any certainty. Compounding the confused status of many of the anomalies is the fact that many of the reported anomalies can be interpreted in any one of several ways with equal or nearly equal probability.

Unquestionably, large numbers of structural alterations must go unrecognized by even the most experienced cytogeneticists. With only the crude criteria of chromosome length and centromere position available for the identification of anomalies, minute exchanges, deletions and duplications will be entirely inapparent. Vast numbers of such changes are catalogued in the large banded chromosomes of *Drosophila* and there is little reason to suppose that similar alterations do not underlie many human defects.

What constitutes a true structural abnormality? There is little question that alterations produced by chromosome breakage, no matter how minute the involved segments, certainly are true abnormalities. There are a number of reports, however, which are in a different category altogether. These are the reports in which alterations of chromosome or satellite size are correlated with clinical abnormalities.

Such alterations of size are difficult to assess. Satellite size is a highly variable characteristic and marked variations can be seen within the complement of apparently normal individuals. The size of satellites, despite their variability from individual to individual and from chromosome to chromosome, remains quite constant within the cells of the individual. Familial alterations of satellite size have been found more or less accidentally in studies of congenital diseases which are known to be associated with some other well defined chromosomal anomaly. Such enlarged satellites, which segregate in an expected Mendelian fashion, may serve as useful chromosome markers in linkage studies.

A constant problem in cytogenetics is assessing the relationship between karyotypic abnormalities and clinical changes. When only isolated reports can be found, coincidence remains an exceptionally troublesome possibility. Despite this probability, chromosome defects which are found in association with congenital disease should be recorded. As such reports accumulate, patterns will eventually be discernible which support cause-effect relationships.

Before any cause and effect relationship can even be postulated in a given instance of structural heterozygosity and clinical abnormality, it must first be established that the anomaly observed and the clinical "syndrome" always segregate together. This requires exhaustive family studies accompanied by karyotyping as many members of the family as possible. With the exception of some exceptionally good studies in familial mongolism, such family studies are still comparatively infrequently available.

One ever-present possibility, not often given adequate consideration, is that the chromosome anomalies which accompany any given defect may, themselves, reflect the *effects* of the condition rather than the cause. Associations between disease and chromosome defects do *not* necessarily imply that the chromosomal defect is primary. As an example, many chromosome defects are present in some tumors and leukemias, particularly after therapy, which by their very inconstancy seem more probably effects than causes.

Another point which deserves emphasis is the fact that structural alterations of chromosomes will *not necessarily* produce any clinical sequelae. As an example, whole-arm translocation between chromosomes does not alter the genetic complement of the affected cell. Unless some position effect (*q.v.*) is induced by the exchange, the functional activity of the cell remains unaltered. If, however, this same defect is present in germ cells, gametogenesis may yield two different types of gametes:

1) *Balanced*—the translocation chromosomes are distributed to one gamete and the unaffected homologues of the translocation chromosomes are distributed to the other.

2) *Unbalanced*—translocation chromosomes and unaffected homologues are distributed to the same gametes.

If large chromosomes are affected, unbalanced gametes often produce nonviable zygotes. If only the balanced zygotes survive, the translocation may pass unnoticed through generation after generation.

Methods are available for the identification of such structural defects in man, though they are difficult to perform and are rarely used. One of these methods is the study of chromosome patterns during meiosis using testicular biopsy material. Structural alterations are reflected by anomalous chromosome relationships during synapsis and meiotic metaphase. The trivalents and tetravalents of translocation chromosomes and the characteristic loops formed by inversion chromosomes are very valuable for detecting otherwise inapparent structural changes. Studies of this type, performed on "carriers" of translocation mongolism have demonstrated trivalent formation.

A second method which offers some promise is wholly experimental. During prophase, chromosomes are long chromonemal threads along which the chromomeres are strung. The chromosomes at this stage seem to be fairly characteristic in both the distribution and the size of the chromomeres they bear. It is the alignment of such chromomeres which produces the bands of the polytene chromosomes of *Drosophila*. Their study may prove equally useful in human material.

AUTOSOMAL TRANSLOCATIONS

A translocation is a reciprocal exchange of genetic material between two non-homologous chromosomes. Of the various types which may occur, the most readily recognizable are those of the so-called "centric fusion" type which occur between acrocentric chromosomes and produce an abnormal metacentric or submetacentric chromosome. The best known translocation in man is that associated with familial mongolism.

Translocation Mongolism

The clinical manifestations of mongolism do not differ significantly in the trisomic and the translocation types. The principal and most important difference lies in the hereditary pattern of these two forms. Whereas trisomic mongolism is usually a sporadic phenomenon affecting the children of older mothers, translocation mongolism is a familial defect transmitted to children of young mothers by clinically normal appearing carrier mothers *or fathers*. Interestingly, there is some evidence that mongolism in the children of translocation-carrying males becomes more frequent with increasing *paternal* age.

Incidence and Etiology

Translocation mongolism is far less common than the sporadic trisomic form. It accounts for about five to ten per cent of the total cases. Its etiology is obscure and can be alluded to in only the most general terms. At the chromosomal level, it is a consequence of reciprocal exchanges between chromosome-21 and a chromosome of the D (13-15) or G (21-22) group. These structural variants are referred to as D/G and G/G mongolism for convenience.

The origin of the chromosome fractures is unknown. Of the intrinsic factors, the fact that these chromosomes are acrocentric chromosomes and concerned with nucleolus-organization seems most significant. Attempts to invoke a constant relationship between translocation mongolism and such extrinsic factors as x-ray, virus infection, *etc.* have been wholly inconclusive.

Hereditary Patterns

The hereditary patterns of D/G and G/G mongolism (with the exception noted later) are similar. An asymptomatic carrier bearing a translocation of the D/G type, for example, has the following chromosome constitution in his cells (assuming the D chromosome is chromosome-14):

$$14, 14/21, 21$$

During gametogenesis, the translocated 14/21 chromosome will be distributed to half of the gametes either alone or in combination with one of the intact homologues. Three possibilities thus exist:

1) 14, 14/21, 21————————>a) 14/21
                                       b) 14, 21 (balanced gametes)
2) 14, 14/21, 21————————>a) 14/21, 21
                                       b) 14, — (unbalanced gametes)
3) 14, 14/21, 21————————>a) 14, 14/21
                                       b) —, 21 (unbalanced gametes)

A fourth possibility, with all of the chromosomes distributed to one gamete and none to the other also exists. Both zygotes would be nonviable and this possibility can be ignored in the discussion.

Fertilization of the six classes of hypothetical gametes outlined above will have the following results:

1 a) 14/21   + 14, 21————>14, 14/21, 21 (normal "carrier")
  b) 14, 21   + 14, 21————>14, 14, 21, 21 (normal)
2 a) 14/21, 21 + 14, 21 ————>14, 14/21, 21, 21 (mongol)
  b) 14   + 14, 21————>14, 14, 21,—(monosomy-21, lethal)
3 a) 14, 14/21 + 14, 21————>14, 14, 14/21, 21 (trisomy—14 ?)
  b) —, 21   + 14, 21————>14, 21, 21 (monosomy-14—lethal)

Gametogenesis of type 3, above, has not been reported, even in families with a large number of progeny bearing a D/G translocation. Thus, for practical purposes, four types of offspring may be expected in approximately equal numbers from the mating of a translocation "carrier" and a normal individual:

              14, 14/21, 21—"normal" translocation carrier
              14, 14/21, 21, 21—translocation mongolism
              14, 14, 21, 21—normal individual
              14, 14, 21,— —monosomy-21, lethal.

In summary, one-third of *viable* children will, in theory, be mongols, one-third will be carriers and one-third will be normal. One-quarter of the pregnancies will be lost.

This proportion of offspring is generally rather closely approximated in matings in which the carrier is a female. For a time, it was thought that fathers bearing such a translocation did not sire abnormal children. This was attributed to impairment of the function of the translocation-bearing spermatozoa. More thorough investigations have revealed several instances of paternal transmission of translocation mongolism, especially of the G/G type. The predominant offspring in most families in which the male is the carrier have also been carriers. In some families, normal offspring have been predominant. In all families, the ratio of mongol

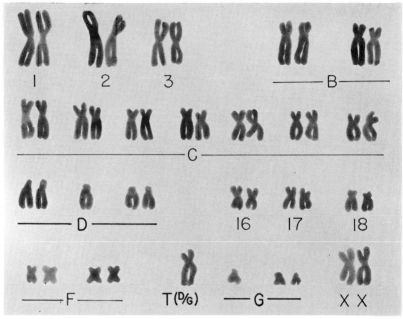

Figure 39. Karyotype of a D/G Translocation "Carrier." The modal number is forty-five. Autosomes are absent from groups D and G and are replaced by an abnormal translocation (T) chromosome which simulates a group C autosome.

children has been far below theoretical expectation (one in sixteen, in one family for example). There is no question that the distribution of gametes from a translocation-carrying father is anything but random. Spermatozoa bearing unbalanced chromosome complements, in translocation mongolism at any rate, have a decided selective disadvantage.

G/G translocation may be of two types, 21/21 or 21/22. A G/G translocation of the 21/22 type behaves much as the D/G type. The 21/21 type, on the other hand, can be distinguished by the fact that all offspring of the 21/21 carrier will be mongols. Only two classes of gametes are possible (21/21 and 0).

Laboratory Findings

Karyotypic patterns vary depending both on the type of translocation present and whether or not the carrier state or the symptomatic mongol state is present.

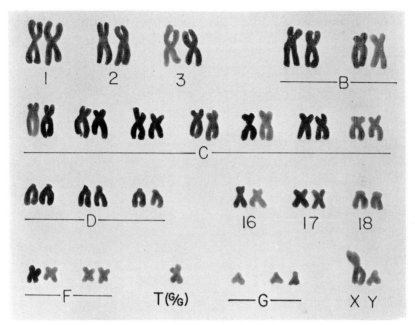

Figure 40. Karyotype in G/G Translocation Mongolism. The modal number is forty-six. Only three group G autosomes are present and there is an abnormal translocation (T) chromosome present which simulates a group F autosome.

The D/G translocation carrier has a modal number of 45 chromosomes. One chromosome is absent from group D (five rather than six) and one member is absent from group G (four rather than five in males; three rather than four in females). In addition, there is an extra abnormal chromosome, the translocation (T) chromosome, which most often appears to be an extra group C autosome. The T chromosome is composed of the long arms of a D chromosome and the long arms of the chromosome-21 joined at the centromere. It is usually submetacentric, and is generally somewhat smaller than the group C autosomes.

The G/G translocation carrier also has a modal number of 45 chromosomes. Two of the group G chromosomes are absent and are replaced by an anomalous T chromosome which most closely resembles one of the group F autosomes. It tends to be slightly larger than either chromosome-19 or chromosome-20. It is usually almost exactly metacentric.

Very infrequently, both of the products of the reciprocal trans-location may be present, particularly if the short arm fragments have retained a centromere (relatively rare). Such translocation carriers have a modal number of 46. In addition to the chromosome pattern outlined above, there is an additional minute "fragment." The "fragment" is the complementary member of the exchange.

A rare morphologic variant of the G/G type of translocation has been described. Usually the T chromosomes have the translocated arms united at the centromere. In the anomalous form, the long arms of the translocated fragment are attached to free ends of the long arms of the recipient chromosome. This type of translocation thus presents as an anomalous acrocentric chromosome with long arms twice as long as usual. On casual inspection, this chromosome rather closely resembles a member of the D group and this type of translocation may be erroneously interpreted as an instance of D-trisomy.

Translocation mongolism has a karyotype which is characterized by a modal number of 46. In either the D/G or the G/G type, the appearance of the karyotype is similar to that described for the carrier state with the addition of a chromosome-21 to the complement producing the modal number of 46. The D/G mongol has five group D chromosomes and a normal complement of G chromosomes. The G/G mongol has either three (females) or four (males) group G chromosomes. The translocation chromo-some is also present in each instance.

The Carrier State

Nearly all authors describe the carrier state in translocations of either the D/G or G/G type as perfectly balanced and asymp-tomatic. This would imply that the translocation invariably in-volves all of the functional genetic material of the long arms of chromosome-21 and that the short arms of chromosome-21 (which are usually lost) contain no genetic material of discernible sig-nificance.

In the main, this generalization is probably correct. There are, however, several reports in which the carrier state has been associ-ated with detectable, though minor, clinical alterations. These occasional reports lead one to question the validity of the blanket references to "asymptomatic" or "normal" carriers. It seems rather improbable that these translocations would follow fractures of such precision that only genetically nonfunctional material is affected in all instances. Occasional loss of small "active" chromosome segments would be expected to produce clinical effects consequent to minor deletions.

Occasional reports indicate that the translocation mongolism has been somewhat less severe than the usual trisomic form. These findings also tend to support the contention that the fractures of the translocation are not invariably precise enough to be totally asymptomatic.

All carriers should be very carefully assessed for minor clinical effects. If minor abnormalities are encountered in sufficient numbers, they may provide useful information as to the physical characteristics governed by the genetic material near the centromere of chromosome-21.

Other Autosomal Translocations

A diverse group of autosomal translocations can be found in the form of isolated case reports. None of these yet approach translocation mongolism in predictability. With the exception of several instances of partial E-trisomy, none bear much recognizable relationship to the better known chromosomal syndromes.

Partial D Trisomy

Production of partial D-trisomy as a result of a translocation is of interest because of its peculiar absence from the literature. The frequency of D/-translocations in mongolism would lead one to expect that at least some instances of D trisomy syndrome might arise on the basis of segregation of the D/- translocation with other members of the D group of chromosomes. We have been unable to find such a case recorded. There are two possible explanations—either such a translocation has a profoundly adverse effect upon the gametes which carry it or the D chromosome involved in translocations is not the same chromosome involved in the D trisomy syndrome.

Partial E Trisomy

Translocations have been associated with incomplete expression of the E trisomy syndrome in several reported instances. Some instances of E translocation have, on the other hand, borne little resemblance to the usual E trisomy syndrome. Translocation of a portion of an E chromosome has involved a recipient of group D or group G with special frequency. In one instance, the exchange was felt to have involved two chromosomes of the E group (16 and 18)—this latter instance was associated with prominent hypertonicity.

Generally speaking, two types of clinical sequelae have been associated with translocations of the E group of chromosomes. The chromosomal defects in each instance may be very straightforward. Loss of one chromosome from group G and one chromosome from group G and one chromosome from group E with an extra chromosome resembling a group C chromosome (a balanced defect) was seen in a mother who had one normal pregnancy in five pregnancies (one abortion and three early fetal deaths). This is somewhat suggestive of the behavior of the translocation of mongolism. Unfortunately, none of the offspring could be karyotyped.

One case report, however, shows more convincingly that a familial translocation pattern similar to that of mongolism does exist, though it is rarely encountered. The mother had a karyotype with a modal number of 45, one chromosome absent from group E and an extra T chromosome similar to those of group C. The affected child had a modal number of 46 with a normal complement of E chromosomes plus the translocated chromosome. The child showed well developed stigmata of E-trisomy syndrome. In a second, very similar, family the mother had a karyotype with a modal number of forty-six. She had five E, five D and two "extra" chromosomes. These latter, both products of the reciprocal translocation, resembled chromosomes of groups G and C.

Translocation may be associated with partial E-trisomy without a familial pattern being noted. In one such instance, the karyotype showed a chromosome absent from the G group, a normal complement in the E group and an "extra group C" chromosome (an unbalanced defect). Deformities present are most consistent with those of E trisomy syndrome.

Miscellaneous Translocations

The following described translocations are only occasional. They are included so that points of comparison are available to those who may encounter similar defects in the laboratory.

A/C Translocations

There have been several case reports, all associated with chromosomal patterns regarded as reciprocal translocation between a group A (1-3) and a group C (6-12) chromosome, which have had unrelated clinical features.

In the first instance, the chromosomes involved were not identified specifically. The chromosomal pattern is difficult to interpret; it may well represent a more complex defect than simple translocation. Two related children each had a convulsive disorder which commenced at three years of age and became progressively more severe, causing the death of one by age six. Though chromosome analysis is available in only one child, it is strongly suspected that the anomaly was present in both.

A father, asymptomatic, and his son showed what was interpreted as a balanced (father) and unbalanced (son) reciprocal translocation between chromosomes 1 and 6. The unbalance in the son was regarded as trisomy of a portion of chromosome-1 and deletion of part of chromosome-6. Most of the anomalies recorded were skeletal and were accompanied by severe mental deficiency.

2/D Translocation

A karyotype was encountered in which the modal number was forty-five with one D chromosome and one chromosome-2 missing. An additional chromosome, an unusually large metacentric was present. The defects were of minor degree and were described as "similar to mongolism."

2/C Translocation

A translocation between chromosome-2 (missing segment, long arm)) and a member of group C (with an unusually long arm) was associated with familial transmission of interatrial septal defects. The mother had mosaicism of the 46/47 type with an extra group C chromosome in the aneuploid line.

B/C Translocation

Two siblings, each with multiple malformations resembling those of mongolism rather closely, were thought to have a reciprocal translocation between chromosomes 4 and 9. The identification of the chromosomes involved is tentative.

D/D Translocation

Reciprocal translocations between acrocentric chromosomes of group D (13-15) have been of the centric fusion type. The karyotype produced by the defect is usually characterized by the absence of two group D chromosomes and the presence of an additional large metacentric chromosome which resembles one of the group A chromosomes (2n = 45).

The first such translocation was encountered in a male with Klinefelter's syndrome. No stigmata other than those of Klinefelter's syndrome were noted.

Familial transmission of this defect has been reported several times. In one family, the defect was associated with nervous system defects including anencephaly. Some members of the family showed mosaicism in which the translocation occurred alone in some stemlines and in the trisomic state in others. In another family, where the translocation was followed for three generations, no clinical correlations were noted.

This translocation seems to be fairly frequent. In addition to the three generation family cited above, the same authors reported its occurrence in several other patients. In only one instance has the translocation been associated with the D-trisomy syndrome.

13/22 Translocation

This is one of the earliest translocations to be described. It was originally encountered in a patient with polydysspondylism (multiple skeletal defects). More recently, a similar translocation was found in several members of a family with mental retardation and speech defects.

?/G Translocation

In a study of one family with habitual abortion, an abnormal paternal chromosome was found. A small acrocentric (group G) had an abnormally long short arm. This was regarded as reflecting a translocation from an unknown donor. It bears a striking similarity to a chromosome regarded as an inversion seen in a family with a similar history (see: "Inversions," below).

G/G Translocation

A most unusual chromosome, an acrocentric with satellites on both long and short arms might represent either a translocation or an inversion. It is more fully discussed in the section below dealing with inversions.

AUTOSOMAL DELETIONS

Deletions are uncommon in the human autosomes and only four case reports are summarized below. In all instances, the deleted chromosome was present as an extra member of the complement (2n = 47). Two of the reports concerned patients with partial E trisomy. The third may represent one of the rare viable anomalies of the group C autosomes. The fourth is an instance of partial mongolism. The Ph[1] chromosome, one of the most important deletions, is discussed in the section on Clones and in Chapter XIV.

Trisomy of Deleted (?) 18

The first of the cases so reported had an extra chromosome which resembled a member of group F with long arms longer than those of other members of the group. The clinical features are entirely in accord with those usually seen in E-trisomy syndrome (mental deficiency, eye defects, ear defects, interventricular septal defect, dextrocardia and defect in the falx cerebri).

The second instance of presumed trisomy of a deleted chromosome-18 is of interest since it affected twin sisters, each of whom had virtually identical clinical findings. The extra chromosome in each instance most closely resembled a group G chromosome but had appreciably larger short arms. The clinical findings are puzzling— features of both the D and E trisomy syndrome are present. The clinical features seem somewhat more in accord with D-trisomy. The morphology of the chromosome is consistent with either interpretation, though the short arms are somewhat longer than one would expect if a D chromosome were involved.

Trisomy of Deleted Group C Autosome

There is one case report in which evidence of group C autosomal anomaly in a viable individual is good. The affected infant suffered complete agenesis of the left lung, pyloric stenosis. Hirschprung's disease and plugging of the bile canaliculi. The extra chromosome was about the size of chromosome-16 but was morphologically unlike the rest of the chromosomes in that group. The short arms were most similar to those of a group C chromosome. The severe and unique defects are more in accord with the expectations one would have in respect to defects of this group.

Trisomy of Deleted 21

A single report of a patient with minimal stigmata of mongolism and an associated small extra "fragment" in the complement seems most consistent with the interpretation of partial trisomy of chromosome-21. However, one almost identical case was regarded by its authors as representing a persistent complementary portion of a reciprocal translocation.

AUTOSOMAL DUPLICATIONS

A duplication is formed as a consequence of an unequal reciprocal interchange between homologous chromosomes. There are some investigators who feel that these have yet to be demonstrated in man. The only instance in which the production of human disease has been attributed to this mechanism is Sturge-Weber syndrome. It has been postulated that partial trisomy (duplication) of chromosome-22 may be associated with this condition.

AUTOSOMAL ISOCHROMOSOMES

Only one example of autosomal isochromosome formation is widely accepted. The large anomalous chromosome which is found in the cells of patients with Waldenstrom's macroglobulinemia (W chromosome) is found as an extra member of the chromosome complement. It is thought to be an isochromosome of the long arms of chromosome-1 or chromosome-2 (see also: Clones).

Consideration must also be given the possibility that at least some examples of G/G translocation mongolism may, in fact, be examples of isochromosome formation involving the long arms of chromosome-21. There is little morphologic evidence which can be used to make the distinction.

AUTOSOMAL INVERSIONS

There are very competent geneticists who are of the opinion that inversions have never been conclusively demonstrated in mammalian cells. In two instances, inversion chromosomes have been tentatively identified in man. The reports are far from widely accepted.

Inversion-21

A normal mother and her mongol daughter each had an abnormal chromosome in group G (chromosome-21?) which was characterized by enlargement of the short arms and shortening of the long arms. A pericentric inversion could well account for such a configuration.

Inversion-G

One of the possible explanations for the occurrence of a very unique acrocentric chromosome which bore satellites on both its long and its short arms is that crossing-over had occurred in a chromosome with a pericentric inversion. Translocation is also a possible explanation. The chromosome was detected in a mentally retarded thirteen year old girl with kyphosis and epilepsy. There were no stigmata of mongolism.

OTHER AUTOSOMAL STRUCTURAL DEFECTS

Other defects which have been described with clinically evident malformations are insertions, ring chromosomes, satellite enlargement and alterations of chromosome size.

Insertions

Microscopic recognition of insertions is very difficult. Those described have been reflected by enlargement of either the long or the short arms in one member of a chromosome pair. Often, an abnormal "puffed," pale or constricted region is thought to reflect the presence of an inserted segment. The donor chromosomes have not been identified in any of the insertions reported with certainty.

An insertion into the long arm of chromosome-1 from an unidentified donor (possibly a member of group C) has been associated with the orofacial-digital (OFD) syndrome. The syndrome occurs in females exclusively (lethal in males?) and is characterized by defects in the palate, lobulation of the tongue, anomalies of the hand and dental deformities.

A similar C/1 insertion has been tentatively identified in a syndrome characterized by cysts of the jaw, multiple basal cell carcinomata and bifid ribs.

Another reported insertion involves a recipient of the group G (21-22) chromosomes and an unidentified donor. The abnormal G chromosome shows enlargement of the short arms, which still bear satellites. It has been encountered in two families with a history of habitual abortion. In one of these families, some normal members (three generations) also had the defect and lacked any phenotypic changes. It is possible that the defect produces nondisjunction which leads to abortion. If the donor chromosome was a large autosome which occasionally paired with the inserted segment in the G chromosome, disjunction involving a large chromosome would be impaired and could well be lethal.

Ring Chromosomes

Ring chromosomes are uncommon structural defects. Their abnormal structure predisposes to nondisjunction during cell division and they gradually become eliminated from the complement as a consequence of such repeated mitotic and meiotic accidents.

A ring configuration of a group E chromosome has been seen in at least three individuals. It was an isolated defect in two of these and was associated with an unidentified translocation to chromosome-3 in the third. In one instance, the ring chromosome was an extra member of the complement (2n = 47) and the clinical effects were those of E trisomy. In the two others, the modal number was 46 but symptoms of partial E trisomy suggest that an undetected translocation might also have been present.

A ring chromosome (unspecified) has been reported in association with mental retardation. Ring-X chromosomes have been seen.

ALTERATIONS IN SIZE

Enlargement of the satellites on the short arms of the acrocentric chromosomes has been reported in association with Marfan's syndrome and familial nervous system defects (anencephaly and spina bifida) as well as in normal individuals. Such enlargement may reflect nothing more than individual or familial normal variation. The value of these large satellites as chromosome markers has not been established. If they segregate with some measureable trait (e.g. blood groups), they can be useful in chromosome mapping.

The significance of apparent alteration in the size of entire chromosomes, reported from time to time, is very difficult to assess. Such apparent enlargement may be due to imperfect coiling of the chromonemal thread, any one of a number of structural defects or may represent nothing more than normal variation. Alterations of whole chromosome length have been seen with Marfan's syndome and other anomalies.

Among the various chromosomal alterations which have been associated with Marfan's syndrome is relative shortening of the long arms of a group G chromosome. This has been described in four unrelated individuals. Enlargement of satellites, also noted in several individuals, has not been seen constantly in any one chromsome. It has been reported with approximately equal frequency in chromosomes of both the D and the G groups.

The article by Carr alluded to earlier lists as one example of the chromosomal changes which can be puzzling an instance of enlargement of chromosome-16. The affected chromosome showed considerable discrepancy in size as compared to its homologue. The patient, a female, had torticollis, a short and broad neck, high arched palate, underdeveloped external genitalia and evidence of slight mental retardation. The patient's father and brothers had the same karotype without clinical changes. The author was therefore tempted to regard the association as coincidental until he became aware of an identical patient studied by others.

Marfan's syndrome and minor defects affecting the acrocentric chromosomes have been associated sufficiently frequently that mere coincidence becomes progressively less probable. The reports to date would at least infer that Marfan's syndrome and defects of the acrocentric chromosomes are related findings.

COMPLEX AUTOSOMAL ANOMALIES

Included in this group are those rare individuals in whom multiple autosomal defects have been reported. They include the following classes of defects:

1) Structurally anomalous mosaics.
2) Structurally anomalous aneuploids.
3) Structurally anomalous aneuploid mosaics.

The rare instances in which such complex anomalies have been recorded are tabulated in Appendix V. There are none which warrant more detailed examination.

CLONES

Strictly defined, a clone is a population of cells (or individuals in the case of some organisms) in which all members have been derived from a common single progenitor exclusively by asexual (mitotic) reproduction. Applying the definition in this strict sense, the cell lines in mosaics are clones. The term has assumed an equally acceptable and more restrictive meaning in which it designates a genetically atypical cell population arising in a single tissue. This narrower definition is widely used in reference to tumors and is used here as a convenient method of distinguishing mosaics from single-tissue chromosomal changes.

Clones of significance in human medicine have so far been confined to tumors and to derangements of the hematopoietic system. Undoubtedly others exist, but their significance is less striking than those alluded to below. Some of the characteristics of tumor clones will be discussed in Chapter XIV. Hematopoietic clones in man exist in at least three diseases.

Waldenstrom's Macroglobulinemia

A very striking chromosome abnormality has been encountered in bone marrow karyotypes prepared in patients with Waldenstrom's macroglobulinemia. The cells contain an extra very large chromosome often paler than the rest of the complement (the "W" chromosome) which appears to be an isochromosome of the long arms of chromosome-1 or chromosome-2. The chromosome is seen only in a portion of cells in culture and is thought to represent a chromosomal change confined to the cells producing the abnormal globulin.

Demonstration of a "W" chromosome in cells of patients suffering from an obscure dysproteinemia should prove a highly acceptable alternative to ultracentrifuge studies.

Erythroblastic Endopolyloidy

A rare variant of familial hemolytic anemia has been associated with abnormal erythropoiesis and the presence of macronuclear and multinuclear erythroblasts in the bone marrow. Bone marrow karyotypes reveal a population of cells which are diploid, hyperdiploid and polyploid. Some may have as many as 92 chromosomes in their complement. Such changes, confined to the erythroblastic series form another type of anomalous clone.

The Ph¹ Chromosome

Chronic myelocytic leukemia is characterized in some ninety percent of cases by the presence of an abnormal deleted chromosome in group G (presumably chromosome-21). Other forms of leukemia have also had clones of cells with abnormal karyotypes. These changes are discussed further in Chapter XIV.

CHAPTER XII

CLINICAL EFFECTS OF SEX CHROMOSOME
ABNORMALITIES

THE comparatively orderly, though sometimes unpredictable, spectrum of anomalies which follows defects in the sex chromosome complement makes discussion of these defects from a clinical point of view quite convenient. The discernible pattern of clinical defects, which roughly parallels the severity of the underlying sex chromosome defect, offers some insight into the eventual patterns which may be seen in autosomal defects. Clinical aberrations probably follow some similar pattern which is related to the severity of the defect affecting the autosome in question.

There are a few basic principles which govern the behavior of sex chromosome anomalies. The first of these, which has been alluded to previously (Chapter IV), is that the agonadal mammal differentiates as a "hypoplastic female." Since the prime derangement induced by any sex chromosome defect is gonadal, each is characterized by a reversion to the agonadal state of greater or lesser degree. Extraneous hormonal effects, such as those of the adrenal, may confuse this broad generalization but do not negate it.

The second basic principle, which seems largely responsible for the comparatively innocuous behavior of even the most elaborate sex chromosome defects, is that the "extra" X chromosomes become inactivated early in fetal development. Thus such defects as monosomy and polysomy, unheard of in autosomes of equal size, are compatible with life when they affect the sex chromosomes. The effects of such extra X chromosomes is, however, appreciable (otherwise the XO and XX constitutions would be much more similar).

The above cited phenomenon, X inactivation, accounts in part for the strikingly greater frequency of sex chromosomal defects than of autosomal defects. The sex chromosomes, which account for only about five percent of the total chromosome complement, account for nearly fifty percent of the case reports in the literature. The preponderance of sex chromosome defects is at least in part more apparent than real. Anomalies of the sex chromosomes can be detected on a mass screening basis using the simple and inexpensive buccal smear techniques. No such simple screening methods are available for the detection of autosomal defects.

GENERAL CLINICAL FEATURES

Sex chromosome defects most commonly become apparent as clinical derangements of sex differentiation in infancy or near puberty. A simple classification, based on the age at which the defects first come to clinical attention, has helped us to keep this rather complex subject under at least partial intellectual control. It is cited below.

Before we consider the syndromes which attend defects in the sex chromosomes, it is mandatory that we define the terms which are used. There is considerable confusion in the application of terms in the field of sexual abnormalities, particularly in regard to the intersex states. We adhere to the following terminology:

CLINICAL INTERSEX—an individual exhibiting sufficient genital ambiguity that the sex is in doubt.

PSEUDOHERMAPHRODITE—an individual in whom the genetic and gonadal sex are in accord but in whom the external genitalia are either ambiguous or are at complete variance with the genetic-gonadal sex.

TRUE HERMAPHRODITE—an individual in whom both testicular and ovarian tissue can be demonstrated unequivocally by histologic study. The diagnosis in this instance is purely histologic and is unaltered by the chromosome complement which is present.

Within the scope of the above definitions, pseudohermaphroditism and clinical intersex are *not necessarily* concomitant conditions. Testicular feminization, particularly, may produce so perfect a female phenotype that the male genetic and gonadal complement remains entirely unsuspected well into adult life.

A more difficult definition is that of *sex* itself. Several types of sex may be alluded to: they include phenotypic sex (the appearance of the patient), *gonadal sex* (the appearance of the gonads), the *chromatin sex* (a term which should be discarded), *gender role* (the sex which the individual assumes socially) and *true* or *chromosomal sex*. Unless otherwise specified, the terms "male" and "female" refer to the chromosomal sex when used in the following discussion.

CLINICAL PRESENTATION OF SEX CHROMOSOMAL ALTERATIONS

A. In infancy—as clinical intersexes with ambiguous genitalia.
B. At puberty—
   1. In "females"
     a) masculinization
     b) sexual infantilism
     c) primary amenorrhea
   2. In males
     a) sexual hypoplasia
   3. As mild degrees of clinical intersex
C. In adults—
   1. Unexplained sterility
   2. Oligomenorrhea.

The above classification is in no wise purported to be a comprehensive classification of sexual developmental anomalies. Its sole purpose is to serve as a point of reference to which the various sex chromosome defects may be related. When the clinical defects cited are encountered, chromatin studies and karyotyping are indicated in the investigation of the patient.

The following discussion will follow the above outline more or less closely. A classification of sex chromosome defects *per se* is given in Appendix V. It must also be remembered that the discussion pertains only to *chromosomal* defects of sexual development. Many hormonal and "idiopathic" states will be alluded to only casually.

Very compreensive treatises are available which discuss all facets of the problem. They cannot be compressed into a single chapter and no attempt has been made to do so.

CHROMOSOMALLY INDUCED INTERSEX

The clinical intersex states are most commonly encountered in the newborn, though some of the more subtle deformities may not command attention until childhood, puberty or even into adult life. An orderly investigative scheme can resolve many of the infantile intersex states without resorting to laparotomy. The diagnostic approach which we recommend is:

A. Perform a buccal chromatin test (*after* fourth day of life)·
   Positive —determine 17-ketosteroid level.
      High—virilizing adrenal hyperplasia.
      Normal—proceed to step B.
   Negative—proceed to step B.

B. Perform a karyotype:
   XY—Testicular feminization
      True hermaphroditism (rare) *
   XX—True hermaphroditism *
      Maternal hormone therapy
      "Idiopathic" pseudohermaphroditism.
   Mosaicism *

Using the above scheme, about half of the instances of infantile intersex (due to adrenal virilism) may be diagnosed without laparotomy. The remainder require laparotomy at some point in a complete evaluation. It is imperative that adequate diagnosis be made early. Current consensus indicates that the gender role is fixed by eighteen months of age. Every effort should be made to make sure that it is an appropriate one.

True Hermaphroditism

Chromosome anlysis has been of comparatively little help in resolving the origin of the true hermaphrodite. The majority of such patients have had an XX chromosome constitution. An XY constitution is uncommon. The reported instances of XY true hermaphroditism have often had recognizable testicular tissue and a "streak" gonad. The "streak" in many instances has been rather liberally interpreted as an ovary and many such patients classified as true hermaphrodites on this basis. It must be admitted that the appearance of these streaks does recapitulate the histology of the "ovaries" seen in gonadal dysgenesis. Bergada *et al.* have alluded to this group as "asymmetrical gonadal differentiation"—all of their cases were chromatin negative. This seems a better term than "true hermaphroditism" when the gonadal histology is not unequivocal.

The clinical appearance of the patients in this group is similar in all of the instances reported. For the most part, the external genitalia are ambiguous and the chromatin pattern is negative. Laparotomy usually shows unilateral Wolffian elements (vas deferens) which are associated with histologically recognizable testicular tissue. On the other side, a Fallopian tube and "streak" gonad are present. Nearly all have a vagina and uterus.

This pattern, no matter how strongly "female" it may appear, does *not* imply that the streak gonad is an ovary. The work of Jost (Chapter IV) has demonstrated that fetal castration in males is followed by Mullerian development and that this effect may be unilateral. Thus there is no real reason to assume that the "streak" gonad is an ovary. Failure of development of testicular tissue has the same ultimate effect, i.e., development of "female" internal genitalia.

Occasionally, interesting mosaics have been encountered. Unfortunately, none seems consistent enough that their discovery on karotyping obviates the need for laparotomy. They will be discussed further later.

The "Ultimate Hermaphrodite"

A single patient has been described whose genetic and gonadal complement is so unique as to surely deserve a designation appropriate to the fascinating picture presented. We herewith define the "ultimate hermaphrodite" as an individual in whom both the genetic complement and gonadal complement are in accord and in whom both testicular and ovarian tissue and normal male (XY) and normal female (XX) cells are present in more or less equal proportions.

The individual who can fulfill these criteria is a mosaic of 46XY / 46XX cells in nearly equal proportions and possesses both testicular and ovarian tissue which is histologically identifiable. The origin of this genetic constitution is amazing. Cytogenetic studies, in company with erythrocyte antigen studies, indicate that the affected individual is a chimera formed by the "grafting" of one fraternal twin to another and their consequent development as a single individual. This type of zygote fusion, which occurs at the one-cell stage, has been accomplished experimentally in the zygotes of lower animal forms. This is the only such instance recorded in man.

Is There an X-Y Translocation?

Several investigators have suggested that an undetected X/Y translocation may underlie some of the human developmental defects which are usually regarded as having an XX constitution. This suggestion, while yet unproven, merits serious consideration. Structural defects of the sex chromosomes are not uncommon and there is little reason to suppose that these chromosomes would be immune to translocation. Should such a condition indeed exist, it would offer much insight into both the function of the Y chromosome and the formation of testicular tissue in "XX" true hermaphrodites.

Mosaicism in Intersex States

One of the more common chromosomal mosaics associated with clinical intersex is XO/XY mosaicism. Alterations which have been associated with this type of mosaicism have been very similar to those which accompany the "asymmetrical gonadal development" of some XY intersex patients. In several instances, the male phenotype has been much better developed than in other intersex states. Thus the XO/XY karyotype is associated principally with defects of male differentiation.

Many of these cases have been called "true hermaphrodites" on the basis of the "ovarian" tissue which has been thought to be present. Though this may occasionally be the true case, the more common pattern is that of severe testicular dysgenesis. The criteria which have been used for the identification of "ovarian" tissue have been very liberal indeed and are typified by such descriptions as

TABLE V

XY/XO Mosaics

(Analysis of Seven Cases)

PHENOTYPIC SEX (as reported)	
Female	3/7
Male	2/7
Intersex	2/7
CHROMATIN	
Buccal chromatin negative	7/7
Absent "drumsticks"	7/7
EXTERNAL GENITALIA	
Bilateral scrotal gonads	0/7
Unilateral scrotal gonad	1/7
Agonadal bifid scrotum	1/7
Penile urethra, hypospadias	1/7
Large phallus, perineal urethra	5/7
Normal clitoris	1/7 (?)
Vagina, normal or hypoplastic	5/7
INTERNAL GENITALIA (6 laparotomies)	
Uterus	6/6
Fallopian tubes	4/6
Wolffian elements	0/6
GONADS	
Bilateral histologic testes	2/7
Unilateral testis	2/7
with ovary 0/7	
with "streak" 1/7	
no biopsy other side 1/7	
Ovary with follicles	0/7
Ovary, stroma only, bilateral	1/7
Ovotestis, unilateral	1/7
No gonadal biopsy	1/7
SECONDARY SEX CHARACTERS	
Gynecomastia in "males"	1/2
Breast hypoplasia in "females"	2/3

"ovarian stroma with theca-like cells." This offhand identification of these virtually structureless gonads has been commented on by other reviewers and a plea for less casual terminology is not unwarranted.

Mosaic patterns other than the XO/XY type are not common. They are summarized in Appendix V.

Non-chromosomal Intersex

There are several variants of infantile intersex which are unrelated to chromosomal defects as far as is now known. The most common examples are those of virilizing adrenal hyperplasia, testicular feminization and the sequelae of intrapartum hormone administration.

CHROMOSOMALLY INDUCED IMPAIRMENT OF FEMALE SEX DIFFERENTIATION

The obvious impairments of sex differentiation in females which occur in infancy have been alluded to. Derangements which become apparent at puberty are more common and may have one of the following clinical presentations:

Masculinization.
Sexual infantilism or hypoplasia.
Primary amenorrhea.
Oligomenorrhea or hypomenorrhea with or without sterility.

Of these, masculinization is least commonly associated with visible chromosomal defects. The major causes of masculinization in the pubertal female are undetected testicular feminization (diagnosed by its XY chromosome constitution), true hermaphroditism and, occasionally, masculinizing ovarian tumors.

The more important group, in respect to their cytogenetic alterations, are those diseases which can be categorized collectively as gonadal dysgenesis. There are two main disease entities within this category—Turner's syndrome and chromatin positive gonadal dysgenesis. The former has a highly characteristic clinical and cytogenetic pattern, the latter is a more miscellaneous group.

Turner's Syndrome

The use of chromosome analysis has clarified the distinction between true Turner's syndrome and chromatin positive gonadal dysgenesis. True Turner's syndrome is characterized by an XO chromosome pattern and a modal number of forty-five chromosomes.

Incidence and Etiology

Turner's syndrome is an uncommon condition for which incidence figures are scanty. The most comprehensive surveys are those conducted on 3,715 newborns from Canada and other series from Berne (3,728) and Edinburgh (6000). Combined incidence figures from these and other series indicate that the incidence of Turner's syndrome in the general female population is somewhere in the neighborhood of 0.4/1,000.

The etiology of the XO constitution is almost always meiotic nondisjunction. Rarely, a structurally anomalous X chromosome such as a ring may become eliminated from an XX constitution leaving an XO pattern. Among the chromosome anomalies, Turner's syndrome has the distinction that it bears no demonstrable relationship to maternal age. Evidence accumulated from studies of such X-borne loci as colorblindness indicates that the preponderant defect resides in spermiogenesis, and that the incidence of paternal X chromosome nondisjunction is about four times that of maternal X chromosome nondisjunction. The X chromosome in the XO pattern is more commonly the maternal X.

An example of the type of study conducted in assessing the site of nondisjunction has been alluded to earlier (see: Determining the Source of the Nondisjunctive Gamete, Chapter VI). The reason for the preponderance of sex chromosome nondisjunction during male gametogenesis is an inherent consequence of the male chromosomal complement. The male sex chromosomes are the only naturally occurring nonhomologous chromosome pair in the complement. The non-homology of these chromosomes is accompanied by imperfect end-to-end pairing during synapsis and thus predisposes to nondisjunction and premature disjunction.

The XO chromosomal constitution is appreciably less common than either XXX or XXY which are the other zygotes which result from meiotic nondisjunction during gametogenesis (XY germ cell produces O and XY spermatozoa in equal numbers). In theory, the incidence of XO and XXY should be almost equal. The difference in incidence has been attributed to functional inadequacy of O sperm.

Clinical Features

Patients with true Turner's syndrome (chromatin negative gonadal dysgenesis) are characteristically short, amenorrheic females with hypoplastic external genitalia and underdeveloped secondary sex characteristics. A complex of soft tissue defects also form an integral part of the syndrome. These various mesenchymal defects are as characteristic of the syndrome as are the sexual changes and serve to differentiate chromatin positive gonadal dysgenesis from true Turner's syndrome.

Affected patients are appreciably shorter than normal females, many being under five feet in height. The external genitalia are hypoplastic and the vagina is frequently so. Axillary and pubic hair are scanty or may even be absent. The soft tissue alterations include neck webbing, a shield-like chest with widely spaced nipples and an increase in the carrying angle of the forearms. The hairline is low on the posterior portion of the scalp, sometimes extending almost to the level of the first thoracic vertebra.

A variety of visceral defects may also be present. Their appearance is less predictable than those above cited. Most significant is the increased incidence of aortic coarctation which occurs in Turner's syndrome. This condition is a rarity in normal females. Peripheral lymphedema is another defect which occurs in Turner's syndrome. It may appear in infancy. The gonads, presumably ovaries, are represented by compact bundles of wavy stroma within which are embedded collections of Leydig-like cells.

Turner's syndrome may make its appearance in the infant female by virtue of the neck webbing which it induces. Peripheral lymphedema is another of the features of Turner's syndrome which may appear in infancy.

One patient with an XO chromosomal pattern (and no evidence of mosaicism) had features at striking variance with the usual clinical pattern associated with this constitution. The only stigma of Turner's syndrome was short stature. In addition to having normal menses and breast development, the patient bore a normal male child. Though one suspects that an undiscovered mosaic is a strong possibility, the possibility that XO patterns may have inconstant clinical sequelae is still worthy of mention.

There are several reports which allude to individuals in whom the XO constitution has been accompanied by ambiguous genitalia and testicular development. It seems unlikely that uncomplicated XO patterns are the true patterns in such individuals. They are virtually identical in all respects with the group cited above under the description of asymmetical gonadal differentiation. Unless some incontrovertible evidence to the contrary can be offered, it seems best to assume that such patients are actually XO/XY mosaics in whom the XY stemline has not yet been detected.

Even less frequently, patients have been reported in whom an "XO" chromatin pattern is associated with a chromatin positive nuclear chromatin pattern. Later reports by some authors of these original reports report the finding of previously undiscovered XX stemline in an XX/XO mosaic. Inconsistencies between chromosomal patterns and expected chromatin patterns should always stimulate a search for an undetected mosaic.

"Male Turner Syndrome"

An interesting clinical syndrome which closely recapitulates the features of Turner's syndrome in the female is seen in males of short stature with neck webbing, low ears and low hairline. The gonadal effects are not usually as striking. There have been no chromosomal anomalies described.

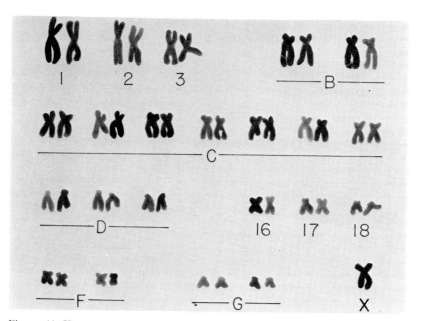

Figure 41. Karyotype in True Turner's Syndrome. The modal number is forty-five and one member of group C (the X chromosome) is absent.

TABLE VI

XO vs. XO/XX

	XO	*XO/XX*
Female phenotype	Yes	Yes
Buccal chromatin	Negative	Positive (85%)
"Drumsticks"	Absent	Present (50%)
		Reduced (35%)
		Absent (15%)
Short stature	Yes	Yes
Breast atrophy	Yes	Yes
Amenorrhea	Yes	Usually
Broad chest	Yes	Variable
Neck webbing	Yes	No
Peripheral lymphedema	Yes	No
Coarctation of aorta	Frequent	No

Laboratory Findings

Buccal or vaginal chromatin preparations have a chromatin negative pattern. The polymorphonuclear drumsticks are either totally absent or, less commonly, present in very much reduced numbers. Karyotyping reveals a modal number of forty-five chromosomes and one member is absent from group C (fifteen instead of the usual sixteen). All the other chromosome groups have a normal complement.

Chromatin Positive Gonadal Dysgenesis

This condition is sometimes referred to as a "chromatin positive Turner's syndrome." The use of this term is to be deplored—it dilutes the specificity of the term "Turner's syndrome" which has both characteristic clinical and chromosomal findings. The clinical and laboratory distinctiveness of the two conditions make the use of equally distinctive terminology a worthwhile goal.

Incidence and Etiology

No incidence figures are yet available which are particularly meaningful. This condition seems to have an incidence which is somewhat similar to that of true Turner's syndrome. The most common chromosomal defect associated with chromatin positive gonadal dysgenesis is mosaicism of the type 45XO/46XX. Other variants are less common.

The XO/XX mosaic reflects nondisjunction in the first or second cleavage division of a zygote whose original constitution might be either XX or XO. If an inherently normal (XX) zygote is affected, either anaphase lagging during first mitosis (produces XO and XX daughter cells) or nondisjunction in the second cleavage division (produces XX, XO and XXX lines) with loss of one of the daughter cells may be postulated. Of the two, anaphase lagging would seem the more probable explanation.

An even more attractive possibility is that nondisjunction occurs in an aneuploid zygote (one chromosome anomaly commonly predisposes to another). For example, nondisjunction in the second cleavage division of an XO zygote would produce an individual with three cell types (XO, XX and OO), with one of these (OO) being a nonviable cell. This and the mechanisms cited above are hypothetical—objective evidence does not favor one above the other.

Clinical Features

Patients with chromatin positive gonadal dysgenesis are short, amenorrheic females with genital hypoplasia and impaired secondary sex development. The overall body habitus is rather similar to that of true Turner's syndrome and the conditions are distinguished clinically by the absence of such features as neck webbing, low hairline, etc. from the chromatin positive variants.

Chromatin Negative Gonadal Dysgenesis

There is a small group of patients in whom the clinical features are consistent with those of chromatin positive gonadal dysgenesis but in whom the buccal and vaginal chromatin patterns are negative. These patients lack any of the stigmata of Turner's syndrome such as neck webbing though their chromatin pattern at first suggests that Turner's syndrome may be present. Most of these patients also have mosaicism. In spite of the chromatin negative pattern, we feel that it is desirable to distinguish this group of patients from those having true XO Turner syndrome.

XX/XO Variants

The clinical features above cited are characteristic of the XO/XX chromosome constitution. Laboratory findings usually include chromatin positive buccal and vaginal epithelial patterns (although occasional negative smears will be encountered). The incidence of positive cells is usually somewhat reduced. The incidence of "drumsticks" in peripheral blood may be normal but is usually somewhat reduced. Asynchrony in the findings of peripheral blood examinations and buccal smears is very suggestive of mosaicism.

Karyotyping reveals a bimodal count with approximately equal numbers of cells with a modal number of forty-five and a modal number of forty-six chromosomes. Chromosome analysis reveals a normal female complement in the euploid (forty-six) line. The aneuploid line lacks one member of group C. On occasion, all findings indicate that chromatin positive gonadal dysgenesis is present but karyotyping reveals a population of cells in peripheral blood which are either wholly euploid or wholly aneuploid. In such instances, chromosome analysis on some other tissuee, such as skin may be necessary to establish a diagnosis.

Other Variants

Isochromosomes of the X chromosome are not uncommon. Their effects are variable and range from amenorrhea to the more severe ranges of chromatin positive gonadal dystenesis. Some of the more severe defects have been associated with mosaicism of such types as 45XO/46X-isoX and with isochromosomes of the long arm type. In such instances, enlargement of both buccal chromatin and of drumsticks may be apparent.

Primary Amenorrhea

There are several abnormalities of sex chromosomal constitution which are reflected only in primary amenorrhea without particularly notable physical alterations. Considering patients with primary amenorrhea as a group, some 28 percent will be found to have sex chromosomal defects as the underlying etiological factor. Or this group, an appreciable number will have fairly readily distinguishable chromosomal defects (such as Turner's syndrome). There is, however, an appreciable residuum of patients in whom primary amenorrhea is the only symptom of some underlying sex chromosomal defect.

Oligomenorrhea and Sterility

Many of the defects which are reflected by primary amenorrhea are not particularly consistent in the effects which they produce. In some patients, they may produce oligomenorrhea or hypomenorrhea and in others sterility may be the only stigma of the underlying chromosome abnormality. Some such defects may, in fact, be discovered accidentally in patients who not only menstruate but who are fertile. Thus an apparently identical defect which produces primary amenorrhea in one patient may be fully compatibile with fertility in another.

Aside from Turner's syndrome and chromatin positive gonadal dysgenesis associated with the XO/XX mosaic pattern, sex chromosome defects are most capricious in the clinical effects which they produce. Some of the more common defects are discussed below.

The most important conclusion which can be drawn from the evidence which has so far accumulated is that cytogenetic techniques deserve a far more prominent place in the investigation of amenorrhea, oligomenorrhea and sterility than they now enjoy. Buccal smears and karyotyping should be among the first laboratory procedures employed in the investigation of any of these conditions. Much frustration and expense to the patient might thereby be obviated.

XXX and XXXX

Both XXX and XXXX chromosome patterns are associated with variable clinical effects. XXX may have no effect on the patient and is, occasionally, encountered in fertile women. This condition is sometimes alluded to as the "superfemale" state—a completely inappropriate term. Mental deficiency is a variable feature and tends to be more pronounced with the tetra-X variant. Either of these patterns can be responsible for otherwise inexplicable sterility. XXX is commoner than Turner's syndrome, its incidence being approximately 1.2/1000.

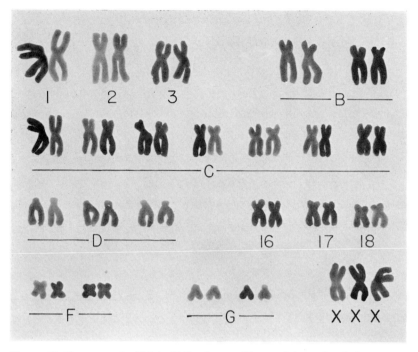

Figure 42. Karyotype in Triplo-X Syndrome. The modal number is forty-seven and there is an extra member in group C (an X chromosome).

X Chromosome Mosaicism

There are at least ten different variant patterns of sex chromosome mosaicism which have been described in which one or more aneuploid stemlines are present. There are also a group of patients in whom mosaicism includes some structurally anomalous chromosome. There is considerable variation in the attendant clinical features. These range from oligomenorrhea to full-blown gonadal dysgenesis. The various mosaics are summarized in Appendix V.

Special mention might be made of chromosome anomalies which have been encountered in the Stein-Levinthal syndrome. These patients have shown the usual stigmata of Stein-Levinthal syndrome including the ovarian changes. They have responded to the usual therapy of wedge resection of the ovary. One such patient, for instance, had mosaicism of the 46XX/46X-deleted X type.

Morphologic Abnormalities of the X Chromosome

Both deletions and isochromosome formation have been encountered. The clinical defects usually parallel those of other forms of chromatin positive gonadal dysgenesis or may be somewhat less severe. Amenorrhea is a common finding. Morphologic abnormalities of the X chromosome are frequently reflected by alterations in the morphology and size of the nuclear sex chromatin. Deletions produce size reductions which are often difficult to assess. Enlargement of the sex chromatin accompanies isochromosome formation. Sometimes a rather striking bilobed configuration is seen.

Though deletions have been reported with moderate frequency, the clinical effects of these deletions have been of comparatively little help in mapping the factors borne of the X chromosome. Both long and short arm deletions tend to produce rather similar clinical alterations. There is a tendency for the abnormal X chromosome in the complement to become "inactivated" and to form the nuclear chromatin mass. This tendency would account in part for the lack of distinctiveness of the clinical sequelae produced.

Isochromosome formation has been accompanied by short stature, short neck, absence of secondary sex characteristics and amenorrhea in chromatin positive females. Such cases have been alluded to as "trisomy-3" in the past since there is a very striking morphologic similarity between X-isochromosomes and chromosome-3. The defect is probably paternal in origin since (in plants) isochromosomes most often form in univalents. Dissociation of the non-homologous X-Y synapsis is not uncommon.

CHROMOSOMAL IMPAIRMENT OF MALE SEX DIFFERENTIATION

The defects of male differentiation which have a chromosomal basis are far less complex than those which affect females. With the exception of testicular feminization (which is not palpably chromosomal) and the infrequent anomalies of the Y chromosome, the abnormalities of male differentiation are those of infantile intersex and Klinefelter's syndrome. The bulk of intersexes are of the "asymmetrical gonadal dysgenesis type" and were discussed earlier.

Klinefelter's Syndrome

The pertinent features of Klinefelter's syndrome are neatly capsuled by the alternative term "chromatin positive testicular tubular dysgenesis." The effects of the syndrome are principally gonadal.

Incidence and Etiology

Klinefelter's syndrome is the commonest of the known defects of human chromosomes and occurs in one of every seven hundred live births. Since the defect is readily detected by buccal smear techniques, several population screenings have established the incidence with fair reliability.

Klinefelter's syndrome is a consequence of meiotic nondisjunction during gametogenesis which yields either XY (sperm) or XX (ova) gametes and the characteristic XXY constitution after fertilization. As with other chromosomal defects, the etiology is obscure. Whether this syndrome, like Turner's syndrome, is most commonly a consequence of paternal nondisjunction is unknown.

Clinical Features

Klinefelter's syndrome is rarely a source of concern during infancy. The patients are essentially normal appearing males and, unless the condition is detected by buccal smear, present no clinical features which draw attention to them.

Symptoms become apparent before or at the time of puberty. The principal clinical feature is a failure of testicular enlargement. The testes are small, firm and relatively insensitive. There is no tendency to cryptorchism and the testes remain scrotal. Testicular measurements of 1.0 to 1.5 cm are common. Azoospermia is an almost constant finding, though instances of oligospermia are recorded (and even an instance of fertility has been reported). Impotence is not a characteristic symptom.

Other findings are variable and are not essential to the diagnosis. The most common associated defects are eunuchoidism and gynecomastia. Of these, eunuchoidism is the more common and these patients are often tall, with long extremities, sparse pubic and axillary hair and, sometimes, high pitched voices. Gynecomastia is fairly frequent. Hypothyroidism of mild degree is a very common finding in patients with testicular tubular dysgenesis.

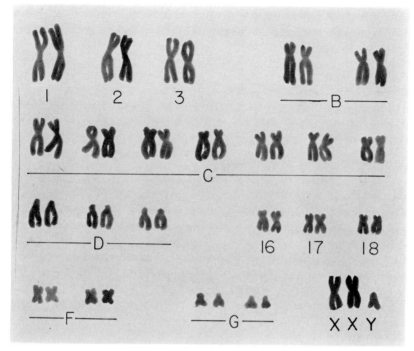

Figure 43. Karyotype in Klinefelter's Syndrome. The modal number is forty-seven and there is an extra member in group C (an X chromosome)—XXY.

Many case reports associate a mild degree of mental deficiency with Klinefelter's syndrome. There is good evidence that Klinefelter's syndrome is more common among the population of institutionalized groups than in the general population. The association is, however, inconstant and many patients have completely normal intelligence.

Laboratory Findings

The epithelial cells of patients with Klinefelter's syndrome are chromatin positive. The combination of testicular hypoplasia and chromatin positive buccal smears are sufficient to make the diagnosis of Klinefelter's syndrome. Karyotyping is not mandatory. The polymorphonuclear leukocyte nuclear appendage pattern is that of the normal female.

Karyotyping reveals a modal number of forty-seven chromosomes with a normal complement in group G (five) and an extra chromosome in group C.

Gonadotrophin levels are elevated.

Variants of Klinefelter's Syndrome

There are a number of cytogenetic variants of Klinefelter's syndrome, all of which have much the same clinical features of the usual XXY type. Variants include polysomic and mosaic chromosomal patterns.

The polysomic variants are XXYY, XXXY, XXXYY and XXXXY. These variants can be detected by buccal smears in which the cells contain double and triple Barr bodies respectively. The XXXY variant differs little from the usual form. Mental deficiency is somewhat commoner and tends to be somewhat more pronounced than that associated with the XXY pattern.

The XXXXY form of Klinefelter's syndrome is, however, considerably more distinctive. Histologically, the degree of testicular dysgenesis appears appreciably more severe than that of the XXY type. Penile hypoplasia and imperfect descent of the testes, not usually features of XXY, are present in the XXXXY form. In addition, mental deficiency is an almost invariable finding and tends to be more severe than in other types. A majority of patients have had an I.Q. of 35 or less.

TABLE VII

The XXXXY Syndrome

Phenotypic males
Chromatin positive (double positive cells and triple positive cells)
Hypoplasia of penis and/or scrotum
Impaired descent of testes
Testicula tubular dysgenesis
Mental deficiency, severe (I.Q. 35 or less)
Skeletal malformations
Defects of forearm predominate
Spinal anomalies
Hyperteleorism
Occasional Defects
Squint
Cleft palate

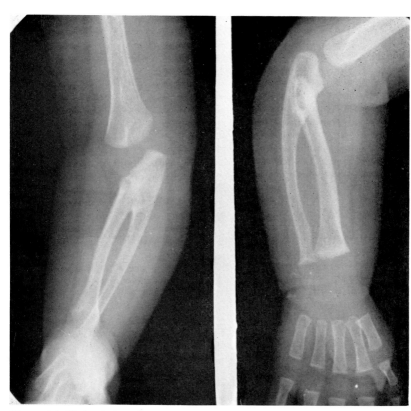

Figure 44. Skeletal Changes in XXXXY Syndrome. Radio-ulnar synostosis is a common and rather characteristic finding. (These photographs were furnished through the kindness of Dr. M. L. Barr and appeared originally in: Barr, M. L., *et al.: Canad. M.A.J., 59.*891-901, 1962.)

Skeletal deformities are another feature unique to the XXXXY variant. These are very common and are highly characteristic. There is often bony synostosis between the radius and the ulna near the elbow joint. Other anomalies, such as hypertelorism and squint are common, but not nearly as characteristic. Multiple buccal nuclear chromatin masses are common. As many as fifty per cent of the cells may have three Barr bodies.

Both XXYY and XXXXY are very uncommon. Once again, the basic defects are those of Klinefelter's syndrome. Mental deficiency has been more severe than in the XXY type. The degree of testicular alteration is hard to assess but seems generally more severe than that of the XXY type. Two of these patients have been unusually tall and "acromegalic." The significance of this feature is obscure, —thyroid defects are also present in XXY Klinefelter's syndrome.

Mosaic patterns are fairly common variants of Klinefelter's syndrome. Their clinical features are those of the usual XXY type. The variants encountered are listed in Appendix V.

Other Defects

Defects of male differentiation other than Klinefelter's syndrome are uncommon and do not have a clinically characteristic pattern.

XYY

The defects associated with XYY have been extremely variable. Several such patterns have been encountered accidentally during family studies initiated in the study of some other anomaly. There is always difficulty in differentiating an XYY pattern from other forms of G trisomy (*vide supra*).

Abnormalities of the Y Chromosome

"Pathological" alterations in the size of the Y chromosome are reported periodically. Many of these reports are concerned with increases in the length of this chromosome. The majority of individuals so affected are wholly asymptomatic. There is great normal variation in the size of the Y chromosome. From the cases reviewed, it seems that such alterations are more probably non-pathological familial variations which may serve as useful "marker" chromosomes.

Deletions of the Y chromosome have been reported several times. In most such cases, mild hypospadias has been present. Hypospadias, being a very minor form of "demasculinization" may very well be related to a chromosomal defect such as Y-deletion in more than a coincidental fashion.

SEX CHROMOSOME DEFECTS AND MENTAL DEFICIENCY

A majority of reports of sex chromosomal defects allude to mental deficiency as one of the clinical features of the afflicted individual. Assessment of degree of mental deficiency range from "slightly subnormal" to severe. While there is little question that sex chromosome defects in general are more common in institutions for the defective than in the general population, the general tenor of most reports tends to leave the impression that mental deficiency is an extremely common, if not invariable feature, of sex chromosome defects.

Considerable caution should be exercised in making such assessments. It has been pointed out, half-facetiously perhaps, that in any given population, slightly less than half will possess "below average" intelligence. This admonition is worth bearing in mind. There is a tendency to equate sex chromosome defects with mental subnormality. If this concept gains wide acceptance, some patients will unnecessarily be labeled as "subnormal."

This error is less likely to occur in an adult or in a pubertal patient. If, however, a sex chromosome anomaly is detected in an infant and the label "mental defective" applied solely because the sex chromosome anomaly has been found, a normally intelligent child may well be burdened by a totally undeserved and premature assessment of his mental capabilities.

Statistical analyses indicate that sex chromosome anomalies are more numerous in the educationally subnormal. Severe mental deficiency is less common than mild subnormality. Sex chromosome anomalies are about three times as frequent in mentally subnormal males than they are in normal males. Mosaicism (XY/XXY) seems less often associated with mental deficiency. Similar figures are quoted in respect to mental deficiency in chromosomally abnormal females. Turner's syndrome is a notable exception and seems no more common in a mentally defective than in a random population.

CHAPTER XIII

UNRELATED CHROMOSOME ABNORMALITES IN FAMILIES AND INDIVIDUALS

In previous chapters, several examples of familial chromosome defects have been explored. Mongolism, in particular, exhibits a familial variant in which a cytogenetic defect (translocation) makes the familial occurrence a predictable event. Similarly, the uncommon phenomenon of secondary nondisjunction is predictable upon the basis of the parental cytogenetic defect which is present.

More interesting is the growing spectrum of family studies in which *unrelated* chromosome defects are concentrated in certain families and even in individuals. Publication of some such reports could, of course, be anticipated merely on the basis of random chance. The increasing accumulation of such reports makes this eventuality progressively less probable. The association between chromosomal defects and various neoplastic diseases, particularly leukemia, is also exceeding chance expectations.

IN INDIVIDUALS

The most frequent form of double aneuploidy is the concomitant presence of mongolism and Klinefelter's syndrome in the same individual. At least five such instances can be found in the cytogenetic literature. Such patients have unfailingly exhibited the clinical sequelae of both of the chromosome aberrations present. All of those which we have reviewed have been of the double trisomy type, with a modal number of forty-eight chromosomes (21, 21, 21 and XXY).

Mongolism and Klinefelter's syndrome are the two most common cytogenetic defects and chance association might well be expected.

On the basis of chance alone, mongolism, with an incidence of 1/800 live births, and Klinefelter's syndrome, with an incidence of 1/700 live births, would be expected to occur coincidentally in about 1/560,000 live births. It is premature to state that the number of cases encountered so far is exceeding these expectations.

Other reported associations are those between mongolism and trisomy-18, triplo-X and trisomy-18, 14/15 translocation and Klinefelter's syndrome, and leukemia and Klinefelter's syndrome. Such reported associations have been isolated events (with the exception of Klinefelter's syndrome and leukemia which has been reported several times).

IN FAMILIES

While the association between unrelated chromosomal abnormalities in individuals might still be attributed to chance, some of the associations which have been encountered in families are unquestionably in excess of the numbers which would be expected based solely on coincidence. The association between mongolism and leukemia is the best documented of such associations.

Mongolism and Leukemia

Leukemia occurs in mongols appreciably more frequently than it does in the general population. Miller, summarizing the findings of the National Cooperative Leukemia Survey (1963), finds that mongolism is about seven times more common among leukemic children than it is among the population in general. Not only is Down's syndrome (mongolism) more frequent among leukemics themselves, but it is also more frequent in the nonleukemic siblings of leukemic patients than in the general population.

In addition, this same survey shows that major malformations other than Down's syndrome are more common among leukemics than they are in others. No specific major anomaly could be implicated in this relationship.

It is of considerable interest that the chromosome which is affected in mongolism, chromosome-21, also seems to be the chromosome which forms the specific Ph[1] chromosome of chronic myelocytic leukemia.

Sex-chromosome Defects and Mongolism

There are many case reports which describe mongolism in one child accompanied by sex-chromosome defects in another sibling. As might be expected, the most frequent such association is that between Klinefelter's syndrome and trisomic mongolism. Other less frequent reports have linked mongolism and Turner's syndrome and mongolism and the triplo-X pattern.

In the majority of such reports, no parental abnormality was present. In one report, a translocation variant of mongolism in one child was accompanied by Klinefelter's syndrome in another. A higher than usual incidence of satellite association between the acrocentric chromosomes was noted in the cells of the affected individuals in the latter family.

One report of parental abnormality with multiple defects in a series of children is of considerable interest. None of the defects present in the offspring were patently related to the defects present in the parental karyotype. A father with an XYY chromosome pattern initiated eight pregnancies. Four of the offspring were normal, there were two abortions, one of the offspring was a mongol and one child demonstrated sex-chromosome mosaicism. Thus, half of the offspring of this particular individual were abnormal and none of the defects present in the offspring seem to represent secondary nondisjunction.

Mongolism, Sex-Chromosomes and Leukemia

The most common associations encountered in families have been those between Klinefelter's syndrome and mongolism and between mongolism and leukemia. Other reported family anomalies have also involved different combinations of this same mongolism-Klinefelter-leukemia triad. One of the few exceptions to this generalization is a family in which trisomy-18 and XO Turner's syndrome were associated. There are increasingly numerous reports of leukemia and sex-chromosome anomalies occurring in the same family and there is at least one family in which all three such defects were present.

IMPLICATIONS

What, if any, conclusions may be legitimately drawn from such examples of unrelated chromosome defects which have a familial predilection? Chance, as always, must be most meticulously eliminated before any other factor can be seriously considered. In the studies relating to the association between mongolism and leukemia, this has already been accomplished. In other associations (mongolism — sex-chromosome, or sex-chromosome — leukemia) chance still bears a high potential for being the etiologic factor concerned.

The reports to date have indicated associations are commonest between the commonest defects. This is most consistent with chance association. Reliable statistics have not been published which indicate that either mongolism or leukemia are more common among patients with sex-chromosome anomalies or their siblings than among the population in general. The sibling aneuploidy of the Klinefelter-mongolism type is a case in point. The expected chance association of such defects is about 1/560,000. Thus, in the United States alone, some five hundred such associations might reasonably be expected to be encountered. Obviously, it is far too soon to implicate any mechanism *other* than chance in these reports except in a speculative manner.

Nevertheless, these associations between chromosomally related diseases call to mind a number of possible implications other than chance association. A brief discussion of some of these may be instructive in suggesting some of the paths which cytogenetic research may be expected to follow.

Mongolism and Leukemia

The proven statistically significant association between mongolism and leukemia seems to offer the most fruitful area for investigation at this point. Most leukemias, and in fact malignant neoplasms in general, are associated with chromosomal aberrations. The association between mongolism and leukemia suggests that either

Leukemia and mongolism are induced by the same chromosome, or,

Chromosome imbalance in general predisposes to neoplasia, or,

Chromosome anomalies and neoplasia both reflect a heritable predisposition to abnormal cell division. All three such factors might well be working in concert.

The association between mongolism and leukemia, when considered in the light of the known chromosome anomaly of chronic myelocytic leukemia makes chromosome-21 highly suspect as the focus of myelocytic neoplasia in general or as the bearer of a locus concerned with leukopoiesis. Trisomy of such a locus may predispose to acute leukemia and deletion of the locus (Ph[1] chromosome) to chronic leukemia.

Whether such inferences are correct remains to be proven. Anomalies of chromosome-21 *per se* are not the sole etiologic agent involved in leukemogenesis since all mongols do not develop leukemia. The most attractive hypothesis would seem to be that chromosome-21 does bear a locus governing leukopoiesis. Further, one may postulate that imbalance at such a locus predisposes to the development of leukemia when the unbalanced genome is subject to some specific, as yet undetermined, environmental stimuli.

Hereditable Mitotic Accidents

The familial concentrations of chromosomal anomalies reported to date may reflect the action of specific genes which encourage mitotic and meiotic accidents. Direct gene control of cell division has been demonstrated in lower animal forms, notably in *Drosophila*. This genus has within its genome several loci which alter normal inheritance patterns. One of these is the *segregation-distorter* (S.D.) gene whose presence modifies meiosis and fertilization in such a fashion that zygotes whose chromosome complement includes the S.D. gene are produced preferentially. Other genes are present which encourage structural rearrangements. Still other genes are associated with repetitious meiotic errors such as asynapsis and premature disjunction.

It seems probable that similar genes are present within the human genome. The nonspecific activity of such genes might well underlie some of the series of unrelated chromosome anomalies which occur in families.

Conclusions

While the family studies available at present allow little else than speculative comment, this line of investigation may be of more than passing import as more comprehensive studies become available. Already these studies have directed attention to the functions of chromosome-21 with ultimate consequences which are yet difficult to envision.

More comprehensive analysis of multiple-anomaly families may ultimately reveal a hereditary pattern which implicates an underlying gene responsible for at least some of the chromosomal anomalies of man. Proof of the existence of such genes, and more important, some mode of recognizing their presence, may ultimately prove one of medicine's more fruitful methods of reducing the static plateau of pregnancy wastage which still exists.

CHAPTER XIV

CHROMOSOME CHANGES IN NEOPLASIA

CYTOGENETIC techniques have been utilized in the study of neoplasia for many years. The literature pertaining to such studies is so voluminous that an attempt to present a comprehensive survey of the various avenues of exploration is entirely beyond our present scope. Only a few of the more recent highlights have been selected for discussion. These are the areas in which cytogenetic techniques seem, to the author at any rate, to offer the greatest potential as clinically useful aids.

Abnormalities of chromosome structure or of chromosome number or both characterize most malignant neoplasms. Such alterations are rare in benign lesions. Although the aneuploidy of most malignancies is random and unpredictable, the very existence of these abnormalities may be put to good use in differentiating malignant from benign neoplasms and from non-neoplastic lesions whose clinical manifestations simulate those of neoplasia.

The aneuploidy of primary tumors tends, in general, to be less striking than that of metastases from the same tumor. There are several most astute investigators who are not, in fact, convinced that aneuploidy is a characteristic feature of malignant neoplasms. This view, though distinctly a minority opinion, may have more than a little pertinence if only primary tumors are being considered. However, analysis of the DNA content of primary tumors reveals DNA concentrations in the near-tetraploid range in most malignancies so studied. It seems improbable that such high DNA concentrations reflect only the increased mitotic activity of such tumors.

The degree of tumor aneuploidy does not always correlate with the biologic activity of the tumor. In some tumors, such as adenocarcinoma of the corpus uteri, the degree of aneuploidy is roughly proportional to the tumor grade. The more malignant tumors of this type are usually the most aneuploid. Other tumors, such as carcinoma of the cervix uteri, exhibit no such demonstrable synchrony between aneuploidy and degree of malignancy.

The ploidy of malignant neoplasms also bears a discernible relationship to radiosensitivity. The relationship is an inverse one, the more aneuploid (hyperploid) tumors are less radiosensitive than are their more nearly euploid counterparts. There is an apparent selective advantage which accrues to polyploid neoplasms. It would seems that polyploid cells have more ample reserve ("spare" chromosomes?) with which to counteract chromosome damage.

The selective advantage enjoyed by polyploid tumor cells may also explain their prevalence in metastases. Polyploid cells, with the increased adaptability consequent to their broadened genetic spectrum, are apparently better able to survive in foreign environments than are those with near-diploid complements.

Much investigation has been directed to the problem of whether chromosomal aberrations in malignancy are the cause of malignant transformation or whether they merely reflect another manifestation of a generally disordered cell metabolism. No conclusive proof can be cited to support either contention. Investigations in this vein have led in turn to studies of relationships between viruses and neoplasms and to investigations of the molecular biology of neoplasms.

One of the more interesting biochemical phenomena observed in neoplasms is the significant difference in both the quantity and the quality of histones which are present in neoplasms. In Chapter I an allusion was made to the function of histones in the control of DNA-directed RNA synthesis. At this point, it should be recalled that one class of histones, the arginine-rich histones, exerts an inhibitory effect upon RNA synthesis. Other histones, notably the "lysine-rich" type, have no such inhibitory action. As an extension of this reasoning, it is suspected that the inhibitory arginine-rich histones function either as the "suppressors" of the Jacob-Monod model or are the compounds which promote segmental heterochromatinization (inactivation) of chromosomes, or both.

The discovery that the nuclei of malignant neoplasms are deficient in arginine-rich histones while containing unusually high quantities of the non-inhibitory lysine-rich histones presents an inescapable corollary: The unbridled nuclear activity of neoplasms must reflect a nuclear response to freedom from the implacable discipline of the arginine-rich histones. The permissive lysine-rich histones not only permit, but may encourage, a biochemical anarchy which eventuates in malignancy.

All one need do is envision a viral metabolic system which commandeers the pathways concerned with the synthesis of arginine-rich histone and a tidy hypothesis results which neatly correlates the observed phenomena of viral carcinogenesis and the above-cited biochemical observations. Sadly enough, such neat hypotheses are seldom borne out by biologic systems. Whether or not such an hypothesis will weather the viscissitudes of scientific investigation, viral carcinogenesis cannot be denied.

Viral carcinogenesis has yet to be proven in relation to human tumors although its existence in other mammalian tumors has been demonstrated. The behavior of the SV40 virus, a tumor producing virus of hamsters, suggests that proof of viral carcinogenesis in man may be nearer than is generally anticipated. The SV40 virus can cause genetic alterations in human tissues, most of which affect the small acrocentric chromosomes. Other suggestive findings are those in which one of the human "viruses in search of a disease," an adenovirus, has been found capable of initiating tumors in other mammalian forms.

One of the most difficult problems which attends research in respect to viral carcinogenesis is the fact that virus can seldom be recovered even from those tumors which are known to be of viral origin. This suggests that the virus may become an inherent part of the host cell's genetic complement. Detection of incorporations of this type demand far more sophisticated techniques than are presently available. The diagnostic import of such sophisticated methods, should they ever become available, will be inestimable.

It would not be unduly difficult to devote an entire monograph to speculations regarding chromosomal activity in carcinogenesis. More important are the implications which cytogenetic techniques have in the clinical evaluation of patients with malignancies. Cytogenetic techniques have a definite, if circumscribed, place in the diagnostic armamentarium.

CHRONIC MYELOCYTIC LEUKEMIA
AND THE Ph¹ CHROMOSOME

Of the many human malignancies studied using cytogenetic techniques, only one has been found in which a predictable chromosome anomaly is present. In 1960, Nowell and Hungerford first described a "minute" chromosome as a constant karyotypic abnormality in seven patients with chronic myelocytic leukemia. Later reports have confirmed that this minute chromosome is unique to chronic myelocytic leukemia and is a fairly constant feature of the karyotypes of affected blood cells. Other leukemias, though they have aneuploid and structurally abnormal cells, have not had this predictable anomaly.

The minute chromosome has been given the name "Philadelphia chromosome" or "Ph¹ chromosome" in accord with a convention which identifies such abnormal chromosomes on the basis of the geographic locality in which they were first discovered. The chromosome is present in the place of one of the four small (21-22) acrocentric chromosomes. It is not a Y chromosome derivative, having been found in affected females. Its presence does not alter the modal number of the affected cells, which remain euploid $(2n = 46)$.

Morphologically, the Ph¹ chromosome is best interpreted as a small acrocentric chromosome from which approximately one-half of the long arm has been deleted. The precise identity of the affected chromosome has not been established though both morphologic and other evidence strongly favors the interpretation that this is a deleted form of chromosome-21. In high quality preparations, the affected member appears to be a member of the larger (21) pair of small acrocentric chromosomes. Inferential supporting evidence is found in the high incidence of leukemia in mongolism, a defect which is also associated with chromosome-21.

The chromosome appears in the complement of affected leukemic cells concomitant with the onset of the leukemia. As yet, the Ph¹ chromosome has not been found in a non-leukemic, normal individual and no evidence presently at hand suggests that a search for the Ph¹ chromosome in non-leukemics might be of any predictive value.

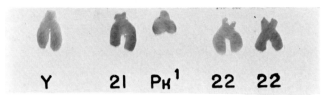

Figure 45. The Ph[1] Chromosome. Only the autosomes of group G are shown. The Ph[1] chromosome is probably a deleted chromosome-21.

Only rarely are cases of chronic myelocytic leukemia encountered in which the Ph[1] chromosome cannot be demonstrated. The incidence of such Ph[1]-negative cases is in the neighborhood of four to six percent of cases of chronic myelocytic leukemia judging from the reports reviewed. The Ph[1]-negative form may represent a distinct subgroup of chronic myelocytic leukemia. The Ph[1]-negative variants have had in common a very long, comparatively "benign" course characterized by good response to irradiation and long intervals between exacerbations. If this preliminary observation bears up under statistical analysis, a valuable prognostic tool will be available.

A second cytogenetic variant of chronic myelocytic leukemia has been noted by several different investigators. In these cases, of which at least five examples have been found, the abnormal cells have had XOPh[1] karotype with a modal number of forty-five.

The morphological distinctiveness of this subgroup has not been accompanied by any evident clinical distinction. The possibility that the unusual karyotype may reflect an etiologic variant, though intriguing, is unproven.

In untreated cases, the Ph[1] chromosome is readily demonstrable in bone marrow preparations. Most investigators recommend the "ultra-short" methods in these studies. Peripheral blood findings are unpredictable and the Ph[1] chromosome may not be demonstrable in blood culture even when it can readily be demonstrated in marrow preparations. The Ph[1] chromosome is confined to hematopoietic tissues and is not demonstrable in cultures of skin or of fascia. Failure to recover the Ph[1] chromosome using peripheral blood preparations when the chromosome is demonstrable in marrow preparations reflects the fact that myeloid elements of sufficient immaturity to reproduce in culture are not invariably present in peripheral blood. In these instances, only the lymphocytes will divide, as they do in blood cultures from normal individuals. Lymphocytes are Ph¹-negative.

The incidence of Ph¹-positive cells in marrow preparations is high in untreated cases (as high as ninety-five per cent in some preparations). This indicates that the Ph¹ anomaly is not confined to the myelocytic series but that it affects all marrow elements which arise from a common precursor. (Myelocytic, erthrocytic and megakaryocytic elements are regarded as having a common ancestry.) This view is supported by occasional observations of the Ph¹ chromosome in megakaryocytes.

These findings are modified by treatment with radiation or with radiomimetic drugs. Radiation therapy induces a sharp decline in the incidence of Ph¹-positive cells obtained in marrow cultures. These cells are more radio-sensitive than are Ph¹-negative marrow elements. Irradiation *per se* induces morphologic chromosome anomalies which may confuse the cytogenetic picture obtained in treated cases. Breaks and dicentrics are common in such preparations and appear in addition to the Ph¹ chromosome. Such alterations should not be interpreted as examples of neoplastic aneuploidy.

From a purely technical standpoint, it is sometimes difficult to obtain good photomicrographs of the chromosomes from a Ph¹-positive cell. For some reason, these cells have a chromosome complement which appears badly fixed and in which the chromosomes are fuzzy in outline and stain poorly. This observation, for which no explanation has been found, has been made by several observers.

Clinical Implications

At present, bone marrow karyotypes offer a diagnostic method by which some ninety to ninety-five percent of the cases of chronic myelocytic leukemia may be diagnosed without equivocation. Much the same claim can be made for morphologic examinations of bone marrow spreads. There are, however, several types of case in which morphologic examination of bone marrow may provide equivocal results. In the aleukemic form of chronic myelocytic leukemia, marrow findings cannot always be interpreted with complete confidence. If karyotyping reveals Ph¹-positive cells in such instances, therapy can be instituted without further equivocation.

In the older age groups, particularly, chronic infections or non-leukemic neoplastic diseases may initiate a leukemoid bone marrow response which is indistinguishable from chronic myelocytic leukemia on purely morphologic grounds. When such diseases are known to be present, the additional diagnosis of chronic myelocytic leukemia is made only with greatest reluctance. Demonstration of Ph[1] chromosome in these cases will solve a knotty clinical problem.

Negative findings are less helpful, for chronic myelocytic leukemia can be present without the Ph[1] chromosome. However, since these variants generally have a more "benign" clinical course, one would not be remiss in temporizing until morphologic evidence of leukemia can be discerned and the diagnosis made with confidence. This consideration is particularly pertinent in relation to cases in which aleukemic leukemia is a diagnostic possibility but not yet a diagnostic certainty.

Conversely, the absence of a Ph[1] chromosome, particularly in the older age group, should stimulate a search for some such disease as tuberculosis. Occasionally, a leukemoid reaction may be the presenting feature of such a condition and Ph[1]-negative karyotype may be the finding which promotes its discovery.

The use of karyotype analysis in the morphologically unequivocal cases of chronic myelocytic leukemia has not reached the point at which it can be recommended as a routine procedure. If further research shows that the Ph[1]-negative variant of chronic myelocytic leukemia is *predictably* and consistently more indolent in its clinical course than is the Ph[1]-positive variant, then karyotyping can be recommended as a routine procedure for its prognostic value. Further reports in this area of investigation will bear careful scrutiny.

OTHER LEUKEMIAS

Karyotype analyses in leukemias other than chronic myelocytic leukemia have been disappointing in that no consistent or predictdable chromosome anomaly has been discovered. The leukemias studied do adhere to the general tendency of neoplasms to be aneuploid and this is almost the only common ground to be found in any of the studies reviewed.

Review of these studies does, however, bring out some illuminating findings. The considerable diversity in the incidence of chromosomal abnormalities reported bears a distinct relationship to the methodology employed. In general, the aneuploid and structurally anomalous karyotypes have been reported more frequently in those studies in which "direct" marrow study was employed rather than the routine two- or three-day peripheral blood culture techniques. Direct marrow methods reflect the true karyotype in such individuals with the greatest possible fidelity and are to be preferred. Longer-term culture methods, particularly those which employ peripheral blood, appear to put the neoplastic stemlines at a selective disadvantage. Proliferation of the non-neoplastic (or euploid neoplastic) cells thereby obscures the aneuploidy which such cells usually demonstrate when recovered from marrow.

While no chromosomal pattern as dramatic as that of the Ph[1] chromosome has been discerned in other leukemias, occasional intriguing similarities have appeared in reports from different authors. These occasional areas of coincidence are worth recording. As greater numbers of case studies accumulate, recognizable etiologic or clinical subtypes may be discovered.

Acute Myelocytic Leukemia

In reviewing reports of some thirty-three cases of acute myelocytic leukemia in which thorough karyotype analyses have been reported, variability of results has been the common denominator. In various reports, the incidence of aneuploidy has ranged from a high of ninety percent of cases to a low of twenty-five percent of cases.

Extra, abnormal, chromosomes are commonly encountered. Extra group C chromosomes are most consistently reported. These have been found by several different groups of investigators. There is no evidence that these constitute a recognizable clinical subgroup.

Acute Lymphocytic Leukemia

Studies of this type of leukemia are infrequent. Hyperdiploid cell lines are frequently encountered but no consistent anomalies have been recorded.

Chronic Lymphocytic Leukemia

Reported karyotype analysis in the study of chronic lymphocytic leukemia have had a predominantly euploid complement devoid of either numerical or structural abnormalities. This may be due in part to the difficulty which has been encountered in getting leukemic lymphocytes to divide. This is one of the few instances in which pooled serum is often superior to autologous serum as a protein source for culture media.

An interesting, consistent chromosomal defect has been reported in both leukemic and non-leukemic members of two families in which familial leukemic patterns were present. Since a familial tendency to chronic lymphocytic leukemia is rather uncommon, finding of a similar, specific chromosome defect in two different families may well be significant.

This chromosome, tentatively designated as the "Ch[1]" chromosome, is one of the small acrocentric chromosomes from which most or all of the short arm has been deleted. The affected chromosome has a horseshoe or a dumbbell configuration. The chromosome is not confined to the leukopoietic cells but has been found in other cells, e.g. skin, as well. The Ch[1] chromosome is also peculiar in that it has been found in the non-leukemic relatives of leukemic patients.

The fact that the chromosome has been found in more than one family intensifies the hope that this may represent a predictable association rather than fortuitous association between a peculiar marker chromosome and familial chronic lymphocytic leukemia.

Myeloproliferative Syndromes

The myeloproliferative disorders are a somewhat diverse group of obscure hyperplasias of bone marrow elements. This hyperplasia may affect either erythroid (polycythemia) or myeloid (myeloid metaplasia) elements. Not obviously neoplastic processes at their inception, these conditions frequently eventuate in either acute or chronic myelocytic leukemia.

Karyotype analysis made during the nonleukemic stages of these diseases have revealed no abnormalities. Similar studies made during the leukemic phases have revealed karyotype alterations in about half of the cases. If one relies on the evidence of these cytogenetic studies, one may conclude that the chronic myelocytic leukemia which follows the myeloproliferative disorders is etiologically unrelated to chronic myelocytic leukemia in general. The Ph[1] chromosome has not yet been found in any of these leukemias.

The karyotype alterations which have been found have affected chromosome groups other than that from which the Ph[1] chromosome is derived (group G). In the "post-myeloproliferative" leukemias, karyotype alterations have been confined to the chromosomomes of groups C, D and E.

CHROMOSOMAL ALTERATION IN SOLID TUMORS

There are comparatively few really satisfactory studies of the karyotype of human solid tumors. Most have been examined by direct squash techniques either applied to the tumor itself or to explants in tissue culture. Recently, Lubs has devised a method in which the cells of the tumor under study are converted to cell suspensions using trypsin. These suspensions are then handled as though they were cells derived from peripheral blood cultures. This latter approach has provided fairly satisfactory metaphase figures.

Regardless of the methods used, no predictable aneuploidy or structural anomaly has been discovered which typifies a given tumor. Each malignant tumor studied, however, has had one or two stemlines in which the alterations of karoptype have been consistent from cell to cell. Each tumor behaves as a highly specialized clone.

In general, multiple stemlines are more characteristic of early than of late tumors. As tumors age, the selective advantage of one or another stemline usually is sufficiently pronounced that the most advantageous stemline predominates. Not uncommonly, late tumors have only a single stemline with a characteristic and uniform karyotype.

Karyotype abnormalities have been found in several lesions which are generally interpreted histologically as "premalignant" lesions. Too few analyses have been conducted to assess the reliability with which such karyotype alterations reflect a physiological alteration from "premalignant" to frank malignancy. It is conceivable that karyotype alterations may antedate the usual morphologic criteria of malignancy and allow a more precise definition of many of the "shades of gray" encountered by histopathologists.

At present, no tumors have been found to have karyotypical alterations which are of sufficient significance to warrant recapitulation here.

DETECTION OF MALIGNANT CELLS USING CYTOGENETIC TECHNIQUES

The aneuploidy common to almost all malignancies would seem to offer a starting point for useful clinical application of cytogenetic techniques in oncology. Only a handful of investigations have been recorded in which such techniques have been applied to the detection of malignant cells in effusions. The results cited in these few reports have been generally disappointing. That these early reports have been unenthusiastic is predicated largely upon the fact that their authors were hoping to adapt cytogenic techniques to "short-cut" screening methods.

If cytogenetic techniques are used in full, including culture, counting and careful photographic karyotyping, the incidence of karyotype abnormalities discovered should be appreciably higher than those reported. It seems unlikely that abbreviated methods, at least those presently available, can provide preparations of sufficient quality for accurate karyotyping.

Adaptation of cytogenetic techniques as screening or as diagnostic methods can hardly be expected to supplant present cytologic techniques used in the diagnosis and detection of cervical carcinoma. There are other areas, however, where cytologic techniques yield many inconclusive findings. Pleural and peritoneal effusions, particularly, are often very difficult to interpret because of the extreme polymorphism which mesothelial cells may exhibit in inflammatory exudates. Early studies indicate that these changes are not accompanied by alterations in karyotype. Thus, there should be a sound basis for the development of cytogenetic techniques valuable for the appraisal of effusions with accuracy greater than that possible using the usual cytologic studies.

Earlier allusions to the comparative radiosensitivity of near-euploid neoplastic cells as compared with increasingly hyperdiploid and polyploid cells suggests that another potentially useful area for cytogenetic techniques might be developed. If this general observation can be extended to a wide variety of tumors, tissue cultures derived from biopsy material may provide a means of deciding between radiotherapy or chemotherapy in the treatment of malignancies.

In present clinical application, the usefulness of cytogenetic techniques in oncology is confined to studies of leukemia and its differentiation from the leukemoid states. It is to be hoped that some of the theoretically valuable applications outlined above will become practically applicable in the near future.

APPENDIX I
GLOSSARY

Every effort has been made to define each new term as it is introduced in the text. The terms which recur with some frequency are defined below for ready reference.

A

Acentric—a chromosome or chromosome fragment which lacks a centromere.

Acrocentric chromosome—a chromosome in which the centromere is situated very near the end of the chromosome, producing very short short arms.

Affinity—variations from expected inheritance patterns which are a consequence of centromere activity.

Alleles (allelomorphs)—functional variants of a single gene which have arisen through mutation.

Allocycly—differences in the timing of DNA replication or mitotic activity which one chromosome may exhibit in relation to the chromosome complement as a whole.

Anaphase—phase of cell division which is initiated by division of the centromere and in which chromatids separate and migrate to the cell poles.

Aneuploid—bearing an abnormal number of chromosomes.

Arresting—colchicine treatment of tissue cultures preparatory to karyotyping.

Association—a recurring relationship between phenotypic features which may result from either linkage of the genes responsible or, more often, reflects the diverse action of a single gene. Association and linkage are *not* synonymous.

Assortment—synonymous with "Segregation" (*q.v.*).

Autoradiography—labeling of dividing chromosomes with radioactive tritium (^{3}H) and determination of the degree to which chromosomes incorporate it (by photographic techniques).

Autosomes—non-sex chromosomes. So called because they are present in homologous pairs.

243

B

Back cross—a mating between two individuals, one of whom bears homozygous recessive genes at the locus under study.

Balbiani rings—pale areas of "puffing" of chromosomes at sites of high metabolic activity.

Barr body—synonymous with "sex chromatin" (*q.v.*).

Bivalent—figure formed by the intimately paired chromosomes of meiosis before visible longitudinal division into chromatids has occurred.

C

C - Mitosis—mitosis which has been arrested at metaphase following damage to the spindle apparatus (a characteristic of colchicine damage).

Centric fusion—a type of translocation in which the number of chromosome arms in the complement remains unaltered but the number of centromeres is reduced by one (e.g., when long-arm translocations between two acrocentric chromosomes produce a single metacentric chromosome).

Centromere—the point of attachment of the spindle body to the chromosome during cell division. This is the point at which chromatids remain united longest.

Centromeric index—a chromosome measurement which expresses the ratio of short arm length to total chromosome length.

Centrosome—a cytoplasmic structure from which the spindle apparatus arises.

Chiasma(ta)—point(s) of contact between chromatids during first meiotic prophase which are sites of crossing-over (*q.v.*).

Chimera—an individual in whom a genetically distinctive line of cells has become established by grafting.

Chromatid—one (longitudinal) half of a chromosome.

Chromomere—a small granule of D.N.A. (mostly) which appears as a "bead" on the stringlike chromonema.

Chromosome—intranuclear body composed of deoxyribose nucleic acid (D.N.A.), histone and protein which carries the genetic information from cell generation to cell generation.

Cistron—synonymous with "site" (*q.v.*).

Cleavage—synonymous with "mitosis" (*q.v.*).

Clone—a line of cells derived by non-sexual reproduction (mitosis) from one and the same progenitor.

Colchicine—a mitotic poison which inhibits spindle body formation and produces an accumulation of metaphase figures in culture media.

Crossing-over—exchange of genetic material between maternal and paternal chromosomes during first meiotic prophase .

D

Deletion—loss of a portion of a chromosome following chromosome breakage.

Denver nomenclature—standard system of nomenclature applied to human metaphase chromosomes.

Deoxyribonucleic acid (D.N.A.)—helical molecule which is a polymer of ribose, phosphate and nucleotide bases which carries genetic information in the nucleus.

Dermatoglyphics—study of dermal ridge patterns, particularly of the hand, as a diagnostic aid in congenital anomalies.

Diakinesis—final stage of first meiotic prophase marked by separation of the paired homologous chromosomes.

Dictyotene—a very long "resting" stage which occurs between diakinesis (which occurs in the fetal ovary) and the completion of meiosis (which occurs following ovulation) in the germ cells of the human ovary.

Differential distance—minimum distance which can occur between the centromere and the nearest chiasma—supposedly imposed on purely mechanical grounds.

Diploid—bearing a paired set of chromosomes (2n)—the normal complement of somatic cells.

Diplotene—stage of meiotic prophase during which crossing-over occurs.

Disjunction—separation of chromatids (or chromosomes in first meiosis) and their migration to opposite cell poles during cell division.

Dominant—a gene which is expressed whenever it is present .

Drumstick—characteristic nuclear appendage present in the polymorphonuclear leukocytes of females.

Duplication—a chromosome anomaly in which one segment of a chromosome is present in duplicate as a consequence of breakage and re-fusion.

E

Equational division—second meiotic division. The chromatids of the haploid daughter cells of the first meiotic division are separated and distributed to the second generation of haploid cells, the gametes.

Euchromatin—chromatin which maintains a more or less constant staining quality throughout cell division. The bulk of genetic information is thought to be borne by euchromatin.

Euploid—bearing a normal number of chromosomes.

Expressivity—a term which reflects quantitative phenotypic differences which may accompany the same genotype.

G

Gametes—ova or spermatozoa. These are haploid (n) cells.

Gene—a chromosome segment which contains the information necessary to control a particular class of chemical reactions. The basic unit of hereditary material.

Genetic code—the sequence of nucleotide bases in the D.N.A. chain which, in turn, determines the sequence of amino acid molecules during protein synthesis.

Genome—the total gene complement.

Genotype—the genetic complement which is responsible for the physical and chemical characteristics (phenotype) of the individual.

H

Haploid—bearing a single set of unpaired chromosomes (n)—the normal chromosome complement of gametes.

Hemizygous—the presence of a single gene, rather than paired genes as may occur in monosomy (single chromosome) and is the normal status of X-borne genes in males (XY).

Heterochromatin—chromatin which condences out of phase with the remainder of the chromatin in the complement. Genetically, heterochromatin is comparatively inactive.

Heterochromatinization—conversion of euchromatin to heterochromatin. This supposedly reflects "inactivation" of the involved chromosome segment.

Heterogametic sex—the sex produced by non-homologous sex chromosomes—in man, the male (XY).

Heteroploidy—numerical chromosome abnormalities which affect all body cells uniformly.

Heteropyknosis—asynchrony of staining which characterizes heterochromatin. Positive heteropyknosis is the term applied to darker staining segments and negative heteropyknosis to lighter segments.

Heterozygous (-ote)—a state (individual) in which the maternally derived and the paternally derived members of a gene pair are dissimilar.

Holandric inheritance—inheritance pattern of genes borne on the Y chromosome.

Homogametic sex—the sex produced by homologous sex chromosomes—in man, the female (XX).

Homozygous (-ote)—a state (individual) in which the maternally derived and the paternally derived members of a gene pair are identical.

Hybrid—a heterozygous individual. The offspring produced by interbreeding between two pure lines.

I

Ideogram—an idealized drawing of a chromosome complement.

Interference distance—minimum distance possible between chiasmata.

Interkinesis—short "resting" phase between first and second meiotic cell divisions.

Interphase—term applied to a cell which is not undergoing cell division.

Inversion—a structural chromosome defect in which a segment of the chromosome is rotated 180° from its normal position.

Isochromosome—a chromosome in which the arms on either side of the centromere are physically identical and bear the same gene loci.

K

Karyotype—a systematic array of the chromosomes of a single cell as depicted by photography or camera lucida drawings. Used to exemplify the chromosome constitution of all of the cells of an individual or even of a species.

Kinetochore—synonymous with "centromere" (*q.v.*).

L

Lampbrush chromosomes—see: Polytene chromosomes.

Leptotene—earliest stage of prophase of first meiotic division. The chromosomes are present as recognizable individual strands.

Linkage—the tendency for genes which are close together on the same chromosome to be distributed to the same gametes.

Locus—the region of a chromosome at which a specific gene is situated.

M

Matroclinous chromosome—a chromosome of maternal origin, i.e., from the ovum.

Meiosis—specialized cell division by which germ cells with a paired set of chromosomes (2n) form gametes with a single set of chromosomes (n).

Mendelian inheritance—hereditary patterns which follow Mendel's laws. Synonymous with chromosomal (as opposed to cytoplasmic) inheritance.

Mendel's laws—basic laws governing chromosomal inheritance. First law ("law of segregation") states that genes are passed unaltered from generation to generation. Second law ("law of independent assortment") states that genes are inherited in a random fashion.

Messenger R.N.A.—R.N.A. which transfers genetic information from nucleus to cytoplasm.

Metacentric chomosome—chromosome with a central centromere.

Metaphase—the phase of mitosis and meiosis in which longitudinal division of chromosmes into chromatids is completed and in which the spindle body forms.

Mitosis—cell division in somatic cells which produces two new (daughter) cells, each of which has the same chromosome complement as the parent cell.

Modal number—the predominant number of chromosomes per cell. Normal modal number in man is forty-six chromosomes.

Monohybrid cross—a mating between two individuals who are heterozygous at the gene locus under study.

Monosomy—bearing a single member of a chromosome pair in an otherwise normal chromosome complement.

Mosaicism—presence of two or more cell lines of differing chromosomal constitution in a single individual.

N

Negative heteropyknosis—see: Heteropyknosis.

Nondisjunction—failure of chromatids (or chromosomes in first meiosis) to separate and migrate to opposite cell poles during anaphase.

O

Operator locus—see: Operon.

Operon—a complex of structural (manufacturing), operator (activating) and regulator (suppressing) subgenes which comprise an entire gene locus.

P

Pachytene—stage of first meiotic prophase in which chromosomes shorten, thicken and split into chromatids.

Pachytene cross—a configuration assumed by translocated chromosomes during meiotic synapsis.

Paracentric defects—structural defects which affect a single chromosome arm.

Paramutation—an alteration of gene function induced by an allele.

Patroclinous chromosome—a chromosome of paternal origin, i.e., from a spermatozoon.

Penetrance—all or none phenomenon which governs expression of dominant genes.

Pericentric defects—structural chromosome defects which affect both chromosome arms, i.e., they occur on both sides of the centromere.

Phenotype—physical or chemical characteristics induced by genes.

Phytohemagglutinin—a plant extract which is both a panagglutinin of red cells and a mitotic stimulant for white cells in tissue culture methods.

Polar bodies—small, nonfunctional daughter cells formed during human oogenesis because of a grossly unequal distribution of cytoplasm.

Polyploid—bearing four (or more) sets of chromosomes.

Polytene chromosomes—very large, banded chromosomes which form as a consequence of multiple divisions of chromonemsta without cell division.

Positive heteropyknosis—see: Heteropyknosis.

Primary constriction—synonymous with "centromere" (*q.v.*).

Prophase—earliest stage of visible cell division.

Propinquity effect—the tendency of broken chromosome ends which lie closest together to fuse.

Pseudoallelism—phenotypic alterations induced by position effects rather than by gene mutations.

Pure line—a population which breeds true for a given character in repeated generations when inbred.

R

Recessive—a gene which is expressed only when its counterpart on the homologous member of the chromosome pair is identical to it.

Reductional division—first meiotic cell division in which the diploid (2n) chromosome complement of the germ cells is reduced to a haploid (n) complement in the daughter cells.

Regulator locus—see: Operon.

Relative length—the length of a chromosome expressed as a percent of the total complement length.

Restitution—reunion of a chromosome break without structural alteration.

Ribonucleic acid—intracytoplasmic (mostly) polymer of ribose, phosphate and nucleotide bases which transfers genetic information within a cell.

Ribosome R.N.A.—site of intracytoplasmic protein synthesis.

S

Salivary gland chromosomes—see: Polytene chromosomes.

Satellite—a heteropyknotic knob attached to the short arm of an acrocentric chromosome.

Secondary constriction—area of achromia or pallor, with or without narrowing, in a chromosome at a point other than the centromere.

Segregation—the distribution of genes to gametes during meiosis.

Sex chromatin—a mass of chromatin applied to the nuclear membrane of cells having two or more X chromosomes.

Sex linkage—inheritance pattern of genes carried by the sex chromosomes and which therefore differ in their effects in the two sexes.

Site—component structural unit of a gene about three nucleotide bases in length.

Spindle body—a system of protein threads which draws chromosomes to the cell poles during cell division.

Subgene—synonymous with "site" (*q.v.*).

Submetacentric chromosome—a chromosome with its centromere situated eccentrically, dividing the chromosome into well defined long and short arms.

Supernumerary chromosomes—extra chromosomes which may appear as normal variants in the karyotype of a species.

Synapsis—intimate side-by-side pairing which occurs between homologous chromosomes during meiosis.

T

Telocentric chromosome—a chromosome bearing a terminal centromere. An unstable form which does not occur in nature.

Telomere—the free end of a chromosome or chromatid whose specialized structure makes it impossible for the telomere to assume an interstitial position.

Telophase—final stage of cell division in which two new nuclei, then two new cells form.

Terminalization—"sliding along" of chiasmata to the ends of the chromatids as the chromosomes separate.

Tetrad—figure formed when the paired chromosomes of first meiosis divide into visible chromatids.

Tetravalent—an abnormal meiotic complex of four chromosomes produced by the synapsis of translocated chromosomes.

Transduction—implantation of chromosomal material from one cell into the complement of another as a consequence of virus infection passing from cell to cell.

Transfer R.N.A.—R.N.A. which carries amino acid molecules to the ribosome for protein synthesis.

Translocation—reciprocal exchange of genetic material between non-homologous chromosomes following chromosome breakage.

Triploid—bearing three sets of chromosomes (3n).

Trisomy—bearing a specific chromosome in triplicate in an otherwise normal complement.

Trivalent—an abnormal meiotic complex of three chromosomes which follows translocation.

Z

Zygote—diploid (2n) product of fertilization of a haploid (n) ovum by a haploid (n) spermatozoon.

Zygotene—one stage of first meiotic prophase characterized by intimate pairing (synapsis) of homologous chromosomes.

APPENDIX II

TECHNICAL METHODS

The methods which have been selected for detailed presentation are, generally, those which we are personally familiar with and from which we have had good results. Also included are a number of techniques which have been devised by various workers to serve some special function. Many techniques which are equally acceptable have been omitted solely in consideration of space limitations.

DEMONSTRATION OF SEX CHROMATIN

Only a few brief remarks need be made regarding the techniques which are used in the examination of polymorphonuclear leukocytes. The three methods which are described for the demonstration of the nuclear sex chromatin body (Barr body) in epithelial nuclei include a rapid (orcein) method, a routine method and a differential (Guard) staining method.

Polymorphonuclear Leukocyte Appendages

No special techniques are necessary for the demonstration of the characteristic "female" appendages of the polymorphonuclear neutrophil (PMN) nuclei. Any of the standard hematologic stains (Wright's, Giemsa, etc.) are satisfactory.

The major difficulty in this technique is that which attends surveying five hundred PMN nuclei. This task may be made less onerous if buffy coat preparations are used. Heparinized blood samples will usually separate into three well defined layers if allowed to stand undisturbed for an hour or so. The leukocyte rich buffy coat immediately above the red cell layer makes very good preparations and a sample of the layer can easily be obtained by aspiration with a Pasteur pipette.

The procedure can also be attenuated without loss of diagnostic significance if examinations are carried out only until six "drumsticks" are encountered or five hundred cells have been examined, whichever occurs first. In those smears with a "female" distribution of appendages, this criterion may shorten the counting time appreciably.

Sex Chromatin - Orcein Stain

The principal advantage of the orcein stain is rapidity of staining. Permanent preparations can be prepared using orcein, though it is more commonly used as a temporary stain. It can be used on fresh material, air dried material or fixed material. Other stains require fixed material for satisfactory results.

Method

1) To fixed (ether:alcohol 1/1) or unfixed material collected as described below on a glass slide, add one or two drops of aceto-orecein or lacto-orecein (see: Reagents, below).

2) Coverslip the preparation, place between layers of bibulous paper and exert firm pressure with the thumb. Take care not to allow the coverslip to slide.

3) For temporary preparations, immediate oil immersion inspection is satisfactory.

    3a) For semipermanent mounts, rim the coverslip with an appropriate cement (rimming with balsam produces very satisfactory and surprisingly long-lasting preparations).

    3b) For permanent mounts, float the coverslip from the preparation using 45 per cent acetic acid. Rinse the material with drops of 45 per cent acetic acid until no further color is noted in the rinse solution. Flood the slide with xylol and mount in balsam or Permount (xylol solvent).

Overall, orcein is a very satisfactory stain. The method has the prime advantage of rapidity. Squashing and flattening the cells leaves them more or less in a single optical plane and facilitates examination. The major disadvantage of orcein staining is that bacteria may take the stain very deeply and be most troublesome.

Sex Chromatin - Thionin Staining

Thionin is probably one of the most popular stains for the demonstration of nuclear sex chromatin. This is the method which we prefer for routine studies.

Method

1) *Sample collection*

1a) *Buccal smears.* Obtain scrapings from the buccal aspect of the cheek using a metal spatula or wooden tongue blade. Firm pressure must be used (but not enough to cause bleeding or oozing) in order that deeper cell layers with vesicular nuclei can be obtained. Insufficiently firm pressure will produce a smear in which superficial cells, with unsatisfactory pyknotic nuclei, predominate.

Spread the smear on a clean glass slide, making an attempt to obtain as thin a smear as possible.

1b) *Vaginal smears.* Where a choice is available, vaginal smears are to be preferred. Chromatin masses are more prominent in vaginal preparations. The same precautions in obtaining deeper cell layers should be observed.

2) *Fixation.* Immerse stains in fixative immediately. Ether:ethyl alcohol (1/1) is a very good fixative. This is the same fixative used for routine Papanicoulau smears and is available in most laboratories. Isopropyl alcohol may be used alone with satisfactory results.

3) Leave smears in fixative for at least one-half hour. Smears may be stored in fixative as long as forty-eight hours if necessary.

4) Transfer slides to absolute ethyl alcohol for three minutes.

5) Immerse slides in 0.25 per cent perlodion solution for two minutes. This makes the cells adhere more firmly during hydrolysis.

6) Air dry slides for fifteen seconds.

7) Immerse slides in 70 per cent alcohol for five minutes.

8) Pass slides through two changes of distilled water of five minutes each.

9) *Hydrolyze* in 1N HCl for *not more* than five minutes at 56°C. This step eliminates the majority of bacteria from the smear.

10) Pass slides through two more changes of distilled water of five minutes each.
11) Stain with thionin working solution (see: Reagents, below) for five minutes.
12) Differentiate in 70 per cent, 95 per cent and absolute ethyl alcohol, one minute in each solution.
13) Clear in xylol (two changes).
14) Mount using permount or balsam.

One of the major advantages of this method is the use of acid hydrolysis. This eliminates almost all of the bacteria which, in large numbers, can make interpretation of smears very difficult. The preparations are permanent. Barr bodies are somewhat less prominently stained than they are with either acetic-orcein or with the differential stains.

Sex Chromatin - Differential (Guard) Stain

Properly performed, this stain produces beautiful, very distinctive preparations in which the sex chromatin mass appears as a prominent, bright red body in a green or blue-background depending on the technique selected. Its major disadvantage is that it is a time-consuming staining method. The stain is most useful in those situations in which many such preparations are being surveyed. The very striking differentiation of the chromatin mass facilitates such mass screenings almost immeasurably.

The method has as its underlying mechanism the displacement of an amphoteric dye (Biebrich scarlet) from nuclear chromatin by a more strongly amphoteric dye (fast green FCF) in a controlled manner. There are two techniques which may be used, fast or overnight. The fast technique (three to four hours) demands repeated microscopic evaluation as staining progresses. The overnight method does not require microscopic control.

Fast Method: (Biebrich scarlet - fast green)
1) Remove slides from fixative, pass through two changes of alcohol (95 per cent, then 70 per cent) two minutes each.
2) Stain in Biebrich scarlet (see: Reagents, below) for two minutes.
3) Rinse in 50 per cent ethyl alcohol.
4) Differentiate in fast green FCF (see: Reagents, below) for one to four hours. Check differentiation hourly. When all of the

cells are green and all of the vesicular nuclei are green, the reaction is complete (usually about four hours). Pyknotic nuclei remain red.

5) Rinse in 50 per cent ethyl alcohol and allow slides to remain in alcohol for five minutes.

6) Dehydrate in successive changes of 70 per cent, 95 per cent and absolute alcohol of two minutes each.

7) Clear in xylol, three changes of two minutes each.

8) Mount in Permount or balsam.

Overnight Method: (Hematoxyln - Biebrich Scarlet - Fast Green)

1) Remove slides from fixative, pass through two changes of alcohol (95 per cent, then 70 per cent) two minutes each.

2) Stain in dilute hematoxylin (see: Reagents, below) for fifteen seconds *only* (about ten dips). Hematoxylin acts as a mordant for the Biebrich scarlet. If the slides are overstained with hematoxylin at this point, the action of Biebrich scarlet will be completely blocked.

3) Without rinsing, stain in Biebrich scarlet (see: Reagents, below) for two minutes.

4) Rinse in 50 per cent ethyl alcohol.

5) Differentiate in fast green FCF (see: Reagents, below) for eighteen to twenty-four hours. No microscopic control is required.

6) Dehydrate, clear and mount as detailed in the above cited fast method (steps 5 through 8).

KARYOTYPE ANALYSIS - PERIPHERAL BLOOD

The general principles upon which karyotype analysis is based have been discussed at some length in Chapter V. From these general principles, almost innumerable variations in technique have been derived. Nearly all of the techniques have as their utilmate basis the "parent" technique originally devised and reported by Moorehead, Nowell, Mellman, Batipps and Hungerford (1960).

In the course of setting up methods in our own laboratory, we have varied many of the phases of the procedure and have finally found a method which has given us the most satisfactory results. It is virtually identical with the method of Moorehead, *et al.*, which is the method we started with at the outset. We cite this experience to save other laboratories the time and frustration which attends "correcting" fancied defects in the procedure. The procedure of of Moorehead *et al.* is a *very* good procedure. Our modification reflects only minor adaptations which suit our particular laboratory.

Method

1) At eight o'clock A.M. on Monday, Tuesday, Friday or Saturday, collect 10 ml. of venous blood from a fasting patient in a sterile, heparinized tube.

Note:

The days suggested are most convenient for the laboratory operating on a five and one-half day schedule. If a technologist familiar with the technique is available on Sunday, samples can be drawn on this day as well.

Though time is not critical, we rarely accept patients later than 9:30 A.M. unless we can be quite sure that they are in a fasting state.

Fasting samples are perferable. Lipemia delays erythrocyte sedimentation and it is our distinct impression that samples from non-fasting patients do not provide cultures which are as satisfactory as those from fasting patients.

Heparin is the anticoagulant of choice. Chelating agents may lower calcium concentrations sufficiently that the cultures fail to grow.

10 ml. samples are desirable since they provide sufficient material for quadruplicate cultures.

2) Allow the heparinized sample to stand at room temperature for one hour. Within this time, about 4 ml. of supernatant cell-rich plasma will accumulate.

Note:

Specimens which are slow to sediment can be separated using *gentle* centrifuging at 6-800 r.p.m. for ten to fifteen minutes.

About half of the workers add phytohemagglutinin to the blood sample to accelerate red cell sedimentation. A concentration of 0.2 ml/10 ml of blood is satisfactory. Since we add phytohemagglutinin to the culture medium as we make it, we rarely use it for sedimenting red cells. Either method is satisfactory.

3) Add aliquots of the supernatant cell-plasma suspension to culture medium (see: Reagents, below) in a ratio of 1 part plasma to 4 parts of medium.

Note:

Some investigators recommend an optimum concentration of $3-5 \times 10^6$ cells/ml. of culture medium and control the cell concentration with hemacytometer counts. Unless the white cell count is very high, or there is a preponderance of polymorphonuclear leukocytes, we have not found these concentrations to be critical. If either of these situations are present, we use smaller aliquots of cell-plasma suspension (0.5 ml/4 ml culture medium) and make up the protein concentration with cell-free autologous plasma obtained by hard centrifugation of the patient's blood sample.

The optimum plasma concentration in the final culture medium is about 20 per cent. Autologous plasma is usually most satisfactory.

With a 10 ml. blood sample, four aliquots of cell-plasma suspension of 1 ml. each can be obtained if 5 ml. total cultures are being used in test tubes. The cultures should be set up in duplicate at least since some twenty-five percent of cultures will fail for no apparent reason. Our recovery rate has been best using quadruplicate samples.

4) Incubate cultures at 37°C. for seventy-two hours. Atmospheric air is satisfactory for the gas phase. Screw-top tubes are best and the lids should be tight. The cultures should be checked daily for evidence of pH change. Do not agitate the cultures unnecessarily.

Note:

The culture vessel choice is a matter of personal preference. The only critical feature is that they be stoppered or capped tightly. The use of centrifuge tubes eliminates the need of transferring the cultures.

Most commercially available media contain a pH indicator. The medium we use (Difco TC 199) contains phenol red which turns orange-yellow when the cultures become hyperacid or deep pink when excess alkalinity develops. The most common pH change is to the acid (yellow) side. Usually this can be corrected by loosening the cap on the tube for a half-hour or so. If the pH does not revert with this step, dropwise addition of a sterile 1 per cent solution of $NaHCO_3$ in saline will usually correct the condition. If hyperacidity recurs, we sometimes have salvaged a culture by the addition of two ml. of culture medium to the tube. Alkalinity is less commonly a problem and can be corrected with 0.1N HC1.

After the first twenty-four hours, fine fibrin clots may be seen in some of the tubes. These can be very troublesome in later handling of the cultures. We remove them, using sterile precautions, as soon as we discover them.

5) On the morning of the fourth day, (i.e., after seventy-two hours incubation), add colchicine to the culture medium in final concentrations of *not over* 0.1 microgram /ml. of culture medium.

6) Incubate for another four to six hours at 37°C.

7) Transfer the cultures to centrifuge tubes. Cells may be adherent to the glass of the original culture tube and can usually be dislodged by gentle swirling or by gentle agitation with a Pasteur pipette. Centrifuge at 800 r.p.m. for ten minutes. Carefully decant the supernatant.

8) Resuspend the cells in prewarmed (37°C) balanced saline such as Ringer's solution using gentle agitation with a Pasteur pipette. Five ml. of saline is sufficient for adequate washing.

9) Centrifuge once again at 800 r.p.m. for five to ten minutes.

10) Aspirate all but 0.5 ml. of supernatant saline and add 1.5 to 2.0 ml. (not more) of prewarmed distilled water. Incubate for 10 minutes at 37°C. From this point on, the cells are very fragile and must be handled gently.

11) Centrifuge slowly (600 r.p.m.) for five minutes.

12) Carefully aspirate the supernatant fluid and drain the cell button by careful inversion.

Note:

—Not uncommonly, the cell button will not be sufficiently firmly packed to withstand inversion. In this case, careful aspiration alone will suffice but inversion is to be preferred whenever it can be done without loss of cells.

13) Layer 4 ml. of acetic alcohol fixative (see: Reagents, below) carefully on top of the cell button taking care not to disturb the cells.

14) Let stand for thirty minutes at room temperature.

15) Resuspend the cells in the fixative gently using a Pasteur pipette and gentle agitation.

16) Centrifuge slowly (600 r.p.m.) for five minutes.

17) Aspirate the supernatant, add another 4 ml. of fresh acetic alcohol fixative and resuspend the cells using a Pasteur pipette.

Note:

Cell clumping may occur at this point. These clumps can usually be dispersed with repeated additions of fixative followed by centrifugation and resuspension in fresh fixative.

18) Centrifuge slowly (600 r.p.m.) for five minutes.

19) Aspirate supernatant and add just enough fresh fixative to produce a hazy suspension when the cells are resuspended. Usually about 0.5 ml. will be sufficient.

20) Use precleaned, first quality glass slides which have been stored in distilled water to prepare stained slides. A drop of cell suspension is dropped on a tilted slide which is still wet with distilled water.

Note:

Even the slides which are marketed as "precleaned" give better results if they are cleaned again before they are used.

Leaving the slides wet when adding the cell suspension takes advantage of the spreading induced by the sudden changes in surface tension which occur when the acetic alcohol fixative contacts the distilled water.

21) Ignite the fixative by touching the slide briefly to a flame.

Note:

As an alternative, the slide may be dried in a stream of warm air or by blowing on it. Rapid and thorough drying is one of the secrets of obtaining good preparations.

22) When the alcohol of the fixative has burned completely, wave the slide vigorously in air to complete drying.

23) Stain in Giemsa stain (see: Reagents, below) for fifteen to twenty minutes.

Note:

Giemsa stain not infrequently has a bluish-green, metalic looking surface scum which should be wiped off the surface of the stain with a piece of filter paper or paper towel if bothersome deposits of stain particles are to be avoided.

24) Wash stained slides in distilled water, allow to dry and mount in balsam or Permount.

Note:

When using this method of preparing slides, we have found that some of the best metaphase figures tend to be at the periphery of the slide and the coverslip should be placed accordingly.

25) Examine slides under medium power or high dry to select metaphase figures for study under oil immersion.

Note:

We have found it most convenient to scan each slide under medium power and to examine likely looking figures under high dry. If they show promise as being good figures, we spot them with an ink dot and do not start oil immersion examination until we have spotted the best figures on a preliminary scan. Thus, if examination is interrupted for some reason, we have a permanent record of the location of the best figures.

26) Enumerate the chromosomes in as many well spread figures as possible using oil immersion.

Note:

This is the most tedious part of karyotyping. We have tried several methods of making it more simple. With a little practice, however, one soon becomes accustomed to mentally dividing the chromosomes into "clumps" and counting each clump separately.

If this technique is being performed only sporadically, photographic counting is a practical method since a whole roll of film is going to be used for each patient anyway. Using a 36-exposure roll (this is the only size that Kodak Copy Film is supplied in in 35 mm. rolls), one may have the processor prepare a contact strip and count the chromosomes from the print. This is facilitated by pricking each image with a pin as it is counted.

If a micro projector is available, counting the chromosomes in the much enlarged fields available with such a projector is one of the easiest methods.

27) Photograph several metaphase figures in which the chromosomes are well spread, in a single optical plane and in which they are present in modal numbers.

Note:

Satisfactory photomicrographs require great care. The most satisfactory film, if the usual 35 mm. attached camera is being used, is Kodak High Contrast Copy (Microfile) film. High intensity illumination is mandatory. Contrast may be increased using one of the Wratten series green filters (e.g. Wratten 58).

Make high contrast black and white prints such that the image of the metaphase figure almost fills the whole of 5″ x 7″ enlargment.

If phase contrast optics are available, these provide some of the best photographs.

28) Cut the individual chromosomes from the photograph and arrange them in homologous pairs and in accordance with the criteria of the Denver system of nomenclature.

We have found it a wise practice to inform both physicians and patients that these methods are subject to unexplainable failures and that a call back for repeated sampling may be necessary.

Peripheral Blood - Micro Method

Although venipuncture samples are to be preferred whenever they are available, excellent preparations may also be obtained using the samples obtained by heel pricks in newborns or small children. The sole disadvantage to such micro methods is the lack of duplicate samples and the increased danger of culture failure on this account.

Method

1) Obtain a free-flowing blood sample from a heel-prick
2) Take up the blood sample in heparinized capillary tubes.

Note:

These tubes, which are available in almost every laboratory, are highly satisfactory for this purpose. Although they are not sterile, the antibiotics which we add to our culture medium (see: Reagents, below) have so far been adequate to prevent culture loss from infection.

3) Stand as many capillary samples as can conveniently be obtained upright in a plasticine block and allow sedimentation to proceed for an hour or so at room temperature.

Note:

If a cell-plasma column has not developed in this time, gentle centrifuging will usually promote separation. If gentle centrifugation is used, the plasticine plug in the end of the capillary tube will not be dislodged.

4) When a good column of plasma has developed, the cell-plasma suspension can be introduced directly into the medium (4 ml.) by attaching a small rubber bulb to the *red cell* end of the tube after breaking off the segment of capillary tubing containing the plasticine plug.

5) The optimum protein concentration is obtained by adding 1 ml. of fetal calf serum or pooled human serum to the culture medium.

The remainder of the technique is that used for larger blood samples. The cell buttons obtained with this method are, of course, much smaller than those obtained using venipuncture samples. All steps must be carried out with great care so that the small collection of cells is not lost. If sufficient numbers of capillary tubes can be filled (four), we prepare duplicate samples despite the small size of the inoculum.

Another method which can be utilized successfully is the introduction of the blood samples directly into the medium without awaiting separation of the layers. The erythrocytes introduced have no untoward effects but we prefer to separate the sample if possible.

Still another method is to introduce the whole blood sample into 1 ml. of either fetal calf serum or pooled human serum and separate the erythrocytes by gentle (600 r.p.m.) centrifugation. We have also used this method with success.

With these methods of micro-analysis available, the age of the patient presents no insurmountable obstacle to successful karyotyping.

Peripheral Blood - Mail-in Method

The hardihood of lymphocytes makes karyotype analysis by mail a possibility if the temperatures to which the mailed sample is exposed do not go below freezing nor exceed the normal body temperature. A method for submitting blood samples for karyotyping has been devised by J. H. Edwards (1963) and consists of defibrinating blood, adding the cell-plasma suspension to medium which contains no phytohemagglutinin and mailing it to the laboratory where the cultures are initiated by adding phytohemagglutinin. The method is successful because lymphocytes will not revert to large mononuclears and start to divide unless phytohemagglutinin is present although they will remain viable for as long as six days.

Method

The following materials are submitted as a mailing kit:

1) Syringes—disposable 10 cc. syringes, each containing three glass beads. The beads should be about 0.5 cm. in diameter and have rough surfaces and a hole in the center.

2) Needles—disposable type in plastic containers, two per syringe.

3) Culture vessel—a container with a capacity of about 30 ml. which is capable of being tightly closed is half filled with TC (Difco, Detroit) medium with added antibiotics but *without* phytohemagglutinin (see: Reagents, below).

4) Dextran solution—6 per cent dextran in saline—2 ml. are sent as part of the kit.

The kits are submitted to the users with the following instructions:

1) Draw *not less* than 4 ml. and *not more* than 8 ml. of venous blood into the syrings.

2) Eject air from the syringe and occlude the needle by sticking into a cork.

3) Shake the needle until the beads stop rattling or for ten minutes by the clock, whichever occurs first.

4) Discard the cork and needle, put on a new needle and draw up all of the Dextran solution. Mix by tilting.

5) Re-cover the needle with the plastic cap supplied, stand the syringe upright away from sunlight for one hour.

6) Remove the plastic cap from the needle, bend the needle to somewhat more than a right angle, taking care not to mix the blood in the syringe. If the blood has clotted, or no separation into layers has occurred, the specimen is not satisfactory for further processing.

7) Inject the supernatant plasma into the culture bottle—do not include any red cells.

8) Return the plasma-culture medium mixture to the laboratory. Mail so that the sample arrives at the laboratory between Monday and Friday.

When the sample arrives at the laboratory, the cell concentration should be checked and adjusted to about 1-2 million cells/ml. of culture. Phytohemagglutinin is added in concentrations of 0.2 ml/5 ml. culture medium. The addition of phytohemagglutinin may be deferred a day or two to make harvesting in three days more convenient. Incubate for three days at 37°C.

The cultures are then handled in the usual fashion except for the washing step. Dextran forms precipitates with acetic acid and must be very carefully washed from the cells. This can be done by layering the cell suspension over 5 per cent (v/v) sucrose and centrifuging them through it. The remainder of the technique is as described previously.

If care is used in washing the Dextran from the cells, this method presents no particular differences from routine blood cultures according to its author.

KARYOTYPE ANALYSIS USING BONE MARROW

Bone marrow cultures may be handled in much the same manner as peripheral blood cultures, the principal differences being predicated upon the greater cellularity of bone marrow and its lack of plasma. Long term cultures can be harvested within forty-eight rather than seventy-two hours.

Method

1) Aspirated bone marrow is added to heparinized autologous plasma or to fetal calf serum in a ratio of 0.5 ml. of marrow to 2.0 ml. plasma or serum and mixed.

2) Erythrocytes are separated by gentle centrifugation at 600 r.p.m.

3) The supernatant is added to culture medium (see: Reagents below) in a ratio of 1 ml. of supernatant for each 6 ml. of culture medium.

4) Culture in an incubator at 37°C for forty-eight hours.

5) The morning of the third day, add colchicine in a concentration of *not over* 0.1 microgram/ml. culture medium.

From this point, the cultures are treated in the same fashion as are cultures from peripheral blood.

Bone marrow aspirate may be added directly to culture medium to which autologous or pooled plasma or fetal calf serum has been added. The erythrocytes may be ignored if desired.

Bone Marrow - Ultra-short Method

One of the prime advantages of bone marrow as a source of material for karyotype analysis is the cellularity which permits very short term culture. These methods are sometimes called "direct" methods. Some investigators have used intravenous injection of colchicine prior to sampling marrow to stimulate an *in vivo* accumulation of metaphase figures. The concentrations used have been less than the usual therapeutic levels of colchicine used in the treatment of gout. This method seems to offer few advantages and has the disadvantage of unnecessary drug administration.

There seems to be little advantage to a method in which colchicine is injected into the patient and four hours allowed elapse as compared with adding colchicine to marrow *in vitro* and waiting four hours. We have not, therefore, used *in vivo* colchicine methods.

Method

1) Aspirated bone marrow is added to culture medium consisting of a mixture of culture medium TC 199 with phytohemagglutinin and antibiotics (see: Reagents, below) and autologous, pooled human or fetal calf serum in a ratio of 4 parts medium to 1 part serum.

2) Use 5 ml. of the above medium for each 0.5 ml. of bone marrow.

3) Add colchicine in a concentration of not more than 0.1 microgram /ml. of culture medium.

4) Incubate six hours at 37°C.

5) Following six hours' incubation, treat the cultures as though they were cultures of peripheral blood at the same stage of karotype analysis.

Using this method, bone marrow preparations may be obtained within one day. Some investigators have treated bone marrow samples directly with hypotonic solutions. Metaphase figures are not numerous with this technique and we prefer the method above cited. Bone marrow is the tissue of choice in the investigation of leukemic patients. It is also useful as a second tissue when mosaicism is being searched for.

KARYOTYPE ANALYSIS USING SOLID TISSUES

There are two general methods for performing karyotype analyses using solid tissues such as skin, fascia or tumor tissue. In the first, the tissue is minced finely and placed on coverslips in culture medium. Cells propagate from the particles as monolayers upon the coverslips, from which they are recovered by trypsinization. These methods require two to three weeks for completion and repeated changes of the culture medium are necessary. Unless a laboratory is already engaged in tissue culture work, this method is probably too cumbersome for the average laboratory.

The second method, which is simpler though much less efficacious, is to convert the solid tissues to cell suspensions by initial treatment with trypsin. The suspensions are then handled as though they were peripheral blood cultures. This method is simpler, more rapid and provides good metaphases for study, particularly from tumor tissue.

Direct Method

This method was described by H. A. Lubs, Jr. (1963) for the examination of tumor tissue

1) Cut tissue into small pieces and place in balanced salt solution (e.g., Hanks' solution) at pH 5 with added colchicine and trypsin (0.25 percent—Difco 1/250).

2) Stir gently with magnetic stirrer.

3) Decant suspension of cells every fifteen to thirty minutes and add more solution to the particles which remain.

4) When sufficient suspension has been obtained, the cells are placed in hypotonic balanced saline (e.g., Hanks' solution) with 160 mg. sodium chloride /100 ml. for a total of thirty minutes, including centrifugation time.

5) After centrifuging the cell suspension which has been treated with hypotonic saline, fix cells with acetic alcohol and proceed as though the cells were cultured leukocytes.

Culture Method

This is the method of Hirschhorn and Cooper (1961).

1) Specimens are obtained by biopsy under local anesthesia and using sterile precautions. A biopsy fragment measuring 5 x 4 x 2 mm is adequate.

   Note:

   Local anesthetics should be injected deep rather than intradermally.

   Local dermbrasion techniques are also useful. The skin behind the ear is anesthetized and abraded. When a crust forms in about three days, it is removed under aseptic conditions and handled like a biopsy specimen. This technique has the advantage that repeated samples may be obtained by removing the crust as it re-forms.

2) Store the sample in sterile saline solution. If culture is to be delayed more than a few hours, the sample should be refrigerated.

3) Using sterile precautions, divide the specimen into fine fragments with maximum diameters of 0.5 x 1.0 mm.

4) Place the tissue fragments into a culture vessel made of a sterile Petri dish into which sterile coverslips have been placed. The fragments should be placed both on and near the coverslips.

5) Add medium (Difco TC 199, single donor AB serum and chicken embryo extract in proportions of 70:20:10) to nearly but not quite completely cover the explants.

6) Incubate at 37°C in a 5 per cent CO_2 atmosphere (expired air from the end of expiration blown through a cotton filter has about 5 per cent CO_2) and change the medium three times weekly using sterile precautions and without disturbing the cells.

7) In one to three weeks, when growth appears active, some coverslip preparations may be made directly (see below) though few mitoses will be seen. Remove the cells and treat them with a 1:1 solution of Versene and trypsin in calcium— and magnesium-free Hanks' solution until a hazy suspension can be obtained.

8) Centrifuge the cell suspension gently for five minutes.

9) Aspirate the supernatant fluid, suspend the cells in fresh culture medium.

10) Distribute aliquots of the cell-medium suspension to sterile Petri dishes containing sterile coverslips.

11) Incubate at 37°C with a 5 per cent CO_2 in air atmosphere for three to four days.

12) Add colchicine in a final concentration of not more than 0.1 microgram/ml. culture medium.

13) Incubate for an additional four hours at 37°C.

14) Remove coverslips and immerse in 0.7 per cent sodium citrate for ten minutes.

15) Immerse coverslips in 2 per cent aceto-orecein (see: Reagents, below) for five minutes.

16) Invert coverslips over a glass slide and squash gently.

17) Seal the coverslip to the slide with an appropriate cement.

The method cited produces temporary slides of good quality. If the slides are rimmed with Permount, they will keep for a surprisingly long time.

ACCENTUATION OF SECONDARY CONSTRICTIONS

Two different methods have been devised for the accentuation of secondary constrictions.

The method of Saksela and Moorhead (1962) consists merely of modifying the fixative and using a glacial acetic acid—methyl alcohol fixative in 1:1 proportions rather than in the usual 1:3 proportion. The secondary constrictions are further accentuated if the preparations are flamed.

The method of Sasaki and Makino (1963) requires brief incubation of the cells in calcium-free medium prior to their treatment with colchicine. The cells are washed three times with prewarmed, calcium-free medium and are then incubated in calcium-free medium for six hours. The cells are then treated with colchicine for one and one-half to two hours. Longer exposure to low calcium media produces sharper constrictions but decreases the mitotic rate.

AUTORADIOGRAPHY

Autoradiography is a specialized technique which is used to study the rate of DNA replication in chromosomes. The replication patterns are fairly characteristic and may be helpful in chromosome identification if an unusual anomaly is discovered. The method is not amenable to routine use.

Method

1) To leukocytes cultured in the usual manner, add tritiated (H^3) thymidine in concentrations of 1 microcurie/ml. of culture medium.

2) Incubate ten minutes, wash cells in saline and reincubate in a medium which contains one hundred times the molar concentration of thymidine used in the labeling solution.

3) After three to four hours incubation, treat the cells with cholchicine and proceed as in a routine peripheral blood culture method.

4) Apply Kodak stripping film AR-10.

5) Expose three weeks, develop film.

6) Counterstain chromosomes through the film with azure B bromide.

This method was devised and reported by Morishima, Grumbach and Taylor (1961) in their studies of the origin of the nuclear sex chromatin.

REAGENTS

Aceto-Orcein Stain

  Stock solution:

Synthetic orcein	1 Gm.
Glacial acetic acid	45 ml.

    Dissolve by boiling. Cool and filter.

  Working solution

Stock solution	9 ml.
Distilled water	11 ml.

Filter. If larger quantities of working solution are made, periodic filtration is required.

Lacto-Aceto-Orcein Stain

Working solution:
Stock solution as above
Lactic acid, 70% solution
Mix in equal parts and filter.
This stain has the advantage that it is hygroscopic and does not dry out as quickly at room temperature as does simple aceto-orcein. Staining takes somewhat longer.

Thionin Stain

Stock thionin
Thionin	1.0 Gm.
Ethyl alcohol, 50%	100 ml.

Stock buffer:
Sodium acetate	9.714 Gm.
Sodium barbiturate	14.714 Gm.
Distilled water to make	500 ml.

Working solution
0.1 N HCl	32 ml.
Stock buffer	28 ml.
Stock thionin	40 ml.

The working solution will keep for six to eight weeks.

Guard Differential Stain for Sex Chromatin

Biebrich scarlet:
Biebrich scarlet, water soluble	1.0 Gm.
Phosphotungstic acid, C.P.	0.3 Gm.
Glacial acetic acid	5.0 ml.
Ethyl alcohol, 50%	100.0 ml.

Fast green FCF:
Fast green FCF	0.5 Gm.
Phosphomolybdic acid	0.3 Gm.
Phosphotungstic acid	0.3 Gm.
Glacial acetic acid	5.0 ml.
Ethyl alcohol, 50%	100.0 ml.

Dilute hematoxylin:
Harris' hematoxylin	0.5 ml.
Ethyl alcohol, 50%	100.0 ml.

Tissue Culture Medium

TC 199 medium (Difco, Detroit). To this commercial medium add:

Penicillin	200 units/ml.
Streptomycin	1-200 micrograms/ml.
Phytohemagglutinin M (Difco, Detroit)	0.01 ml/ml.

Fixative, Karyotyping

Glacial acetic acid	15.0 ml.
Absolute methyl alcohol	45.0 ml.

This provides sufficient fixative for quadruplicate cultures from a single patient.

Make up fresh for each culture.

Giemsa Stain

Stock stain:

Giemsa powder	1.0 Gm.
Glycerine	66.0 ml.
Absolute methyl alcohol	66.0 ml.

Grind Giemsa powder with a little glycerine, add the remainder of the glycerine. Transfer to a flask in a 56°C water bath until dissolved. Cool. Add methyl alcohol. Let stand two to three weeks. Filter. Store in a brown bottle in subdued light.

Stock buffer:

Na_2HPO_4 solution	9.5 Gm./L.
NaH_2PO_4 solution	9.2 Gm./L.

Mix 61.1 ml. of Na_2HPO_4 solution and 38.9 ml. of NaH_2PO_4 solution in 900 ml. of distilled water to produce a buffer of pH 7.0.

Working solution:

Stock stain	2.0 ml.
Stock buffer	40.0 ml.

This quantity is convenient for use in a Coplin jar.

APPENDIX III
SOURCES OF ERROR

THROUGHOUT the text, an effort has been made to point out the possible sources of error which may arise in either the technical or interpretive aspects of each test. In the course of our work with these techniques, we have managed to accumulate a certain expertise on the subject of errors, much to our chagrin. For readers who are initiating these examinations for the first time, this compendium of problems gleaned from both personal experience and from the literature may prove helpful.

TECHNICAL DEFECTS

Success in cytogenetic techniques demands meticulous attention to technical detail. Though sex chromatin techniques are quite simple, there are nevertheless a number of technical errors to which they are subject which may eventuate in errors of interpretation. Karyotyping procedures have great potentiality for unexpected failure.

Chromatin Preparations

Despite the comparative simplicity of the nuclear sex chromatin (Barr) tests and the examination of polymorphonuclear leukocyte (PMN) appendages, these tests are still prone to technical error. Merely having some of these technical hazards brought to mind may ensure against their occurrence.

Polymorphonuclear Neutrophil Leukocyte Appendages

A major source of error encountered in surveying peripheral blood smears for "drumsticks" is *overstaining*. Size is not the only criterion by which drumsticks are differentiated from small clubs. The size of some "small" clubs approximates that of drumsticks rather closely and, unless a micrometer eyepiece is being used, other differential criteria must be employed. One such criterion is the presence of an internal chromatin structure in small clubs which is not present in drumsticks, which are stained homogenously. In overstained smears, where all nuclear chromatin assumes a dark homogeneous appearance, this criterion cannot be used and errors may be made.

Other errors may arise by misidentification of *platelets* and *accessory lobes*, either of which may simulate the appearance of drumsticks or sessile nodules. A platelet superimposed upon a leukocyte in a fortuitous relationship to the nucleus can produce temporary confusion. The difference in focal plane of the two structures is readily demonstrable if it is thought of. Accessory lobes should provide little difficulty as long as their existence is borne in mind. Since they are isthmic structures, they have two "stalks" and are attached to two nuclear lobes.

Nuclear Sex Chromatin

A smear which is heavily populated by *bacteria* can be extremely difficult to interpret and a chromatin negative smear can be misinterpreted by confusing bacteria with nuclear sex chromatin masses. This is one of the major drawbacks of the orcein stain. An error which is perhaps even more easily made is to interpret some cells in a chromatin positive smear as "double positive," implying an XXX or XXXY constitution.

Smears which contain large numbers of *superficial cells* are unsatisfactory for examination. Pyknotic and near-pyknotic nuclei cannot be used for the demonstration of nuclear sex chromatin. *Incomplete differentiation* in differential stains such as Guard's stain may leave some of the larger intranuclear chromatin masses other than the sex chromatin stained with the "specific" sex chromatin stain. This problem is less acute if only the masses related to the nuclear membrane are counted as sex-chromatin. However, one of the advantages of such differential staining is that it permits identification of the chromatin mass when it is not intimately associated with the nuclear membrane. This advantage is lost in poorly differentiated preparations.

Karyotype Preparations

There seems to be rather general agreement that despite the most meticulous technique some twenty-five percent of cultures initiated for karyotype analysis will unaccountably fail. There are a number of errors of technique which will elevate this basic "failure rate" and some of these are avoidable.

The most important single technical maneuver for keeping sample losses at a minimum is the use of *duplicate*, or even better *quadruplicate* aliquots of sample from each patient. We have observed the puzzling phenomenon of having one or two aliquots of some cultures fail to produce any cells whatever while two or three ostensibly identical aliquots, handled identically, produce very satisfactory preparations. Since we have adopted the use of small quadruplicate cultures as a routine prodedure, the need for call-back of patients for repeated sampling has diminished appreciably.

The causes, known and hypothetical, of repeated culture failure are summarized in the table. Of these causes, the "idiopathic" are usually the most common. This does not obviate the need for investigating each phase of the procedure to see if errors have crept in unnoticed.

The next more frequent cause of culture failure has, in our experience, been *hyperacidity*. Generally, this has been most troublesome on weekends when the cultures are sometimes forgotten and no pH correction made. If cultures are checked daily, preferably morning and evening, pH adjustment can be made in time to obviate any damage to the culture. Cultures which are beginning to become acid (yellow) are treated in the following manner: First, the cap of the culture tube is loosened for one-half to one hour. CO_2

TABLE VIII

CAUSES OF CULTURE FAILURE

Faulty sampling	— non-fasting patient
Faulty medium	— failure to add PHA
	— failure to add protein
Hyperacidity	— bacterial contamination
	— neutrophil leukocytosis
	— hypercellular inoculum
Colchicine	— too much
	— overexposure
Hypotonic	— overtreatment
solution	— rough handling after treatment
Idiopathic	— antigen-antibody reactions?
	— to nonhomologous serum
	— to antibiotics

is blown off and this simple maneuver will correct about half of the instances of hyperacidity.

If the cultures still remain acid, add sterile 1% $NaHCO_3$ in saline, drop by drop. Wait for about twenty seconds between each drop and do not succumb to the temptation to wave the culture vessel about. Very gentle agitation should be used, if any. Arbitrarily, we regard eight drops (in a five ml. culture) as a maximum addition.

Cultures which resist both of these corrective measures are either infected or hypercellular. Infected cultures may as well be discarded. Differentiating infection from hypercellularity at this stage can be done without sampling the culture. We add two or three ml. of fresh culture medium (with initial 5 ml. cultures) and this sometimes provides enough corrective capacity that hypercellular cultures can be salvaged. More often than not, however, cultures which do not respond to $NaHCO_3$ to not respond to this treatment either. Only about twenty-five per cent of cultures can be salvaged at this point.

Blood samples from *non-fasting* patients are lipemic and often separate badly. They also fail to grow more often than fasting samples. *Phytohemagglutinin* is mandatory to the success of peripheral blood cultures. We add it directly to the culture medium as we make it up. Failure to add *protein* is generally an oversight which attends the preparation of micro-samples.

Excess concentrations of *colchicine* follow dilution errors when the arresting solution is being made. Colchicine in final concentrations of four micrograms per ml. of culture medium is almost invariably lethal and no suitable metaphases will be found. Concentrations between the lethal level of four micrograms per ml. and the optimum of 0.1 micrograms per ml. are accompanied by a variety of toxic changes. At their mildest, these are reflected in hypercontraction of chromatids. Progressively more severe changes are splitting of the centromeres (so-called "colchicine anaphase") and finally chromosome fragmentation and dissolution.

Overtreatment with *hypotonic* solution may result from failure to leave any saline on the washed cells (when distilled water is being used as the hypotonic agent). Careless addition of too much distilled water should not occur (but does). The optimum *total* time for

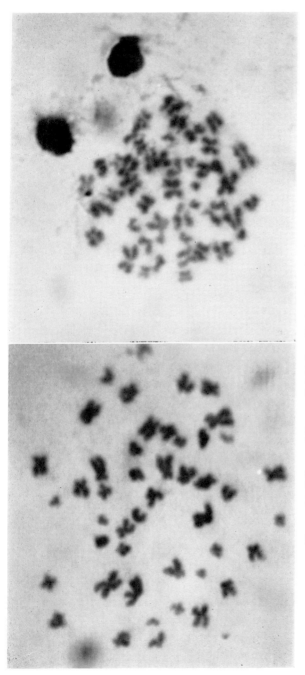

Figure 46. Effects of Excess Colchicine. Early effects (*left*) include marked contraction and shortening of the complement and "fuzziness" of outline. Later effects (*right*) include centromere splitting (colchicine anaphase), further contraction and eventual fragmentation.

hypotonic treatment is fifteen minutes, *including* centrifugation time. As simple an error as leaving the preparations in the centrifute for ten rather than five minutes results in appreciable loss of metaphase figures.

When one delegates responsibility for the technical aspects of karyotyping, it is well to emphasize the necessity for strict adherence to established routine.

SOURCES OF INTERPRETIVE ERROR

All of the technical errors outlined lead in turn to some resultant error in interpretation. Even in the absence of technical error, there are a number of pitfalls which are peculiar to the interpretation of these tests.

Sex Chromatin (Barr) Tests

The sex chromatin body of epithelial nuclei may undergo artefactual alterations in both number and size. Before a report reflecting abnormalities in either of these moieties is issued, possible artefacts should be recalled. These are:

1) Artefactual variations in number (reduced incidence of chromatin positive nuclei in phenotypic females):
   Due to exogenous hormone (steroid) therapy.
   Following parturition.
   In newborns.
2) Artefactual variations in size.
   Reduced size following oral antibiotics.
   Apparent increases or decreases in size following either:
     a) Altered staining technique (Barr bodies appear smaller in hematoxylin-eosin or Papanicoulau preparations than with specific stains).
     b) Source of tissue—bodies in vaginal smears appear larger than bodies in oral smears.

These artefacts have been discussed at some length in Chapter IV.

Reporting buccal or vaginal chromatin preparations as "male" or "female" rather than "chromatin negative" or "chromatin positive" is erroneous (see Chapter IV).

Polymorphonuclear Leukocyte Appendages

The principal source of interpretive error is mistaking small clubs, common to the nuclei of both males and females, with drumsticks. This error is very commonly made by neophytes.

Karotypes

Probably the most common error made in karyotype analysis is failure to recognize the presence of a mosaic chromosome pattern. This error can occur most readily if only a few metaphases are available for study. When karyotyping is used as a diagnostic test, karyotype analyses which do not agree with the clinical appearance of the patient should be most carefully reappraised.

Instances of apparent structural anomalies, particularly if these are present in a "mosaic" pattern or if they bear no relationship to the usual findings in the clinical defect under investigation, should be reinvestigated with repeated examination. Though not a frequent event, structural anomalies have been shown to arise artefactually in *in vitro* preparations. In at least one such instance, pooled serum rather than autologous serum was employed as a protein source. Generally, such artefacts are fortuitous and non-repetitive and will be inapparent on repeated examination.

An insufficient number of good metaphases for examination may also lead to a diagnosis of mosaicism where none exists. False hypermodal counts are often made on cells subject to colchicine overexposure with centromere splitting. Chromatids may be erroneously identified as whole chromosomes in such instances. False hypomodal counts are a common consequence of cell disruption. Disruption is not always apparent from the shape of the metaphase figure—even round and fairly compact chromosome clusters may lack a chromosome due to artefactual loss. Any metaphase in which the chromosomes are strung out in an elongated ellipse or are very widely dispersed should be suspect.

Failure to elicit a history of exposure to X-irradiation or to radiomimetic drugs when these have been administered will frequently lead to errors in interpretation. The alterations produced by these agents are primarily structural and may persist for many years. The presence of bizarre structural anomalies such as dicentrics and

rings should make one particularly alert to the possibility of previous exposure to radiation.

Errors in interpretation are less troublesome than are technical
defects in karyotype analyses. The very complexity of these tests
seems to lend caution to interpretations made when these tests are
used as diagnostic media. It is those cases in which some "new"
defect is discovered that most of the trouble arises (*vide infra*).

REPORTING

In a field as new as cytogenetics, anyone who is at all active in the
use of these techniques has a very good chance of encountering some
abnormality which has either never been reported before or has
been encountered only once or twice. Fortuitous local circumstances may offer one the opportunity to accumulate a significant
series of related cases. New and useful techniques are often born of
expediency where "routine methods" have not become entrenched
with institutional solidarity.

Failure to report any such findings wastes useful scientific data.
What is most needed in the field of cytogenetics is an accumulation
of well documented case reports so that the significant features of
various syndromes can be assessed statistically and defects which
are now recognized only as solitary case reports either accepted or
rejected as diagnostic entities.

Conversely, careless reporting is worse than no reporting at all.
Exposure to the literature in cytogenetics makes one acutely aware
of some of the shortcomings therein. Consideration of some of these
shortcomings has led the author to formulate a series of criteria
which he feels should be satisfied before a case report is submitted
for publication:

1) The reported anomaly should conform to the general principle "the bigger the chromosome affected, the more severe
   the defect," unless there is overwhelming evidence that this
   general principle does not hold for the case being reported.
2) The affected chromosome or chromosomes should be identified
   by number only if this identification can be made wholly
   without equivocation.
3) Terminology should conform to generally accepted criteria.

This is particularly pertinent if eponymic syndromes are being considered. For example, a menstruating female, five feet eight inches tall and with good breast development would hardly be appropriately described by the appellation "atypical Turner's syndrome." Though such exaggerated examples are infrequent, they do exist. Less flagrant abuse of terminology is, perhaps, even more undesirable since it is harder to detect.

4) Cases reported as examples of mosaicism should conform to the criteria for the identification of mosaics as originally enumerated by Court Brown *et al.* (1960). These are:

   a) Counts differing from the mode must be too frequent to be attributed to chance.

   b) An excess of nonmodal cells should be found on more than one examination and, preferably, in more than one tissue.

   c) The nonmodal cells should themselves have a smilar karyotype.

5) Cases reported as examples of significant structural heterozygosis should conform to the following criteria (Edwards *et al.*, 1962).

   a) At least one chromosome arm of unquestionably abnormal length must be repeatedly demonstrable.

   b) The chromosome abnormality and the supposedly related clinical syndrome must segregate together.

   c) Caution should be exercised in relating observed chromosome abnormalities to phenotypic changes which are not generalized, congenital and uncommon.

6) *All* phenotypic alterations should be meticulously recorded whether or not they strike the reporter as being significant.

7) The phenotypic changes reported should be compared, in detail, with reported phenotypic alterations in other patients with similar chromosomal abnormalities.

8) When the chromosome pattern is amenable to more than one interpretation this fact should not only be noted but examined in some detail.

APPENDIX IV

CONVERSION OF PERSONAL NOMEN-CLATURES TO DENVER TERMINOLOGY

Prior to the Denver Conference of 1960, the workers in the field of human cytogenetics each devised a personal classification for the human chromosomes. To aid readers who may wish to refer to articles published before the time of the Denver conference, the following table presents the Denver equivalents of the personal nomenclatures in use prior to 1960.

Denver	Tijo & Puck	Chu & Giles	Levan & Hsu	Ford, Jacobs & Jajtha	Book, Fraccaro & Lindsten	Lejeune, Turpin & Gauthier
1						G1
2						G2
3						G3
4						G4
5						G5
6						M1
7				(8)		M2
8				(9)		Md1
9				(11)		M3
10				(12)		Md2
11				(12)		M4
12				(13)		Md3
13	18	14	20	14	14	T1
14	19	15	18	15	15	T2
15	20	13	19	16	13	T3
16	13	17	15	19		C1
17	14	16	13	17		P1
18	15	18	14	18		P2
19	16	19	16	20		C2
20	17		17	21		C3
21			22	22		Vh
22			21	23		Vs
X			21	(7)		

Only the designations which differ from the Denver nomenclature are indicated.

APPENDIX V

CLASSIFICATION OF KNOWN CHRO-
MOSOMAL DEFECTS (WITH REFERENCES)

FOR the convenience of those who wish a more detailed exposition of the anomalies which have been encountered in the various chromosomal abnormalities in man, the following table has been constructed. As nearly as possible, we have recorded all of the chromosome abnormalities described in the literature surveyed. The diversity of chromosome abnormalities described is surprising.

The anomalies are classified on the basis which was proposed in Chapter VIII. Many of the anomalies which have been reported are open to varying interpretation. Case reports alluding to such defects have been classified under the several different categories which seem most applicable. For example, most of the case reports of "trisomy G" are also classified in the table as reports of the "XYY" anomaly.

A convenient method of cytogenetic shorthand proposed by Hustinx, Eberle, Geerts, Ten Brink and Woltring (1961) has much to recommend it. It is used, with minor modification, throughout the table. It contains the following symbols:

AA = normal autosome set (can be omitted when only sex chromosome defects are considered)

$\mathrm{AA} - \mathrm{A}_a$ = monosomy of autosome A_a

$\mathrm{AA} + \mathrm{A}_a$ = trisomy of autosome A_a

$\mathrm{AA}\ (\mathrm{Ta/b})$ = translocation chromosome a/b as part of a euploid chromosome set $(2\mathrm{n} = 46)$

$\mathrm{AA} + \mathrm{Ta/b}$ = translocation chromosome a/b in addition to a euploid chromosome set $(2\mathrm{n} = 47)$

iso-a = isochromosome of chromosome a (if the arm involved is known, it is specified, *e.g.*, iso-long-a)

XY = the sex chromosomes (may be omitted if only autosomes are abnormal)

$\bar{\mathrm{x}}$ = deleted X chromosome (long $\bar{\mathrm{x}}$ = deleted long arm X, short $\bar{\bar{\mathrm{x}}}$ = deleted short arm X)

283

$\bar{y} =$ deleted Y

$/ =$ the stemlines of a mosaic are separated by a bar

References which are designated in bold face type are, in general, selected as good review articles which summarize appreciable numbers of cases. Bracketed references, *e.g.* (123, 124), indicate a single case which has been reported in two or more separate publications.

I—ANEUPLOIDY

IA—HETEROSOMAL ANEUPLOIDS

1—Isolated Monosomy

1a. Autosomal:
None reported

1b. Sex chromosomal:
45 XO—Turner's syndrome—**21**, 486, 529, (531, 532), 538, 540, **547**, 607
—hermaphrodites with testes—489, 490, 491, 562
—Turner's syndrome, fertile—525

2—Isolated Trisomy

2a. Autosomal:
Group C, unspecified (47AA + A_C)—374, 377, 579
Group D, (47AA + A_D)—D trisomy syndrome
—327, 332, 346, 348, 349, (350, 351), (352, 353, 355), 354, (356, 366, **367**), 359
Group E, (47AA + A_E)—E trisomy (18-tri-somy) 291, (332, **357**, 366) 352, 360, 361, 362, 364, 368, **370**, 371, 372, 382
Group F, unspecified (47AA + A_F)—heart dis-ease—326
, chromosome 19 (47AA + A_{19})—asymptomatic—417
Group G, unspecified (47AA + A_G)—schizo-phrenia—(373, 380)
—benign myotonia
—375
—resembling D or E trisomy—453

, chromosome 21 (47AA + A₂₁)—
mongolism—326,
334, 335, 337, 340,
344, 345, 405, 613,
625, 628
— mongolism, leukemia
—618, 617, 632
— mongolism, Ph¹
chromosome—657
— (mongolism, normal
chromosomes)—
338
, chromosome 22 (47AA + A₂₂)—
Sturge-Weber syn-
drome—378
— schizophrenia, other
defects—381

b. Sex chromosomal:

47 XXX —"sexual hypoplasia"—168, 374,
427, 547, **552**, 562, 605, 607
—fertile—550, 554, 613

47 XXY —Klinefelter's syndrome—571, 574,
585, 607, 609, **674**, 738
—Klinefelter's syndrome, fertile—
583, 586
—hypospadias—584

47 XYY —congenital myotonia—375
—enuresis—600
—asymptomatic—596, 601

3—Isolated Polysomy

3a. Autosomal:
49AA + A₂₁ + A₂₁ + A₂₁—mongolism and
leukemia—627

3b. Sex chromosomal
48 XXXX —**549**
48 XXXY —Klinefelter's syndrome—168,
573, 578, 607
48 XXYY —572, 575, 576, 588, 589, 607
49 XXXXX —168
49XXXXYY —740

49 XXXXY —Klinefelter's variant—569, **570**, 580, 582, 592, 625

4—Complex Aneuploidy
  4a. Autosomal:
    i. Trisomy—monosomy:
      $46AA + A_F - A_G$ — heart disease—326
      $46AA + A_{19} - A_{21}$ — mongolism—417
    ii. Multiple trisomy:
      $48AA + A_{21} + A_{18}$ — 386
  4b. Combined autosomal-sex chromosomal
    $48AA + A_{21}XXY$—mongolism and Klinefelter's syndrome—(316, 622), (621, **622**), 387, 605, 607, 615, 617
    $48AA + A_{18}XXX$ — E trisomy uncomplicated —(629 **630**)
    $49AA + A_8 + A_{11}XXY$—later proven to be XXXXY—579

5—Triploidy
  69 AAA—in abortus—388 (see also mosaics)

IB—ANEUPLOID MOSAICS
  1. Autosomal:
  $46 AA/47 AA + A_C$
    —familial interatrial septal defect—434
    —sexual hypoplasia—547
    —multiple anomalies, mental retardation— 377
  $46 AA/47 AA + A_D$
    —incomplete D trisomy syndrome—399
    —complete D trisomy syndrome—372
    —generalized congenital analgesia—347
  $46 AA/47 AA + A_D/48 AA + A_D + A_D$
    —generalized congenital analgesia—347
  $46 AA/47 AA + A_G$
    —dystrophia myotonica—407
  $46 AA/47 AA + A_{21}$
    —partial mongolism—192, 326, 334, 389, 394, (395, **396**), 397, 400, 750
  $46 AAXX/47 AA + A_{21}XX$
    —partial mongol with mongol children—393, 398

46 AA/47 AA + A₂₁/48 AA + A₂₁ + A₂₁
  —atypical mongolism—(390, 391)
46 AA/47 AA + A₂₁/48 AA + A_F + A₂₁
  —mongolism—392
46 AAXY/69 AAAXXY
  —in fetuses—147, 326
46 AAXX/69 AAAXXX
  —multiple anomalies—383, 385

2. Sex chromosomal:
  45 XO/46 XX
      —gonadal dysgenesis—481, **542**, (543, 544,
        545), 546, **547**
  45 XO/46 XY
      —amenorrhea—504
      —true hermaphrodite—508, 510
      —male with sexual hypoplasia—505
      —atypical XO females—489, 491
      —asymmetrical gonadal differentiation—481,
        506, 507, 509, **513**, 544, 547
  45 XO/47 XXX
      —gonadel dysgenesis—547, 562
  45 XO/47 XXY
      —Klinefelter's syndrome—251, 557, 744
  45 XO/47 XYY
      —gonadal dysgenesis—742
  45 XO/48 XXXY
      —male pseudohermaphrodite—755
  46 XX/46 XY
      —true hermaphrodite—(**498**, 499, 501, 572)
      —(?) mother of mongol—396
  46 XX/47 XXX
      —severe oligomenorrhea—556, 607
  46 XY/47 XXY
      —mental retardation, multiple anomalies—
        377, 607, 751
      —Klinefelter's syn drome—587
  46 XY/48 XXXY
      —mental defective, no Klinefelter's syndrome
        —737
  47 XXX/48 XXXX
      —mild sexual hypoplasia—549

47 XXY/48 XXYY
—Klinefelter's syndrome—738
48 XXXY/49 XXXXY
—mental deficiency—607
45 XO/46 XX/46 XY
—asymmetrical gonadal differentiation—754
45 XO/46 XX/47 XXX
—gonadal dysgenesis—168, 558, 559, 741, 745
46 XY/47 XXY/48 XXYY
—mental deficiency—607
46 XX/47 XXY/49 XXYYY
—true hermaphrodite—749

IC—SUPERNUMERARY CHROMOSOMES
—in dystrophia myotonica—407

II—STRUCTURAL ANOMALIES

IIA—STRUCTURALLY ANOMALOUS
HETERPLOIDS
1—Translocations (in general, 446)
1a. Autosomal:
group A /group C —convulsive disorder—438
1 /6—familial, symptomatic in
offspring—439
2 /C—familial atrial septal defect
—434
2 /group D—minor anomalies—443
group B /group C—multiple anomalies—439
group D /group D—cerebral palsy—442
—asymptomatic—441, (**448**,
449)
—D trisomy—436, 437
group D /group E—partial E trisomy—440, 775
—familial E trisomy—435, 447
group D /group G—familial mongolism—408,
409, 411, 412, 413, 435,
416, **418**, 419, 420, 422,
424, 426, 427, **428**, 429,
430, 444, 616
—familial mongolism, sym-
tomatic carrier?—355

13 /21—(satellite ends only)—
Marfan's syndrome—276
13 /22—polydysspondylism—445
—speech defects—444
₹ ₁ᴜ] E /group G—abortions—414
—partial E trisomy—467
16 /18—mental retardation, hypertonicity—756
16 /21—partial mongolism—410
18 /group G—partial E trisomy—467
? /group E—partial E trisomy—450
? /group E or F—multiple intestinal defects,
lung agenesis—451
group G /group G—familial mongolism—324,
325, 334, 336, 431
—unusual chromosome
mongolism—443
—kyphosis, epilepsy, no
mongolism—459
21 /21—familial mongolism—394,
417, 418, 421, 425, 612
21 /22—mental retardation—459
? /group G—abortions—321
1b. Sex chromosomal:
X /X—primary amenorrhea—148
—hemophiliac male with hypospadias—
746
? /X—cerebral palsy—739
X /Y—intersex—502
2—Deletions
2a. Autosomal:
47 AA + deleted A_C—multiple intestinal defects—451
47 AA + deleted A_{18}—partial E trisomy—452,
453
47 AA + deleted A_{18}—partial mongolism—
421, 750
2b. Sex chromosomal:
46 AAX-long $\bar{x}$—primary amenorrhea—547,
556

46 AAX-short x̄—sexual hypoplasia—547
46 AA Xx̿—562
46 AA Xȳ—mild hypospadias (598, **599**)
                —female, gonadal dysgenesis—602

3—Duplications
  3a. Autosomal:
      None proven—discussed in relation to Sturge-
                Weber syndrome—271
  3b. Sex chromosomal
      ? of deleted long arm of X-gonadal dysgenesis
      —747

4—Isochromosomes
  4a. Autosomal:
      isochromosome—1—Waldenstrom's macroglo-
                bulinemia—455, 456, 457
      isochromosome—2—Waldenstrom's macroglo-
                bulinemia—454
      isochromosome—21—mongolism—394, 417
  4b. Sex chromosomal:
      46 X-iso-long-X—gonadal dysgenesis—168,
                547, 561, **564**, 605
      46 X-iso-X—familial transmission, sexual hypo-
                plasia—(**448**, 449)
                —primary amenorrhea—148, 568
                —multiple anomalies—560
      46 iso-X Y—hemophiliac male with hypospa-
                dias—746

5—Inversions
  5a. Autosomal:
      inversion-21—mongolism—461
      inversion-G—kyphosis, epilepsy and mental re-
                tardation—459
  5b. Sex chromosomal:
      none reported

6—Other Structural Defects
  6a. Autosomal:
      ring-D, unspecified—partial trisomy—468
      ring-E, unspecified—partial trisomy—468
      ring, unspecified—mental retardation—466

insertion ? /1—orofacialdigital syndrome—
(460, 463, 464, 465)
insertion ?C /1—skeletal defects, multiple basal
cell carcinomas—469
insertion ? /short arm group G—abortions—
321, 458
enlarged chromosome 16—spina bifida, torticollis, small
mandible—458
enlarged chromosome G group—Marfan's syndrome—475
satellite enlargement—Marfan's syndrome—
470, 474, 477
—central nervous defects
—472

6b. Sex chromosomal:
long Y chromosome—asymptomatic—229, 594
603
—multiple (non-sex) ano-
malies—597

IIB—STRUCTURALLY ANOMALOUS MOSAICS

1—Autosomal:
46 AA /46 A(T 2 /13-15)—asymptomatic—75
46 AA /46 A(T 13 /15)—asymptomatic—442
2—Sex chromosomal:
46 XX /46 X$\bar{\text{x}}$—oligomenorrhea, Stein-Levinthal
type—556

III—STRUCTURALLY ANOMALOUS ANEUPLOIDS

46 AA − A$_D$ − A$_D$ + T D /D XXY—Klinefelter's syndrome—752

IV—STRUCTURALLY ANOMALOUS ANEUPLOID MOSAICS

1—Autosomal:
46 AA /47 AA + A$_{21}$ /48 AA + A$_{21}$ + iso-21— mongolism—392
46 AA /47 AA + centric fragment—mongolism—394
47 AA + A$_{21}$ /47 AA − A$_F$ + A$_{21}$ + iso-21 /48
AA + A$_{21}$ + A$_{18}$

—mongol with hyperthyroidism and finger deform
ities—395

2—Sex chromosomal:
    45 XO /46 X iso-X—gonadal dysgenesis—541, 563
    45 XO /46 X$\bar{\text{x}}$—gonadal dysgenesis—168, 555
    45 XO /46 XY—asymmetrical gonadal differentiation
        —544, 595
    45 XO/47 X$\bar{\text{x}}$Y—asymmetrical gonadal differentiation
        —511
    47 XXY /48 XX$\bar{\text{x}}$Y—Klinefelter's syndrome—743
    45 XO /46 X ring-X /47 X 2-ring-X—gonadal dys-
                    genesis—565
    45 XO /47 XX$\bar{\text{y}}$ /48 XX$\bar{\text{y}}$—gonadal dysgenesis, mas-
                    culinization—748

3—Combined autosomal—sex chromosomal:
    46 AA(Ph[1])XY /47 AA(Ph[1])XXY—leukemia—661

V—CLONES
    46 diploid /49-60 hyperdiploid /60 polyploid—
    erythroblastic endopolyploidy—478
    46 AA(Ph[1])—chronic myelocytic leukemia—624, 651, 652,
    653, **660**, 661
    45 AA(Ph[1])XO /46 AA(Ph[1])XY—aneuploid clone in leu-
    kemic stemline—661
    isochromosome-1 (or 2?)—Waldenstrom's macroglobulin-
    emia—454, 455, 456, 457

REFERENCES

References which we found to be particularly useful as review sources are designated in bold face.

GENERAL REFERENCES

1. Bearn, A. G. (guest editor): Symposium on genetics, Am. J. Med., 34: 583-720, 1963
2. Childs, B. and Young, W. S.: Genetic variations in man, Am. J. Med., 34:663-673, 1963
3. Editorial: Complicating the chromosomal anomalies, Lancet, 2:31, 1961
4. Eggen, R. R.: Cytogenetics: A review of recent advances in a new field of clinical pathology, Am. J. Clin. Path., 39:3-37, 1963
5. Evans, D. A. P.: Pharmacogenetics, Am. J. Med., 34:639-662, 1963
6. Ferguson-Smith, M. A.: Cytogenetics in man, Arch. Int. Med., 105:627-639, 1960
7. Ferguson-Smith, M. A.: Chromosome abnormalities with congenital disease, Mod. Med., March 6, 1961, pp. 77-87
8. Ferguson-Smith, M. A. and Johnston, A. W.: Chromosome abnormalities in certain diseases of man, Ann. Int. Med., 53:359, 1960
9. Ford, C. E.: Human cytogenetics: its present place and future possibilities, Am. J. Human Genet., 12:104-117, 1960
10. Ford, C. E. and Hamerton, J. L.: The chromosomes of man, Nature (Lond.), 178:1020-1023, 1956
11. Gardner, L. I. (editor): Molecular genetics and human disease (1st Ed.) Charles C Thomas, Springfield, 1961
12. Gates, R. R.: Human genetics (1st Ed.), Macmillan, New York, 1946
13. Hirschhorn, K. and Cooper, H. L.: Chromosomal aberrations in human disease. A review of the status of cytogenetics in medicine, Am. J. Med., 31:442-470, 1961
14. Lennox, B.: Chromosomes for beginners, Lancet, 1:1046-1051, 1961
15. **McCusick, V. A. (editor): Medical genetics, 1958, J. Chron. Dis., 10:255-363, 1959**
16. **McCusick, V. A. (editor): Medical genetics, 1959, J. Chron. Dis., 12:1-202, 1960**
17. **McCusick, V. A. (editor): Medical genetics, 1960, J. Chron. Dis., 14:1-198, 1961**
18. **McCusick, V. A. (editor): Medical genetics, 1961, J. Chron. Dis., 15:417-572, 1962**

293

19. McCusick, V. A.: Genetics in medicine and medicine in genetics, Am. J. Med., 34:594-599, 1963

20. Moore, K. L. and Hay, J. C.: Human chromosomes. Preparation, analysis and diagnostic implications of abnormalities, I, Canad. M.A.J. 88:1022-1028, 1963; II, Canad. M.A.J., 88:1071-1079, 1963

21. Penrose, L. S. (editor): Recent advances in human genetics (1st Ed.), Little, Brown and Co., Boston, 1961

22. Rappaport, S. and Kaplan, W. D.: Chromosomal aberrations in man J. Pediat., 59:415-428, 1961

23. Robinson, A.: The human chromosomes, Am. J. Dis. Child., 101:369-398, 1961

24. Robinson, A., Puck, T. T. and Tjio, J. H.: Some applications of human chromosomal analysis to problems in medicine (Abstract—Trans. Am. Ped. Soc., 1960), Am. J. Dis. Child., 100:777-778 1960

25. Sohval, A. R.: Recent progress in human chromosome analysis and its relation to the sex chromatin, Am. J. Med., 31:397-441, 1961

26. Stern, C.: Principles of Human Genetics (2nd Ed.), Freeman, San Francisco, 1960.

27. Warkany, J. and Kalter, H.: Congenital malformations, New England J.M., Part I, 265:993-1001, 1961; Part II, 265:1046-1052, 1961

28. Wolstenholme, G. E. W. and O'Connor, E. M. (editors): Ciba Foundation Symposium on Congenital Malformations, Little, Brown and Co. Boston, 1960

Chapter I - Chromosome Structure and the Chemistry of Heredity

Historical

29. Arnold, J.: Beobachtungen uber Kerntheilungen in den Zellen der Geschwulste, Virchow's Arch., 78:279-301, 1879

Chromosome Structure

30. Brooke, J. H., Jenkins, D. P., Lawson, R. K. and Osgood, E. E.: Human chromosome uncoiling and dissociation, Ann. Human Genet., 26:139-143, 1962

31. Gall, J. G. and Callan, H. G.: H³ uridine incorporation in lampbrush chromosomes, Proc. Nat. Acad. Sci., 48:562-570, 1962

32. Heitz, E.: in: Chromosome problems (report on Landbouwhageschool conference, April, 1956—Springall, H. D., editor), Nature (Lond.), 178:782-784, 1956

33. Lima-de-Faria, A.: Incorporation of tritiated thymidine into meiotic chromosomes, Science, 130:503-504, 1959

34. White, M. J. D.: The chromosomes (5th Ed.), John Wiley and Sons, New York, 1961

Chemistry of Heredity, General

35. Avery, O. T., MacLeod, C. M. and McCarty, M.: Studies on chemical nature of substance inducing transformation of pneumococcal types: induction of transformation by desoxyribonucleic acid fraction isolated from pneumococcus type III, J. Exper. Med., 79:137-158, 1944

36. **Cohen, S. S.: Recent advances in the chemistry of inheritance, J. Pediat., 60:586-600, 1962**

37. Cole, A.: A molecular model for biological contractility: implications in chromosome structure and function, Nature (Lond.), 196:211-214, 1962

38. Davern, C. I. and Cairns, J.: Nucleic acids and proteins, Am. J. Med., 34:600-608, 1963

39. Gall, J. G.: Kinetics of deoxyribonuclease action on chromosomes, Nature (Lond.), 198:36-38, 1963

40. Hay, E. D.: Recent studies of embryonic induction, New England J. M. 268:1114-1122, 1963

41. Ingram, V. I.: Biochemical genetics at the molecular level, Am. J. Med., 34:674-679, 1963

42. Littlefield, J. W.: The expression of genetic information, New England J.M., 268:873-881, 1963

43. **Siminovitch, L.: The chemical basis of heredity in viruses and cells, Canad. M.A.J., 86:1137-1142, 1962**

D.N.A.

44. Cairns, J.: Proof that the replication of DNA involves separation of the strands, Nature (Lond.), 194:1274, 1962

45. Kornberg, A.: Biologic synthesis of deoxyribonucleic acid, Science, 131: 1503-1508, 1960

46. Rolfe, R.: Changes in the physical state of DNA during the replication cycle, Proc. Nat. Acad. Sci., 49:386-392, 1963

47. Watson, J. D. and Crick, F. H. C.: Molecular structure of nucleic acids: A structure for deoxyribose nucleic acid, Nature (Lond.), 171:737-738

48. Watson, J. D. and Crick, F. H. C.: Genetical implications of the structure of deoxyribonucleic acid, Nature (Lond.), 171:964-967, 1953

49. Woods, P. S. and Schairer, M. U.: Distribution of newly synthesized deoxyribonucleic acid in dividing chromosomes, Nature (Lond.), 183: 303-305, 1959

R.N.A. and the Genetic Code

50. Bretscher, M. S. and Grunberg-Manago, M.: Polyribonucleotide-directed protein synthesis using an *E. coli* cell-free system, Nature (Lond.), 195: 283-284, 1962

51. Champe, S. P. and Benzer, S.: Reversal of mutant phenotypes by 5-fluorouracil: an approach to nucleotide sequences in messenger RNA, Proc. Nat. Acad. Sci., 48:532-546, 1962

52. Chargaff, E.: Calculated composition of a "messenger" ribonucleic acid, Nature (Lond.), 194:86-87, 1962

53. **Crick, F. H. C., Barnett, L., Brenner, S. and Watts-Tobin, R. J.: General nature of the genetic code for protein Nature (Lond.) 192:1227-1232, 1961**

54. Genetic code for the synthesis of protein, Lancet, 1:32-33, 1962.

55. Golomb, S. W.: Plausibility of the ribonucleic acid code, Nature (Lond.), 196:1228, 1962

56. Kano-Suekoa, T. and Spiegelman, S.: Evidence for a nonrandom reading of the genome, Proc. Nat. Acad. Sci., 48:1942-1949, 1962

57. Lengyel, P., Speyer, J. F. and Ochoa, S.: Synthetic polynucleotides and the amino acid code, I, Proc. Nat. Acad. Sci., 47:1936, 1961

58. Lengyel, P., Speyer, J. F., Basilio, C. and Ochoa, S.: Synthetic polynucleotides and the amino acid code, III, Proc. Nat. Acad. Sci., 48: 282-284, 1962

59. Love, R.: Distribution of ribonucleic acid in tumor cells during mitosis, Nature (Lond.), 180-1338-1339, 1957

60. Lowe, C. U.: Some aspects of the structure and function of cytoplasm, J. Pediat., 60:601-613, 1962

61. Nirenberg, M. W. and Matthaei, J. H.: An intermediate in the biosynthesis of phenylalanine directed by synthetic template RNA, Proc. Nat. Acad. Sci., 47:1558, 1961

62. Roberts, R. B.: Further implications of the doublet code, Proc. Nat. Acad. Sci., 48:1245-1250, 1962

63. Spencer, M., Fuller, W., Wilkins, M. H. F. and Brown, G. L.: Determination of the helical configuration of ribonucleic acid molecules by X-ray diffraction study of crystalline amino-acid transfer ribonucleic acid, Nature (Lond.), 194:1014-1020, 1962

64. Speyer, J. F., Lengyel, P., Basilio, C. and Ochoa, S.: Synthetic polynucleotides and the amino acid code, II, Proc. Nat. Acad. Sci., 48: 63-68, 1962

65. Speyer, J. F., Basilio, C. and Ochoa, S.: Synthetic polynucleotides and the amino acid code, IV, 48:441-448, 1962

66. Wall, R.: Overlapping genetic codes, Nature (Lond.), 193:1268-1270 1962

67. Woese, C. R.: Nature of the biological code, Nature (Lond.), 194:1114-1115, 1962

68. Zalokar, M.: Nuclear origin of ribonucleic acid, Nature (Lond.), 183: 1330, 1959

Transfer of Genetic Information

69. Brachet, J.: Ribonucleic acids and the synthesis of cellular proteins, Nature (Lond.), 186:194-199, 1960

70. Chamberlin, M. and Berg, P.: Deoxyribonucleic acid directed synthesis of ribonucleic acid by an enzyme from *Escherichia coli*, Proc. Nat. Acad. Sci., 48:81-94, 1962

71. Medvedev, Zh. A.: A hypothesis concerning the way of coding inter-

action between transfer RNA and messenger RNA at the later stage of protein synthesis, Nature (Lond.), 195:38-39, 1962

72. Protein synthesis, Lancet, 1:1333, 1961
73. Risebrough, R. W., Tissieres, A. and Watson, J. D.: Messenger RNA attachment to active ribosomes, Proc. Nat. Acad. Sci., 48:430-436, 1962

Genes, General

74. **Demerec, M.; The nature of the gene, Am. J. Human Genet., 13: 122-127, 1961**
75. Frota-Pessoa, O.: On the number of gene loci and the total mutation rate in man, Am. Naturalist, 95:217-222, 1961
76. The gene, Lancet, 2:1018, 1960
77. Genes and their products, Lancet, 1:469-470, 1962
78. Woolf, L. I.: Gene expression in heterozygotes, Nature (Lond.), 194: 609-610, 1962

The Operon

79. Gates, R. R.: Fractionation of genes, Nature (Lond.), 186:739-740, 1960
80. Jacob, F., Perrin, D., Sanchez, C. and Monod, J.: (Structural, operator and regulator genes), Compt. rend. Acad. Sci., Paris, 250:1727, 1960
    Quoted by Parker, W. C. and Bearn, A. G. (ref. 91)
81. **Jacob, F. and Monod, J.: Genetic regulatory mechanisms in the synthesis of proteins, J. Molec. Biol., 3:318-356, 1961**
82. Motulsky, A. G.: Controller genes in synthesis of human hemoglobin Nature (Lond.), 144:607-609, 1962

Histones

83. Allfrey, V. G., Littau, V. C. and Mirsky, A. E.: On the role of histones in regulating ribonucleic acid synthesis in the cell nucleus, Proc. Nat. Acad. Sci., 49:414-421, 1963
84. Bartalos, M.: A possible chemical term for the operator-gene, Nature (Lond.), 198:109, 1963

Mutations

85. Baglioni, C.: The fusion of two peptide chains in hemoglobin Lepore and its interpretation as a genetic deletion, Proc. Nat. Acad. Sci., 48:1880-1886, 1962
86. Benzer, S. and Champe, S. P.: A change from nonsense to sense in the genetic code, Proc. Nat. Acad. Sci., 48:1114-1121, 1962
87. Brink, R. A.: Paramutation and chromosome organization, Quart. Rev. Biol., 35:120, 1960
88. Freese, E. B.: Transitions and transversions induced by depurinating agents, Proc. Nat. Acad. Sci., 47:540-545, 1961
89. Garen, A. and Siddiqi, O.: Suppression of mutations in the alkaline phosphatase structural cistron of *E. coli*, Proc. Nat. Acad. Sci., 48: 1121-1127, 1962

90. Gerald, P. S., Efron, M. L. and Diamond, L. K.: A human mutation (the Lepore hemoglobinopathy) possibly involving two "cistrons", Am J. Dis. Child., 102:514-515, 1961
91. Parker, W. C. and Bearn, A. G.: Control gene mutations in the human haptoglobulin system, Nature (Lond.), 198:107-108, 1963
92. **Penrose, L. S.: Mutation, in: Recent advances in human genetics (Penrose, L. S., editor), Little, Brown and Co., Boston, 1961**
93. **Zamenhof, S.: Mutations, Am. J. Med., 34:609-626, 1963**

Cell Differentiation

94. Davidson, E. H., Allfrey, V. G. and Mirsky, A. E.: Gene expression in differentiated cells, Proc. Nat. Acad. Sci., 49:53-60, 1963
95. Eisonstadt, J. M., Kameyama, T. and Novilli, G. D.: A requirement for gene-specific deoxyribonucleic acid for the cell-free synthesis of a galactosidase, Proc. Nat. Acad. Sci., 48:652-659, 1962
96. Fox, A. S., Yoon, S-B. and Mead, C. G.: Evidence for the persistence in protein synthesis of an information transfer mechanism after the removal of gencs, Proc. Nat. Acad. Sci., 48:546-561, 1962
97. Gluck, L. and Kulovich, M.: RNA and the sequence of differentiation in embryonic cells, Am. J. Dis. Child., 104:549, 1962
98. **Jarvik, L. F.: Senescence and chromosomal changes, Lancet 1:114-115, 1963**
99. Markert, C. L.: Biochemical embryology and genetics, J. Nat. Cancer Inst. Monograph No. 2, p. 3, 1960
100. **Sonneborn, T. M.: The gene and cell differentiation, Proc. Nat. Acad. Sci., 46:149-165, 1960**

Pertinent discussions will also be found in the following articles: 22, 84, 167 (heterochromatin); 270 (DNA synthesis); 272 (chromosome structure).

Chapter II - Normal Cell Division

101. Carriere, R., Leblond, C. P. and Messier, B.: Increase in the size of liver cell nuclei before mitosis, Exp. Cell. Res., 23:625-628, 1961
102. Edwards, R. G.: Meiosis in ovarian oocytes of adult mammals, Nature (Lond.), 196:446-450, 1962
103. German, J. L.: Synthesis of deoxyribonucleic acid during interphase, Lancet, 1:744, 1962
104. Harris, H.: Formation of the nucleolus in animal cells, Nature (Lond.) 190:1077-1078, 1961
105. Martin, P. G.: Evidence for the continuity of nucleolar material in mitosis, Nature (Lond.), 190:1078-1079, 1961
106. Ohno, S., Kaplan, W. D. and Kinosita, R.: Demonstration of bi-partite spiral structure on spermatogonial chromosomes of *Mus musculus*, Exp. Cell. Res., 15:426-428, 1958

107. Ohno, S., Klinger, H. P. and Atkin, N. B.: Human oogenesis, Cytogenetics, 1:42-51, 1962

108. Ohno, S., Makino, S., Kaplan, W. D. and Kinosita, R.: Female germ cells of man, Exp. Cell. Res., 24:106-110, 1961

109. Schneiderman, L. J. and Smith, C. A. B.: Nonrandom distribution of certain homologous pairs of normal human chromosomes in metaphase Nature (Lond.), 195:1229-1230, 1962

110. Slizyoski, B. M.: The pachytene stage in mammalian oocytes, Nature (Lond.), 189-683-684, 1961

111. Smithies, O., Connell, G. E. and Dixon, G. H.: Chromosomal rearrangements and the evolution of haptoglobin genes, Nature (Lond.), 196: 232-236, 1963

112. Wilson, J. Y.: Simultaneous changes in both differential and interference distances of chiasmata, Nature (Lond.), 184:207-208, 1959

Pertinent discussions will also be found in the following articles: 34, 272 (cell division, general); 49, 103 (DNA distribution during cell division); 107 (functions of meiosis).

Chapter III - Principles of Heredity

113. Braden, A. W. H.: Influence of time of mating on the segregation ratio of alleles at the T locus in the house mouse, Nature (Lond.), 181: 786-787, 1958

114. Darlington, C. D.: (Effects of triploidy on crossing-over), J. Genet., 41: 35, 1941, *quoted by* Jain, H. K. and Basak, S. L. (ref. 118)

115. de la Chapelle, A., Ikkala, E. and Nevanlinna, H. R., Hemophilia in a girl: a probable exception from sex-linked recessive inheritance, Lancet 2:578-580, 1961

116. Graham, J. B., Tarleton, H. L., Race, R. R. and Sanger, R.: A human double cross-over, Nature (Lond.), 195:834, 1962

117. Gates, R. R.: Y chromosome inheritance of hairy ears, Science, 132: 145, 1960

118. Jain, H. K. and Basak, S. L.: Interchromosome effects of chiasmata and crossing-over, Nature (Lond.), 197:725-726, 1963

119. Li, C. C.: Genetic aspects of consanguinuity, Am. J. Med., 34:702-714, 1963

120. McConnell, R. B.: Associations and linkage in human genetics, Am. J. Med., 34:692-701, 1963

121. Musto, D. F.: The theory of hereditary disease of Luis Mercado, chief physician to the Spanish Hapsburgs, Bull. Hist. Med., 35:346, 1961

122. Riley, R., Chapman, V. and Kimber, G.: Genetic control of chromosome pairing in intergeneric hybrids with wheat, Nature (Lond.), 183:1244-1246, 1959

123. Schultz, J. and Redfield, H.: (Interchromosomal effects of crossing-over),

Cold Spring Harbor Symp. Quant. Biol., 16:175, 1951, *quoted by* Jain H. K. and Basak, S. L. (ref. 118)

124. Smith, C. A. B.: Methodology in human genetics, Am. J. Human Genet. 13:128-136, 1961

125. Stern, C.: The problem of complete Y-linkage in man, Am. J. Human Genet., 9:147-166, 1957

126. Wallace, M. E.: Affinity: evidence from crossing inbred lines of mice Heredity, 16:1-24, 1961

127. White, M. J. D. and Morley, F. H. W.: (Effect of pericentric structural changes on chiasma formation), Genetics, 40:604, 1955, *quoted by* Jain, H. K. and Basak, S. L. (ref. 118)

Pertinent discussions will also be found in the following articles: 78 (expressivity); 112 (environmental effects); 138 (position effects); 140, 243, 244 (X-linked genes in man).

Chapter IV - Sex Differentiation and the Chromatin Test

Sex Differentiation

128. Jost, A.: Réchérches sur la différenciation sexuelle de l'embryon de lapin: III: Rôle des gonads foetales dans la différenciation sexuelle somatique, Arch. Anat. Micr. Morph. Exp., 36:271, 1947

129. **Jost, A.: Problems of fetal endocrinology: the gonadal and hypophyseal hormones, Rec. Prog. Hormone Res., VIII: 379-418, 1953**

130. Mainx, F.: Sex determination in man and in *Diptera*, Lancet, 1:673, 1961

131. Renkonen, K. O., Makela, O. and Lehtovaara, R.: Factors affecting the human sex ratio, Nature (Lond.), 194:308-309, 1962

132. **Stern, C.: The genetics of sex determination in man, Am. J. Med., 34:715-720, 1963**

133. Weiman, H. L.: The chromosomes of human spermatocytes, Am. J. Anat., 21:1-22, 1917

Function of Sex Chromosomes

134. Garn, S. M. and Rohmann, C. G.: X-linked inheritance of developmental timing in man, Nature (Lond.), 196:695-696, 1962

135. Melander, Y. and Hansen-Melander, E.: Activities of the X chromosome Lancet, 2:53-54, 1962

136. Mittwoch, U.: Properties of X chromosomes, Lancet, 2:880, 1961

137. Ohno, S.: Properties of X chromosomes, Lancet, 2:723-724, 1961

138. **Russell, L. B.: Genetics of mammalian sex chromosomes, Science, 133:1745-1803, 1961**

139. Singular behavior of an X chromosome, Lancet, 2:29-30, 1962

140. **Stewart, J. S. S.: The X chromosome of man, Lancet, 2:1269-1271, 1962**

Chromatin Test, General

141. Barr, M. L. and Bertram, E. G.: A morphological distinction between the neurones of the male and female, and the behavior of the nucleolar satellite during accelerated nucleoprotein synthesis, Nature (Lond.), 163:676-677, 1949

142. Barr, M. L.: Sex chromatin and phenotype in man, Science, 130:679, 685, 1959

143. Barr, M. L.: Sexual dimorphism in interphase nuclei, Am. J. Human Genet., 12:118-127, 1960

144. Barr, M. L. and Carr, D. H.: Sex chromatin, sex chromosomes and sex anomalies, Canad. M.A.J., 83:979-986, 1960

Recognition of Sex Chromatin

145. Ashley, D. J. B.: Occurrence of sex chromatin in the cells of the blood and bone marrow in man, Nature (Lond.), 179:969-970, 1957

146. Ashley, D. J. B.: Occurrence of sex chromatin in the basal cells of the epidermis and in basal cell carcinomas, Nature (Lond.), 181:427, 1958

147. Book, J. A. and Santesson, B.: Nuclear sex in triploid XXY human cells Lancet, 2:318, 1961

148. Edwards, J. H.: Barr bodies, Lancet, 1:616, 1961

149. Fraccaro, M. and Lindsten, J.: Observations on the so-called "sex chromatin" in human somatic cells cultivated *in vitro*, Exp. Cell. Res., 17:536-539, 1959

150. Grob, H. S. and Kupperman, H. S.: Experiences with technics of chromatin sex determination, Am. J. Clin. Path., 36:132-138, 1961

151. Harnden, D. G.: Nuclear sex in triploid XXY human cells, Lancet, 2: 488, 1961

152. James, J.: The "sex chromatin" and the nucleic acids, Exp. Cell Res., 21:205-208, 1960

153. Klinger, H. P.: The fine structure of the sex chromatin body, Exp. Cell Res., 14:207-211, 1958

154. Klinger, H. P. and Schwarzacher, H. G.: Sex chromatin in polyploid nuclei of human amnion epithelium, Nature (Lond.), 181:1150-1151, 1958

155. Miles, C. P.: Sex chromatin in cultured human tissues, Nature (Lond.), 184:477-478, 1959

156. Miles, C. P.: Morphology and functional relations of sex chromatin in cultured amnion cells, Exp. Cell Res., 20:324-337, 1960

157. Miles, C. P.: Size of the sex chromatin body, Lancet, 2:660, 1962

158. Mittwoch, U. and Delhanty, J. D. A.: Nuclear sex in triploi XXY human cells, Lancet, 2:552, 1961

159. Orsi, E. V. and Ritter, H. B.: A report of sex chromatin in human tissue culture, Exp. Cell Res., 15:244-245, 1958

160. Orsi, E. V., Wallace, R. E. and Ritter, H. B.: Changes in incidence of sex chromatin in subcultured cells, Science, 133:43-44, 1961

161. Serr, D. M., Ferguson-Smith, M. A., Lennox, B. and Paul, J.: Representation of the X chromosome in intermitotic nuclei in man, Nature (Lond.), 182:124, 1958

162. Therkelsen, A. J. and Petersen, G. B.: Frequency of sex-chromatin-positive cells in the logarithmic and postlogarithmic growth phases of human cells in tissue culture, Exp. Cell Res., 28:588-589, 1962

Origin of the Sex Chromatin

163. Barr, M. L.: Sex chromatin, Science, 130:1302, 1959

164. Beutler, E., Yeh, M. and Fairbanks, V. F.: The normal human female as a mosaic of X-chromosome activity: studies using the gene for G-6-P.D.-deficiency as a marker, Proc. Nat. Acad. Sci., 48:9-16, 1962

165. Cattanach, B. M.: (Heterochromatinization of X-autosome translocation in mouse), Z. Vererbungslehre, 92:165, 1961, *quoted by* Grumbach, M. M., Morishima, A. and Taylor, J. H. (ref. 168)

166. Grumbach, M. M., Morishima, A. and Chu, E. H. Y.: On the sex chromatin and sex chromosomes in sexual anomalies in man. Relation to origin of the sex chromatin, Am. J. Dis. Child., 100:548-549, 1960

167. Grumbach, M. M., Marks, P. A. and Morishima, A.: Erythrocyte glucose-6-phosphte dehydrognease activity and X chromosome polysomy, Lanet, 1:1330-1332, 1962

168. Grumbach, M. M., Morishima, A. and Taylor, J. H.: Human six chromosome abnormalities in relation to DNA replication and heterochromatinization, Proc. Nat. Acad. Sci., 49:581-589, 1963

169. Lyon, M. F.: Gene action in the X chromosome of the mouse, (*Mus musculus*, L), Nature (Lond.), 190:372-373, 1961

170. Lyon, M. F.: Sex chromatin and gene action in the mammalian X chromosome, Am. J. Human Gene., 14:135-148, 1962

171. McCusick, V.: Barr body in polyploidy, *in* Medical Genetics, 1961, J. Chron. Dis., 15:417-572, 1962

172. Miles, C. P.: Cytogenetic abnormality in man: wider implications of theories of sex chromatin origin, California Med., 96:21-25, 1962

173. Morishima, A., Grumbach, M. M. and Taylor, J. H.: Asynchronous duplication of human chromosomes and the origin of sex chromatin, Proc. Nat. Acad. Sci., 48:756-763, 1962

174. Muldal, S.: Origin of the Barr body, Lancet, 2:1384-1385, 1962

175. Ohno, S.: Dynamics of the condensed female X-chromosome, Lancet, 1:273-274, 1963

176. Ohno, S. and Cattanach, B. M.: Cytological study of an X-autosome translocation in *Mus musculus*, Cytogenetics, 1:129-140, 1962

177. Ohno, S. and Hauschka, T. S.: Allocycly of the X-chromosome in tumors and normal tissues, Cancer Res., 20:541-545, 1960

178. Ohno, S., Kaplan, W. D. and Konosita, R.: Formation of the sex chro-

matin by a single X-chromosome in liver cells of *Rattus norvegicus*, Exp. Cell Res., 18:415-418, 1959

179. Ohno, S., Kaplan, W. D., and Kinosita, R.: The basis of nuclear sex difference in somatic cells of the opossum, *Didelphis virginiana*, Exp Cell Res., 19:417-420, 1960

180. Ohno, S., Kaplan, W. D. and Kinosita, R.: On isopycnotic behavior of the XX-bivalent in oocytes of *Rattus norvegicus*, Exp. Cell Res., 19:637-639, 1960

181. Ohno, S., Kaplan, W. D. and Kinosita, R.: X-chromosome behavior in germ and somatic cells of *Rattus norvegicus*, Exp. Cell Res., 22:535-544, 1961

182. Ohno, S., Kovacs, E. T. and Kinosita, R.: On the X-chromosomes of mouse mammary carcinoma cells, Exp. Cell Res., 16:462-465, 1959

183. **Ohno, S. and Makino, S.: The single-X nature of the sex chromatin in man, Lancet, 1:78-79, 1961**

184. Ohno, S. and Weiler, C.: Sex chromosome behavior pattern in germ and somatic cells in *Mesocricetus auratus*, Chromosoma, 12:362-373, 1961

185. Stewart, J. S. S.: Genetic mechanisms in human intersexes, Lancet, 1:825-826, 1960

186. Stewart, J. S. S. and Sanderson, A. R.: Sex chromatin in normal human testis, Lancet, 1:79-80, 1961

187. Vandenberg, S. G., McKusick, V. A. and McKusick, A. B.: Twin data in support of the Lyon hypothesis, Nature (Lond.), 194:505-506, 1962

Interpretation of Chromatin Tests

188. Ashley, D. J. B.: Are ovarian pregnancies parthenogenetic?, Am. J. Human Genet., 11:305-310, 1959

189. Carpentier, P. J., Stolte, L. A. M. and Visschers, G. P.: Determination of genetic sex by the vaginal smear, J. Clin. Endocr., 16:155-160, 1956

190. Del Campo, M. S. B. and Ramirez, O. E. G.: Fluctuations of the sex chromatin during the menstrual cycle, Inter-society Cytology Council, Inc., Memphis, Tennessee, November 2-4, 1961, *quoted by* Smith, D. W., *et al.*, Pediatrics, 30:707-711, 1962

191. Grumbach, M. M. and Barr, M. L.: Cytologic tests of chromosomal sex in relation to sexual anomalies in man, Rec. Prog. Hormone Res., XIV:255-334, 1958

192. Moore, K. L. and Barr, M. L.: Smears from the oral mucosa in the detection of chromosomal sex, Lancet, 2:57-58, 1955.

193. Polani, P. E.: Sex reversal: genetic, chromosomal and nuclear sex, Lancet, 1:629-630, 1959

194. Sohval, A. R. and Casselman, W. G. L.: Alteration in size of nuclear sex chromatin mass (Barr body) induced by antibiotics, Lancet, 2:1386-1388, 1961

195. Taylor, A. I.: Ambiguous sex and sex chromatin in the newborn, Lancet, 2:1059, 1962

Polymorphonuclear Leukocyte Appendages

196. Davidson, W. M.: Inherited variations in leukocytes, Brit. Med. Bull., 17:190-195, 1961

197. Davidson, W. M. and Smith, D. R.: A morphological sex difference in the polymorphonuclear neutrophil leukocytes, Brit. M. J., 2:6-7, 1954

198. Harnden, D. G. and Jacobs, P. A.: Cytogenetics of abnormal sexual development in man, Brit. Med. Bull., 17:206-212, 1961

199. Maclean, N.: The drumsticks of polymorphonuclear leukocytes in sex-chromosome abnormalities, Lancet, 1:1154-1158, 1962

200. Procópio-Valle, J,, Chagas, W. A. and Manceau, J. N.: Value of drumsticks and other nuclear appendices in the determination of sex. Discriminatory analysis based on findings in 804 normal subjects, J. Clin. Endocr., 21:965-975, 1961

201. Ruhren, R.: "Sex" chromatin in neutrophils from male and female C³H mice, Exp. Cell Res., 19:424-427, 1960

Pertinent discussions will also be found in the following articles: 103 (X-asynchrony in females)

Chapter V - Identification of Human Chromosomes

202. Hansemann, D.: Ueber pathologische Mitosen, Virchow's Arch., 123: 356-370, 1891

203. Lejeune, L., Gautier, M. and Turpin, R.: Les chromosomes humains en culture de tissues, Compt. Rend. Acad. Sci. Paris, 248:602, 1959

204. Painter, T. S.: The Y chromosome in mammals, Science, 53:503-504, 1921

205. Painter, T. S.: Studies in mammalian spermatogenesis, II. The spermatogenesis of man, J. Exp. Zool., 37:291-334, 1923

206. Tjio, J. H. and Levan, A.: The chromosome number of man, Hereditas, 42:1-6, 1956

207. de Winiwarter, H.: Etudes sur la spermatogenese humaine. (I. Cellule de Sertoli. II. Hétérochromosome et mitoses de l'epithélium seminal.), Arch. Biol., 27:91-190, 1912

Culture Media

208. Basrur, V. R. and Baker D. G.: Human chromosome breakage in low-calcium values, Lancet 1:1106-1107, 1963

209. Hsu, T. C.: Mammalian chromosomes *in vitro* I. The karyotype of man, J. Hered., 43:167-172, 1952

210. Hughes, A.: Some effects of abnormal tonicity on dividing cells in chick tissue cultures, Quart. J. Micr. Sci., 93:207-220, 1952

211. McDonald, M. R. and Kaufmann, B. P.: Production of mitotic abnormalities by EDTA, Exp. Cell Res., 12:415-417, 1957

Phytohemagglutinin

212. Beckman, L.: Effect of phytohemagglutinin on human serum and cell proteins, Nature (Lond.), 195:582-583, 1962

213. Cooper, E. H., Barkhan, P. and Hale, A. J.: Mitogenic activity of phyto-hemagglutinin, Lancet, 2:210, 1961
214. de la Chapelle, A.: Factor stimulating cell division in cultured leucocytes, Lancet, 1:1348, 1961
215. Elves, M. W. and Wilkinson, J. F.: Effects of phytohemagglutinin on the morphology of cultured leucocytes, Nature (Lond.), 194:1257-1259 1962
216. Elves, M. W. and Wilkinson, J. F.: The effects of phytohemagglutinin on normal and leukaemic leucocytes when cultured *in vitro*, Exp. Cell Res., 30:200-207, 1963
217. Nowell, P. C.: Phytogemagglutinin: an initiator of mitosis in cultures of normal human leukocytes, Cancer Res., 20:462-466, 1960
218. Quaglino, D., Hayhoe, F. G. J. and Flemans, R. J.: Cytochemical observations on the effect of phytohaemagglutinin in short term tissue cultures, Nature (Lond.), 196:338-340, 1962.

Chromosome Enumeration

219. Jacobs, P. A., Brunton, M., Court Brown, W. M., Doll, R. and Goldstein, H.: Change of human chromosome count distributions with age: evidence for a sex difference, Nature (Lond.), 147:1080-1081, 1963
220. Jacobs, P. A., Court Brown, W. M. and Doll, R.: Distribution of human chromosome counts in relation to age, Nature (Lond.), 191:1178-1180, 1961

Chromosome Identification, General

221. Book, J. A., Lejeune, J., Levan, A., Chu, E. H. Y., Ford, C. E., Fraccaro, M., Harnden, D. G., Hsu, T. C., Hungerford, D. A., Jacobs, P. A., Makino, S., Puck, T. T., Robinson, A. and Tjio, J. H., (Counsellors: Catcheside, D. G., Muller, H. J. and Stern, C.): A proposed standard system of nomenclature of human mitotic chromosomes, Lancet, 1: 1063-1065, 1960
222. Chu, E. H. Y.: The chromosome complements of human somatic cells, Am. J. Human Genet., 12:97-103, 1960
223. Chu, E. H. Y. and Giles, N. H.: Human chromosome complement in normal somatic cells in culture, Am. J. Human Genet., 10:63-79, 1959
224. Harnden, D. G.: The chromosomes, *in:* Recent advances in human genetics (1st Ed.), Little, Brown and Co., Boston, 1961
225. Makino, S. and Sasaki, M.: A study of somatic chromosomes in a Japanese population, Am. J. Human Genet., 13:47-63, 1961
226. Tjio, J. H. and Puck, T. T.: Genetics of somatic mammalian cells II. Chromosomal constitution of cells in tissue culture, J. Exptl. Med. 108:259-268, 1958
227. Yerganian, G.: Cytologic maps of some isolated human pachytene chromosomes, Am. J. Human Genet., 9:42-54, 1957

Identification of Specific Chromosomes

228. Ann Josephine, Sr. and Brown, M. C.: Secondary constrictions of chromosomes, Lancet, 2:1282, 1962

229. Bender, M. A. and Gooch, P. C.: An unusually long human Y chromosome, Lancet, 2:463-464, 1961
230. Boyes, J. W.: Human X-chromosome arm ratios and percentages of total
complement length, Am. J. Human Genet., 13:104-105, 1961
231. de la Chapelle, A.: Constrictions in normal human chromoscmes, Lancet,
2:460-462, 1961
232. Giannelli, F.: The pattern of X-chromosome desoxyribonucleic acid synthesis in two women with abnormal sex-chromoscme complements,
Lancet, 1:863-865, 1963
233. Gromults, J. M. and Hirschhorn, K.: Satellites of acrocentric chromosomes, Lancet, 2:54, 1962
234. Jacobs, P. A.: Symposium on genetics in medicine, Royal College of
Physicians, Brit. M.J., 2:1638-1639, 1961
235. Matthey, R.: Etudes sur les chromosomes d'*Ellobius lutescens* Th. (Mam-
malia-Muridae-Microtinae) I. Essai critique sur le valeur critéres pro-
posés par le ≪ Systeme Denver ≫ pour l'identification des chromosomes homologues, Cytogenetics, 1:180-195, 1962
236. Miller, O. J., Cooper, H. L. and Hirschhorn, K.: Recent developments
in human cytogenetics, Eugen. Quart., 8:23-33, 1961
237. Miller, O. J., Mukherjee, B. B. and Bray, W. R.: Normal variations in
the human karyotype, Trans. N. Y. Acad. Sci., 24:372-382, 1962
238. Muldal, S. and Ockey, C. H.: The Denver classification and group III,
Lancet, 2:462-463, 1961
239. **Patau, K.: The identification of individual chromosomes especially
in man, Am. J. Human Genet., 12:250-276, 1960**
240. Patau, K.: Chromosome identification and the Denver report, Lancet,
1:933-934, 1961
241. Petersen, G. B. and Therkelsen, A. J.: Observations on satellited human
chromosomes, Lancet, 1:1229, 1961

Chromosome Mapping

242. Cooper, H. L.: The use of human chromosome markers in linkage studies,
Trans. N.Y. Acad. Sci., 24:383-394, 1962
243. Lyon, M. F.: Genetic factors on the X chromoscme, Lancet, 2:434, 1961
244. Mann, J. D., Cahan, A., Gelb, A. G., Fisher, N., Hamper, J., Tippett, P.,
Sanger, R. and Race, R. R.: A sex-linked blood group, Lancet, 1:
8-10, 1962
245. McCusick, V. A.: Chromosome mapping, *in:* Medical genetics, 1961, J.
Chron. Dis., 15:417-572, 1962
246. Polani, P. E. and Hamerton, J. L.: Genetic factors on the X chromosome,
Lancet, 2:262-263, 1961
247. Renton, P. H., Stratton, F. and Bateman, A. J.: Genes on the mongol
chromosome?, Lancet, 2:727, 1962
248. Sachs, L. and Krim, M.: Some systems for the genetic analysis of mammalian cells, Am. J. Human Genet., 12:128-133, 1960

249. Stewart, J. S. S.: Genetic factors on the X chromosome, Lancet, 2:104-105, 1961

Pertinent discussions will also be found in the following articles: 21 (chromosome mapping); 270 (autoradiography); 594, 597 (hereditable variations in chromosomes); 724, 725 (secondary constrictions).

Chapter VI - Nondisjunction and Aneuploidy

Nondisjunction, General

250. Bridges, C. B.: Nondisjunction as proof of the chromosome theory of heredity, Genetics, 1:107, 1916
251. Hayward, M. D.: Sex chromosome mosaicism in man, Heredity, 15: 235-240, 1960
252. Stewart, J. S. S.: Mechanisms of meiotic nondisjunction in man, Nature (Lond.), 187:804-805, 1960
253. **Stewart, J. S. S.: Mechanisms of non-disjunction in man, Nature (Lond.), 194:258-260, 1962**
254. Twiesselmann, Fr., Defrise-Gussenhoven, E. and Lequebe, A.: Incidence on genetics of mechanism of segregation and disjunction at meiosis in man, Nature (Lond.), 196:1232-1233, 1962

Timing Nondisjunction

255. Gartler, S. M., Vullo, C. and Gandini, E.: Glucose-6-phosphate dehydrogenase deficiency in an XO individual Cytogenetics, 1:1-4, 1962
256. Lindsten, J., Bowen, P., Lee, K. S. N., McCusick, V. A., Polani, P. E., Wingate, M., Edwards, J. H., Hamper, J., Tippett, P., Sanger, R. and Race, R. R.: Source of the X in XO females: the evidence of Xg Lancet, 1:558-559, 1963
257. Polani, P. E., Lessof, M. H. and Bishop, P. M. F.: Color blindness in "ovarian agenesis" (gonadal dysplasia), Lancet, 2:118-120, 1956
258. Saldanha, P. H.: Population cytogenetics, Lancet, 2:728, 1962
259. Stern, C.: Colour-blindness in Klinefelter's syndrome, Nature (Lond.) 183:1452-1453, 1959

Chimeras

260. Ford, C. E., Hamerton, J. L., Barnes, D. W. H. and Loutit, J. F.: Cytological identification of radiation-chimeras, Nature (Lond.), 177: 452-454, 1956
261. Tarkowski, A. K.: Mouse chimera developed from fused eggs, Nature (Lond.), 190:857-860, 1961

Supernumerary Chromosomes

262. Bantock, C.: Chromosome elimination in *Cecidomyidae*, Nature (Lond.) 190:466-467, 1961
263. Hayward, M. D. and Bower, B. D.: The chromosomal constitution of the Sturge-Weber syndrome, Lancet, 1:558-559, 1961

264. Kodani, M.: The supernumerary chromosome of man, Am. J. Human Genet., 10:125-140, 1958
265. Kodani, M.: Three chromosome numbers in whites and Japanese, Science, 127:1339-1340, 1958
266. Stern, C.: The chromosomes of man, Am. J. Human Genet., 11:301-314, 1959

Pertinent discussions will also be found in the following articles: 138, 140, 244, 258, 480 (source of nondisjunctive gametes); 174 (nondisjunction of sex chromosomes); 225 (supernumerary chromoscmes).

Chapter VII - Structural Abnormalities of Chromosomes

267. Edwards, J. H.: Chromosomal association in man, Lancet, 2:317-318, 1961
268. Ferguson-Smith, M. A. and Handmaker, S. D.: Observations on the satellited human chromosomes, Lancet, 1:638-640, 1961
269. Ferguson-Smith, M. A. and Handmaker, S. D.: Observations on the satellited human chromosomes, Lancet, 2:1362, 1961
270. Gilbert, C. W., Muldal, S., Lajtha, L. G. and Rowley, J.: Time-sequence of human chromosome duplication, Nature (Lond.), 195:869-873, 1962
271. Patau, K., Therman, E., Smith, D. W., Inhorn, S. L. and Picken, B. F.: Partial trisomy syndromes. I. Sturge-Weber disease, Am. J. Human Genet., 13:287-298, 1961
272 **White, M. J. D.: Animal Cytology and Evolution (2nd Ed.), Cambridge University Press, 1954**

Pertinent discussions will also be found in the following articles: 140, 246 (genes on isochromosomes); 266 (evidence of inversion in man).

Chapter VIII - Etiology and Classification of Human Chromosome Abnormalities

Age

273. Bodmer, W. F.: Effects of maternal age on the incidence of congenital abnormalities in mouse and man, Nature (Lond.), 190:1134-1135, 1961
274. Book, J. A., Fraccaro, M., Hagert, C. G. and Lindsten, J.: Congenital malformations in children of mothers aged 42 and over, Nature (Lond.) 181:1545-1546, 1958

Genetic Complement

275. Levitan, M.: Spontaneous chromosome aberrations in *Drosophila robusta*, Proc. Nat. Acad. Sci., 48:930-937, 1962
276. Ohno, S., Trujillo, J. S., Kaplan, W. D. and Konosita, R.: Nucleolus organizers in the causation of chromosomal anomalies in man, Lancet, 2:123, 1961
277. Shaw, M. W.: Association of acrocentric chromosomes with the centromere region of chromosome No. 1, Lancet, 1:1351-1352, 1961

Radiation

278. Boyd, E., Buchanan, W. W. and Lennox, B.: Damage to chromosomes by therapeutic doses of radioiodine, Lancet, 1:977-978, 1961

279. Carter, C. O., Evans, K. A. and Stewart, A. M.: Maternal radiation and Down's syndrome, Lancet, 2:1042, 1961

280. Chu, E. H. Y., Giles, N. H. and Passano, K.: Types and frequencies of human chromosome aberrations induced by X-rays, Proc. Nat. Acad. Sci., 47:830-838, 1961

281. Conen, P. E.: Chromosome damage in an infant after diagnostic X-irradiation, Lancet, 2:47, 1961

282. **Conen, P. E., Bell, A. G. and Aspin, N.: Chromosomal aberrations in an infant following the use of diagnostic X-rays, Pediatrics, 31: 72-79, 1963**

283. Fetner, R. H.: Ozone induced chromosome breakage in human cell cultures, Nature (Lond.), 194:793-794, 1962

284. Macintyre, M. N. and Dobyns, B. M.: Anomalies in chromosomes of the circulating leukocytes in man following large doses of radioactive iodine, J. Clin. Endocr., 22:1171-1181, 1962

285. Oster, I. I.: Radiation effects on genetic systems, Proc. Conf. Res. Radiotherapy Cancer, 1960, p. 45

286. Pollard, E. C.: Effects of ionizing radiation on nucleoproteins, Proc. Conf. Res. Radiotherapy Cancer, 1960.

287. Russell, W. L.: An augmenting effect of dose fractionation on radiation-induced mutation rate in mice, Proc. Nat. Acad. Sci., 48:1724-1727, 1962

288. Snell, G. D.: The induction by X-rays of hereditary changes in mice, Genetics, 20:545-567, 1935

289. Stewart, J. S. S. and Sanderson, A. R.: Chromosomal aberration after diagnostic X-irradiation, Lancet, 1:978-979, 1961

290. Tough, I. M., Buckton, K. E., Baikie, A. G. and Court Brown, W. M.: X-ray induced chromosome damage in man, Lancet, 2:849-857, 1960

291. Uchida, I. A. and Curtis, E. J.: A possible association between maternal radiation and mongolism, Lancet, 2:848-850, 1961

292. Wahrman, J. and Robinson, E.: Chromosome damage after X-ray therapy, Lancet, 1:505-506, 1963

293. Whitfield, J. F., Rixon, R. H. and Rhynas, P. O. W.: Cytological consequences of chromosome bridges in X-irradiated L strain mouse cells, Exp. Cell Res., 18:591-593, 1959

Chemicals

294. Arrigh, F. E., Hsu, T. C. and Bergsagel, D. E.: Chromosome damage in marine and human cells following cytoxan therapy, Tex. Rep. Biol. Med., 20:544-549, 1962

295. Conen, P. E. and Lansky G. S.: Chromosome damage during nitrogen mustard therapy' Brit. M.J., 2:1055-1057, 1961

296. Craveri, R. and Veronesi, U.: Effect upon mitosis in *Allium cepa* of an antifungal antibiotic produced by *Streptomyces* sp., Exp. Cell Res., 11: 560-567, 1956

297. Elves, M. W., Buttoo, A. S., Israels, M. C. G. and Wilkinson, J. F.: Chromosome changes caused by 6-azauridine during treatment o acute myeloblastic leukemia, Brit. M.J., 1:156-159, 1963

298. Hsu, T. C. and Somers, C. E.: Effect of 5-bromodeoxyuridine on mammalian chromosomes, Proc. Nat. Acad. Sci., 47:396-403, 1961

299. Somers, C. E. and Hsu, T. C.: Chromosome damage induced by hydroxylamine in mammalian cells, Proc. Nat. Acad. Sci., 48:937-943, 1962

Viral Infections

300. Lindgren, C. C.: A hypothesis of viral pathogenesis, Nature (Lond.), 194:130-133, 1962

301. Roman, H.: Genetics of some microorganisms, Am. J. Human Genet., 13:107-112, 1961

302. Sabin, A. B. and Koch, M. A.: Evidence of continuous transmission of noninfectious SV40 viral genome in most or all SV40 hamster tumor cells, Proc. Nat. Acad. Sci., 49:304-311, 1963

303. Zamenhof, S., de Giovanni-Donnelly, R. and Heldenmuth, L. H.: Transfer, by transformation, of information determining mutation rates in *Bacillus subtilis*, Proc. Nat. Acad. Sci., 48:944-947, 1962

Pertinent discussions will also be found in the following articles: 34 (gene effects on cell division); 304 (radiation effects); 422 (paternal age).

Chapter IX - Indications for Cytogenetic Testing

304. Bender, M. A. and Gooch, P. C.: Types and rates of X-ray-induced chromosome aberrations in human blood irradiated *in vitro*, Proc. Nat. Acad. Sci., 48:522-532, 1962

305. Blank, C. E., Gemmell, E., Casey, M. D. and Lord, M.: Mosaicism in a mother with a mongol child, Brit. M.J., 2:378-380, 1962

306. Carr, D. H.: Chromosome studies in abortuses and stillborn infants, Lancet, 2:603-606, 1963

307. Carter, C. O. and Evans, K.A.: Risk of parents who have had one child with Down's syndrome (mongolism) having another child similarly affected, Lancet, 2:785-787, 1961

308. Dixon, A. D. and Torr, J. B. D.: Sex chromatin as an aid to the identification of sex in forensic medicine, Nature (Lond.), 178:797, 1956

309. Edwards, J. H.: The genetic basis of common disease, Am. J. Med., 34: 627-638, 1963

310. Hsia, E. Y.: Inborn errors of metabolism, New England J.M., 262-1222-1227; 1273-1278; 1318-1323, 1960

311. First International Conference on Congenital Malformations, Lancet 2:257-258, 1960.
312. Fraser Roberts, J. A.: Genetic prognosis, Brit. M.J., 1:587-592, 1962
313. Gans, S. L. and Rubin, C. L.: Apparent female infants with hernias and testes, Am. J. Dis. Child., 104:82-86, 1962
314. Hamerton, J. L., Briggs, S. M., Giannelli, F. and Carter, C. O.: Chromosome studies in detection of parents with high risk of second child with Down's syndrome, Lancet, 2:788-791, 1961
315. Herndon, C. N.: Basic contributions to medicine by research in genetics, J.A.M.A., 177:695-699, 1961
316. Lee, C. H., Schmid, W. and Smith, P. M.: Definitive diagnosis of mongolism in newborn infants by chromosome studies, J.A.M.A., 178: 1030-1032, 1961
317. Lubs, H. A., Jr.: Causes of familial mongolism, Lancet, 2:881, 1961
318. Nilsson, I. M., Bergman, S., Reitalu, J. and Waldenstrom, J.: Hemophilia A in a "girl" with male sex chromatin pattern, Lancet, 2:264-266, 1959
319. Parker, W. C. and Bearn, A. G.: Application of genetic regulatory mechanisms to human genetics, Am. J. Med., 34:680-691, 1963
320. Riis, P. and Fuchs, F.: Antenatal determination of foetal sex in prevention of hereditary disease, Lancet, 2:180-182, 1960
321. Schmid, W.: A familial chromosome abnormality associated with repeated abortions, Cytogenetics, 1:199-209, 1962
322. Tips, R. L. and Lynch, H. T.: The impact of genetic counseling upon the family milieu, J.A.M.A., 184:183-186, 1963
323. Waxman, S. H., Gartler, S. M. and Kelley, V. C.: Apparent masculinization of the female fetus diagnosed as true hermaphrodism by chromosomal studies, J. Pediat., 60:540-544, 1962
324. Zellweger, H.: Familial mongolism and eugenic counselling, Lancet, 2: 455-456, 1962
325. Zellweger, H.: Familial mongolism, Lancet, 2:660-661, 1962

Chapter X - Mongolism and Other Autosomal Aneuploidy Syndromes

General

326. Book, J. A., Santesson, B. and Zetterquist, P.: Association between congenital heart malformations and chromosomal variations, Acta. paediat. 50:217-227, 1961
327. Ellis, J. R. and Marwood, J. C.: Autosomal trisomy syndromes, Lancet, 2:263, 1961
328. Engel, D.: Chromosomal anomalies in "bleb diseases," Lancet, 2:369, 1961
329. Ferguson-Smith, M. A.: Abnormal sex ratio in the autosomal trisomy syndromes, Lancet, 2:357-358, 1962
330. Lewis, A. J.: Autosomal trisomy, Lancet, 1:866, 1962

331. Penrose, L. S.: Finger-prints, palms and chromosomes, Nature (Lond.), 197:933-938, 1963
332. Smith, D. W., Patau, K. and Therman, E.: Autosomal trisomy syndromes, Lancet, 2:211-212, 1961
333. Uchida, I. A., Patau, K. and Smith, D. W.: The dermal patterns of the new autosomal trisomy syndromes, Am. J. Dis. Child., 102:588, 1961

Mongolim

334. **Carr, D. H.: The chromosome abnormality in mongolism, Canad. M.A.J., 87:490-495, 1962**
335. Conen, P. E., Bell, A. G. and Rance, C. P.: A review of chromosome studies in the diagnosis of mongolism. Case report of a Chinese infant, J Pediat., 60:533-539, 1962
336. Forssman, H. and Lehmann, O.: Chromosome studies in 11 families with mongolism in more than one member, Acta. paediat., 50:180-188, 1962
337. German, J. L. and Bearn, A. G.: Family studies on the chromosomal complement of mongols, J. Clin. Invest., 39:989-990, 1960
338. Hall, B.: Down's syndrome (mongolism) with normal chromosomes, Lancet, 2:1026-1027, 1962
339. Hall, B.: Down's syndrome (mongolism) with normal chromosomes, Lancet, 1:947-948, 1963
340. Jacobs, P. A., Baikie, A. G., Court Brown, W. M. and Strong, J. A.: The somatic chromosomes in mongolism, Lancet, 1:710, 1959
341. Lejeune, J.: Le mongolisme, trisomie degressive, Ann. genet., 2:1, 1960
342. Lejeune, J., Gauthier, M. and Turpin, R.: Etude des chromosomes somatiques de neuf enfants mongoliens, Compt. rend. Acad. Sci. Paris, 248:1721-1722, 1959
343. Lejeune, J. and Turpin, R.: Chromosomal aberrations in man, Am. J. Human Genet., 13:175-184, 1961
344. Opie, L. H., Spaulding, W. B. and Conen, P. E.: Masked mongolism. Group 21 trisomy in a fifty-three year old woman, Am. J. Med., 35: 135-142, 1963

D Trisomy Syndrome

346. Atkins, L. and Rosenthal, M. K.: Multiple congenital abnormalities associated with chromosomal trisomy, New England J.M., 265:314-318, 1961
347. Becak, W., Becak, M. L. and Schmidt, B. J.: Chromosome trisomy of group 13-15 in two cases of generalized congenital analgesia, Lancet, 1:664-665, 1963
348. Conen, P. E., Phillips, K. G. and Mauntner, L. S.: Multiple developmental anomalies and trisomy of a 13-15 group chromosome ("D' syndrome), Canad. M.A.J., 87:709-712, 1962
349. **Lubs, H. A., Jr., Koenig, E. U. and Brandt, L. K.: Trisomy 13-15: a clinical syndrome, Lancet, 2:1001-1002, 1961**

350. Miller, Q. J., Alkan, M., Picard, E., Warner, S. and Gerald, P. S.: A specific congenital defect of brain associated with 13-15 trisomy, Am. J. Dis. Child., 104:532-533, 1962

351. Miller, J. Q., Picard, E. H., Alkan, M. K., Warner, S. and Gerald, P. S.: A specific congenital brain defect (arhinencephaly) in 13-15 trisomy, New England J.M., 268:120-124, 1963

352. Patau, K., Smith, D. W., Therman, E., Inhorn, S. L. and Wagner, H. P.: Multiple congenital anomaly caused by an extra autosome, Lancet, 1:790-793, 1960

353. Patau, K., Therman, E., Smith, D. W. and Inhorn, S. L.: Two new cases of D¹ trisomy in man, Hereditas, 47:239-242, 1961

354. Sergovich, F., Madrovich, J. S., Barr, M. L., Carr, D. H. and Langdon, W. A.: The D trisomy syndrome: a case report with a description of ocular pathology, Canad. M.A.J., 89:151-157, 1963

355. Smith, D. W., Patau, K. and Therman, E.: A new syndrome of multiple congenital anomalies caused by an extra autosome, Am. J. Dis. Child., 100:492-493, 1960.

356. Smith, D. W., Patau, K., Therman, E. and Inhorn, S. L.: A new autosomal trisomy syndrome: Multiple congenital anomalies caused by an extra chromosome, J. Pediat., 57:338, 1960

357. **Smith, D. W., Patau, K., Therman, E., Inhorn, S. L. and Demars, R. I.: The D₁ trisomy syndrome, J. Pediat., 62:326-341, 1963**

358. Therman, E., Patau, K., Smith, D. W. and Demars, R. I.: The D trisomy syndrome and XO gonadal dysgenesis in two sisters, Am. J. Human Genet., 13:193-204, 1961

359. Townes, P. L., DeHart, G. K., Hecht, F. and Manning, J. A.: Trisomy 13-15 in a male infant, J. Pediat., 60:528-532, 1962

E Trisomy Syndrome

360. Edwards, J. H., Harnden, D. G., Cameron, A. H., Crosse, V. M. and Wolff, O. H.: A new trisomic syndrome, Lancet, 1:787-789, 1960

361. German, J. L., III, Rankin, J. K., Harrison, P. A., Donovan, D. J., Hogan, W. J. and Bearn, A. G.: Autosomal trisomy of a group 16-18 chromosome, J. Pediat., 60:503-512, 1962

362. Holman, G. H., Erkman, B., Zacharias, D. L. and Koch, H. F.: The 18-trisomy syndrome—two new clinical variants, New England J.M., 268:982-988, 1963

363. Muldal, S.: Trisomy and group V, Lancet, 2:879-880, 1961

364. Patau, K., Therman, E., Smith, D. W. and DeMars, R. I.: Trisomy for chromosome No. 18 in man, Chromosoma, 12:280-285, 1961

365. Potter, E. L.: Pathology of the fetus and infant (2 Ed.), Year Book, Chicago, 1961

366. Smith, D. W., Patau, K. and Therman, E.: The 18 trisomy syndrome and the D¹ trisomy syndrome, Am. J. Dis. Child., 102:587, 1961

367. **Smith, D. W., Patau, K., Therman, E. and Inhorn, S. L.: The No. 18 trisomy trisomy syndrome, J. Pediat., 60:513-527, 1962**

368. Steinberg, J. B. and Jackson, J. F.: The 16-18 trisomy syndrome, Am. J. Dis. Child., 105:213-215, 1963

369. Townes, P. L., Manning, J. A. and DeHart, G. K.: Trisomy 18 (16-18) associated with congenital glaucoma and optic atrophy, J. Pediat., 61:755-758, 1962

370. Uchida, I. A., Bowman, J. M. and Wang, H. C.: The 18-trisomy syndrome, New England J.M., 266:1198-1201, 1962

371. Voorhees, M. L., Vaharu, T. and Gardner, L. I.: Trisomy 16-18 syndrome, Lancet, 2:992, 1962

372. Weiss, L., DiGeorge, A. M. and Baird, H. W., III.: Four infants with the trisomy 18 syndrome and one with trisomy 18 mosaicism, Am. J. Dis. Child., 104:533-534, 1962

Other Trisomy "Syndromes"

373. Biesele, J. J., Schmid, W. and Lawlis, M. G.: Mentally retarded schizoid twin girls with 47 chromosomes, Lancet, 1:403-405, 1962

374. DeCarli, L., Nuzzo, F., Chiarelli, B. and Poli, E.: Trisomic condition of a large chromosome in a woman with mongoloid traits, Lancet, 2:130-131, 1960

375. Dunn, H. G., Ford, D. K., Auersperg, N. and Miller, J. R.: Benign congenital hypotonia with chromosomal anomaly, Pediatrics, 28:578-590, 1961

376. Dunn, H. G., Ford, D. K., Auersperg, N. and Miller, J. R.: Benign congenital hypotonia with chromosomal anomaly, Am. J. Dis. Child., 102:581, 1961

377. El-Alfi, O., Powell, H. C. and Biesele, J. J.: Possible trisomy in chromosome group 6-12 in a mentally retarded patient, Lancet, 1:700-701, 1963

378. Hayward, M. D. and Bower, B. D.: Chromosomal trisomy associated with Sturge-Weber syndrome, Lancet, 2:844-846, 1960

379. Poli, E.: Extra chorosomes and Barr chromatin bodies, Lancet, 2:46-47, 1960

380. Schmid, W., Biesele, J. J. and Lawlis, M. G.: Mentally retarded schizoid twin girls with 47 chromosomes, Lancet, 2:409, 1962

381. Turner, B. and Jennings, A. N.: Trisomy for chromosome 22, Lancet, 2:49-50, 1961

382. van Wijk, J. A. M., Stolte, L. A. M., van Kessel, H. I. A. M. and Tijdink, G. A. J.: A trisomic child of a hyperthyroid mother, Lancet, 1:887-888, 1961

Complex Aneuploidy and Triploidy

383. Book, J. A. and Santesson, B.: Malformation syndrome in man associated with triploidy (69 chromosomes), Lancet, 1:858-859, 1960

384. Delhanty, J. D. A., Ellis, J. R. and Rowley, P. T.: Triploid cells in a human embryo, Lancet, 1:1286, 1961

385. Ellis, J. R., Marshall, R., Normand, I. C. S. and Penrose, L. S.: A girl with triploid cells, Nature (Lond.), 198:411, 1963

386. Gagnon, J., Katyk-Longin, N., de Groot, J. A. and Barbeau, A.: Double trisomie autosomique a 48 chromosomes (21 + 18), Union Med. Canada, 90:1220, 1961

387. Hustinx, T. W. J., Eberle, P., Geerts, S. J., TenBrink, J. and Woltring, L. M.: Mongoloid twins with 48 chromosomes (AA + A²¹XXY), Ann. Human Genet., 25:111-115, 1961

388. Penrose, L. S. and Delhanty, J. D. A.: Triploid cell cultures from a macerated fetus, Lancet, 1:1261-1262, 1961

Autosomal Mosaicism

389. Clarke, C. M., Edwards, J. H. and Smallpiece, V.: 21-trisomy/normal mosaicism in an intelligent child with some mongoloid characters, Lancet, 1:1028-1030, 9161

390. Fitzgerald, P. H. and Lycette, R. R.: Mosaicism in man, involving the autosome associated with mongolism, Heredity, 16:509-512, 1961

391. Fitzgerald, P. H. and Lycette, R. R.: Mosaicism involving the autosome associated with mongolism, Lancet, 2:212, 1961

392. Gustavson, K.-H. and Ek, J. I.: Triple stemline mosaicism in mongolism Lancet, 2:319, 1961

393. Hayashi, T., Hsu, T. C. and Chao, D.: A case of mosaicism in mongolism, Lancet, 1:218-219, 1962

394. Lindsten, J., Alvin, A., Gustavson, K.-H. and Fraccaro, M.: Chromosomal mosaic in a girl with some features of mongolism, Cytogenetics, 1:20-31, 1962

395. Nichols, W. W., Fabrizio, D. P. A., Coriell, L. L., Bishop, H. C. and Boggs, T. R., Jr.: Mongolism with a mosaic chromosome pattern, Am. J. Dis. Child. 102:453-454, 1961

396. Nichols, W. W., Coriell, L. L., Fabrizio, D. P. A., Bishop, H. C. and Boggs, T. R.: Mongolism with mosaic chromosome pattern, J. Pediat., 60:69-76, 1962

397. Richards, B. W. and Stewart, A.: Mosaicism in a mongol, Lancet, 1: 275-276, 1962

398. Smith, D. W., Therman, E. M., Patau, K. A. and Inhorn, S. L.: Mosaicism in a mother of two mongoloids, Am. J. Dis. Child., 104:534, 1962

399. Warkany, J., Rubinstein, J. H., Soukup, S. W. and Curless, M. C.: Mental retardation, absence of patellae, other malformations with chromosomal mosaicism, J. Pediat., 61:803-812, 1963

400. Zellweger, H. and Abbo, G.: Chromosomal mosaicism and mongolism, Lancet, 1:827, 1963

Chimeras

401. Booth, P. B., Plaut, G., James, J. D., Ikin, E. W., Moores, P., Sanger, R. and Race, R. R.: Blood chimerism in a pair of twins, Brit. M.J., 1:1456-1458, 1957
402. Dunsford, I., Bowley, C. C., Hutchison, A. M., Thompson, J. S., Sanger, and Race, R. R.: A human blood-group chimera, Brit. M.J., 2:81, 1953
403. Nicholas, J. W., Jenkins, W. J. and Marsh, W. L.: Human blood chimeras: a study of surviving twins, Brit. M.J., 1:1458-1460, 1957
404. Woodruff, M. F. A., Fox, M., Buckton, K. A. and Jacobs, P. A.: The recognition of human blood chimeras, Lancet, 1:192-194, 1962

Secondary Nondisjunction

405. Hanhart, E.: Mongoloide Idiote bei Mutter und zwei Kindern aus Inzesten, Acta. genet. med. et. gemell., 9:112, 1960
406. Hanhart, E., Delhanty, J. D. A. and Penrose, L. S.: Trisomy in mother and child, Lancet, 1:403, 1961

Supernumerary Chromosome

407. Fitzgerald, P. H.: A possible supernumerary chromosome associated with dystrophia myotonica, Lancet, 2:456-457, 1962

Pertinent discussions will also be found in the following articles: 147, 158 (triploidy); 260 (chimeras); 279, 291 (maternal radiation in mongolism); 316 (mongolism).

Chapter XI - Clinical Effects of Autosomal Structural Anomalies

Translocation Mongolism

408. Atkins, L., O'Sullivan, M. A. and Pryles, C. V.: Mongolism in three siblings with 46 chromosomes, New England J.M., 266:631-635, 1962
409. Biesele, J. J., Schmid, W., Lee, C. H. and Smith, P. M.: Translocation between acrocentric chromosomes in a 46-chromosome mongoloid and his 45-chromosome mother, Am. J. Human Genet., 14:125-134, 1962
410. Book, J. A., Gustavson, K.-H. and Santesson, B.: Chromosomal abnormality in a mongolism-like syndrome, Acta. paediat., 50:240, 1961
411. Breg, W. R., Miller, O. J. and Schmickel, R. D.: Chromosome studies in mongolism with particular reference to translocation, Am. J. Dis. Child., 102:578-579, 1961
412. Breg, W. R., Miller, O. J. and Schmickel, R. D.: Chromosomal translocations in patients with mongolism and in their normal relatives, New England J.M., 266:845-851, 1962
413. Carter, C. O., Hamerton, J. L., Polani, P. E., Gunalp, A. and Weller, S. D. V.: Chromosome translocation as a cause of familial mongolism, Lancet, 2:678-680, 1960

414. de Lozzio, C. B. and Valencia, J. I.: A case of translocation 21-22/17-18, Lancet, 1:1106, 1963

415. Ek, J. J., Falk, V., Bergman, S. and Reitalu, J.: A male mongoloid with 46 chromosomes, Lancet, 2:526-527, 1961

416. Forssman, H. and Lehmann, O.: Translocation carrying phenotypically normal males and the Down syndrome, Lancet, 1:1286, 1961

417. Fraccaro, M., Kaijser, K. and Lindsten, J.: Chromosomal abnormalities in father and mongol child, Lancet, 1:724-727, 1960

418. Hamerton, J. L., Cowie, V. A., Giannelli, F., Briggs, S. M. and Polani, P. E.: Differential transmission of Down's syndrome (mongolism) through male and female translocation carriers, Lancet, 2:956-958, 1961

419. Hamerton, J. L. and Steinberg, A. G.: Progeny of D/G translocation heterozygotes in familial Down's syndrome, Lancet, 1:1408, 1962

420. Macintyre, M. N., Staples, W. I., Steinberg, A. G. and Hempel, J. M.: Familial mongolism (trisomy-21 syndrome) resulting from a "15/21" chromosome translocation in more than three generations of a large kindred, Am. J. Human Genet., 14:335-344, 1962

421. Migeon, B. R., Kaufmann, B. N. and Young, W. J.: A chromosome abnormality with centric fragment in a paramongoloid child, Am. J. Dis. Child., 104:533, 1962

422. Penrose, L. S.: Paternal age in mongolism, Lancet, 1:1101, 1962

423. Penrose, L. S. and Delhanty, J. D. A.: Familial Langdon Down anomaly with chromosomal fusion, Ann. Human Genet., 25:243-252, 1961

424. Penrose, L. S., Ellis, J. R. and Delhanty, J. D. A.: Chromosomal translocation in mongolism and in normal relatives, Lancet, 2:409-410, 1960

425. Pfeiffer, R. A.: The transmission of G/G translocation, Lancet, 1:1163, 1963

426. Polani, P. E., Briggs, J. H., Ford, C. E., Clarke, C. M. and Berg, J. M.: A mongol girl with 46 chromosomes, Lancet, 1:721-724, 1960

427. Scherz, R. G.: Negro female mongol with 46 chromosomes, Lancet, 2:882, 1962

428. Sergovich, F. A., Soltan, H. C. and Carr, D. H.: A 13-15/21 translocation in carrier father and mongol son, Canad. M.A.J., 87:852-858, 1962

429. Shaw, M. W.: Segregation ratios and linkage studies in a family with six translocation mongols, Lancet, 1:1407, 1962

430. **Shaw, M. W.: Familial mongolism, Cytogenetics, 1:141-179, 1962**

431. Sheppard, P. M.: Differential transmission of Down's syndrome (mongolism), Lancet, 2:1455-1456, 1961

432. Walker, N. F., Carr, D. H., Sergovich, F. R., Barr, M. L. and Soltan H. C.: Trisomy-21 and 13-15/21 translocation chromosome patterns in related mongol defectives, J. Ment. Def. Res., 7:150-163, 1963

433. Zellweger, H., Mikamo, K. and Abbo, G.: An unusual translocation in a case of mongolism, J. Pediat., 62:225-229, 1963

Other Autosomal Translocations

434. Book, J. A., Santesson, B. and Zetterquist, P.: Translocation hetero-
     zygosity in man, Lancer, 1:167, 1961
435. Brodie, H. R. and Dallaire, L.: The E syndrome (trisomy 17-18) resulting
     from a maternal chromosomal translocation, Canad. M.A.J., 87, 559-
     561, 1962
436. Buhler, E. and Rossier, R.: (13/15 translocation) *quoted by* Walker, S.
     and Harris, R. (ref. 448)
437. Cooper, H. L. and Hirschhorn, K.: (13/15 translocation) *quoted by* Walker,
     S. and Harris, R. (ref. 448)
438. Dobson, R. and Ohnuki, Y.: Chromosomal abnormalities in a child with
     a convulsive disorder, Lancet, 2:627-630, 1961
439. Edwards, J. H., Fraccaro, M., Davies, P., Young, R. B., Penrose, L. S.
     and Holt, S. B.: Structural heterozygosis in man: analysis of two
     families (with a note on dermal ridge configurations), Ann. Human
     Genet., 26:163-178, 1962
440. Hecht, F., Bryant, J., Arakaki, D., Kaplan, E. and Gentile, G.: Trisomy-18
     syndrome due to *de novo* translocation, Lancet, 1:114, 1963
441. Hirschhorn, K., Oikawa, K., Gromults, J. M. and Novins, J.: (Familial
     transmission of 13/15 translocation with one D trisomy) *quoted by*
     Walker, S. and Harris, R. (ref. 448)
442. Jagiello, G. M.: Familial 13-15 translocation abnormality (Denver
     classification) associated with one case of cerebral palsy, New England
     J.M., 269:66-69, 1963
443. Mercer, R. D. and Darakjian, G.: Apparent translocation between chro-
     mosome 2 and an acrocentric in group 13-15, Lancet, 2:784, 1962
444. Moorehead, P.S., Mellman, W. J. and Wenar, C.: A familial transloca-
     tion associated with speech and mental retardation, Am. J. Human
     Genet., 13:32-46, 1961
445. Turpin, R., Lejeune, J., LaFourcade, J. and Gautier, M.: Aberrations
     chromosomiques et maladies humaines. La polydysspondylie a 45 chro-
     mosomes, Compt. rend. Acad. Sci. Paris, 248:3636-3638, 1959
446. Turpin, R. and Lejeune, J.: Chromosomal translocations in man, Lancet
     1:616, 1961
447. Vislie, H., Wehn, M., Brøgger, A. and Mohr, J.: Chromosome abnor-
     malities in a mother and two mentally retarded children, Lancet,
     2:76-78, 1962
448. Walker, S. and Harris, R.: Familial transmission of a translocation be-
     tween two chromosomes of the 13-15 group (Denver classification),
     Ann. Human Genet., 26:151-162, 1962
449. Walker, S. and Harris, R.: Investigation of a family showing transmission
     of a 13-15 chromosomal translocation (Denver nomenclature), Brit.
     M.J., 2:25-26, 1962
450. Zaleski, W. A.: Autosomal trisomies and partial trisomy syndromes (with

presentation of two cases of partial trisomy for the E group of chromosomes), Canad. M.A.J., 88:389-396, 1963

Deletions

451. Butler, L. J., France, N. E., Russell, A. and Sinclair, L.: A chromosomal
aberration associated with multiple congenital anomalies, Lancet, 1:
1242, 1962
452. Crawfurd, M. d'A.: Multiple congenital anomaly associated with an
extra autosome, Lancet, 2:22-24, 1961
453. Gustavson, K.-H., Hagberg, B., Finley, S. C. and Finley, W. H.: An
apparently identical extra autosome in two severely retarded sisters
with multiple malformations, Cytogenetics, 1:32-41, 1962

Isochromosomes

454. Benirschke, K., Brownell, L. and Ebaugh, F. G.: Chromosomal abnormalities in Waldenstrom's macroglobulinemia, Lancet, 1:594-595, 1962
455. Bottura, C., Ferrari, I. and Veiga, A. A.: Chromosome abnormalities in
Waldenstrom's macroblobulinemia, Lancet, 1:1170, 1961
456. German, J. L., Biro, C. F. and Bearn, A. G.: Chromosomal abnormalities in Waldenstrom's macroglobulinemia, Lancet, 2:48, 1961
457. **Patau, K.: Chromosomal abnormalities in Waldenstrom's macroglobulinemia, Lancet, 2:600-601, 1961**

Other Structural Anomalies

458. **Carr, D.H.: Chromosomal abnormalities and their relation to disease,
Canad. M.A.J., 88:456-461, 1963**
459. Ellis, J. R., Marshall, R. and Penrose, L. S.: An aberrant small acrocentric chromosome, Ann. Human Genet., 26:77-82, 1962
460. Gorlin, R. J. and Psaume, J.: Orodigitofacial dysostosis—a new syndrome.
A study of 22 cases, J. Pediat., 61:520-529, 1962
461. Gray, J. E., Mutton, D. E. and Ashby, D. W.: A possible further cytogenetic mechanism in mongolism, Lancet, 1:21-23, 1962
462. Kaplan, H., Vaharu, T., Voorheess, M. L. and Gardner, L. I.: Chromosomal analysis in a case of orofacial-digital syndrome, New England
J.M., 266:774-775, 1962
463. Patau, K., Therman, E., Inhorn, S. L., Smith, D. W. and Ruess, A. L.:
Partial trisomy syndromes. II. An insertion as the cause of the OFD
syndrome in mother and daughter, Chromosoma, 12:573-584, 1962
464. Ruess, A. L., Pruzansky, S., Lis, E. F. and Patau, K.: The orofacial-
digital syndrome: a recently identified disease apparently associated
with a previously unidentified chromosomal abnormality, Am. J. Dis.
Child., 102:586-587, 1961
465. Ruess, A. L., Pruzansky, S., Lis, E. F. and Patau, K.: The oral-facial-
digital syndrome: a multiple congenital condition of females with
associated chromosomal abnormalities, Pediatrics, 29:985-995, 1962

466. Smith-White, S., Peacock, W. J., Turner, B. and denDulk, G. M.: A ring chromosome in man, Nature (Lond.), 197:102-103, 1963

467. vanWijk, J. A. M., Tijdink, G. A. J. and Stolte, L. A. M.: A case of partial trisomy, Lancet, 2:1454, 1961

468. Wang, H-C, Melnik, J., McDonald, L. T., Uchida, I. A., Carr, D. H. and Goldberg, B.: Ring chromosomes in human beings, Nature (Lond.), 195:733-734, 1962

469. Yunis, J. J. and Gorlin, R. J.: Chromosomal studies in patients with cysts of the jaw, multiple nevoid basal cell carcinomata and bifid rib syndrome, Chromosoma, 14:146-153, 1963

Alterations in Size

470. Cooper, H. L. and Hirschhorn, K.: (Large satallites on chromosome 22), *quoted by* Ellis, J. R. and Penrose, L. S. (ref. 472)

471. Cooper, H. L. and Hirschhorn, K.: Enlarged satellites as a familial chromosome marker, Am. J. Human Genet., 14:107-124, 1962

472. Ellis, J. R. and Penrose, L. S.: Enlarged satellites and multiple malformations in the same pedigree, Ann. Human Genet., 25:159-162, 1961

473. Handmaker, S. D.: The satellited chromosomes of man with reference to the Marfan syndrome, Am. J. Human Genet., 15-11-18, 1963

474. Hirschhorn, K. and Cooper, H. L.: (Large satellites on chromosome 13), *quoted by* Ellis, J. R. and Penrose, L. S. (ref. 472)

475. Kallen, B. and Levan, A.: Abnormal length of chromosomes 21 and 22 in four patients with Marfan's syndrome, Cytogenetics, 1:5-19, 1962

476. McKusick, V. A.: Chromosomes in Marfan's disease, Lancet, 1:1194, 1960

477. Tjio, J. H., Puck, T. T. and Robinson, A.: The human chromosomal satellites in normal persons and in two patients with Marfan's syndrome, Proc. Nat. Acad. Sci., 46:532-539, 1960

Clones

478. de Lozzio, C. B., Valencia, J. I. and Acame, E.: Chromosomal study in erythroblastic endopolyploidy, Lancet, 1:100 -1005, 1962

Pertinent discussions will also be found in the following articles: 249 (inversions); 317, 324, 325 (familial mongolism); 363 (unequal crossing-over).

Chapter XII - Clinical Effects of Sex Chromosome Abnormalities

General

479. Alexander, D. S. and Ferguson-Smith, M. A.: Clinical, pathological and chromosomal studies in male pseudohermaphroditism and other abnormalities of sex development, Am. J. Dis. Child., 100:563, 1960

480. Bateman, A. J.: Maternal *vs* paternal nondisjunction as the source of sex chromosome unbalance, Lancet, 2:1383-1384, 1962

481. Bergada, C., Cleveland, W. W., Jones, H. W. J. and Wilkins, L.: Gonadal histology in patients with male pseudohermaphroditism and atypical gonadal dysgenesis: relation to theories of sex differentiation, Acta. Endocr., 40:498-520, 1962

482. Griboff, S. I. and Lawrence, R.: The chromosomal etiology of congenital gonadal defects, Am. J. Med., 30:544-563, 1961

483. Maclean, N., Harnden, D. G. and Court Brown, W. M.: Abnormalities of sex chromosome constitution in newborn babies, Lancet, 2:406-408, 1961

484. Moore, K. L.: Sex reversal in newborn babies, Lancet, 1:217-219, 1959

485. Moore, K. L. and Edwards, C. H. C.: Medicolegal aspects of intersexuality: criteria of sex, I, Canad. M.A.J., 83:709-714, 1960; II, Canad M.A.J., 83:756-760, 1960

486. **Polani, P. E.: Turner's syndrome and allied conditions: clinical features and chromosomal abnormalities, Brit. Med. Bull., 17: 200-205, 1961**

487. Polani, P. E.: The sex chromosomes in Klinefelter's syndrome and in gonadal dysplasia. Evidence for non-disjunction, cleavage loss or other sex-chromosome aberration in man and the function of the Y chromosome, *in*: Molecular Genetics and Human Disease (Gardner, L. I., ed.), Thomas, Springfield, 1961 pp. 153-181

488. Polani, P. E.: Sex anomalies due to chromosome errors, Postgrad. M.J., 38:281-283, 1962

Chromosomal Intersex

489. Atkins, L. and Engel, E.: Absence of Y chromosome (XO sex chromosome constitution) in a human intersex with extra-abdominal testes, Lancet, 2:20-23, 1962

490. Bishop, P. M. F. and Polani, P. E.: True hermaphroditism and Klinefelter's syndrome, Lancet, 2:928-929, 1960

491. Bottura, C. and Ferrari, I.: Male pseudohermaphroditism with XO chromosomal constitution on bone marrow cells, Brit. M.J., 2:1100-1101, 1962

492. de Assis, L. M., Epps, D. R., Bottura, C. and Ferrari, I.: Chromosomal constitution and nuclear sex of a true hermaphrodite, Lancet, 2:129-130, 1960

493. Ferguson-Smith, M. A., Johnston, A. W. and Weinberg, A. N.: The chromosome complement in true hermaphroditism, Lancet, 2:126-128, 1960

494. Fraccaro, M., Kaijser, K. and Lindsten, J.: Further cytogenetical observations in gonadal dysgenesis, Ann. Human Genet., 24:205-211, 196:

495. Gordon, R. R., O'Gorman, F. J. P., Dewhurst, C. J. and Blank, C. E.: Chromosome counts in a hermaphrodite with some features of Klinefelter's syndrome, Lancet, 2:736-739, 1960

496. Harnden, D. G. and Armstrong, C. N.: The chromosomes of a true hermaphrodite, Brit. M.J., 2:1287-1288, 1959

497. Shah, P. N., Naik, S. N., Mahajan, D. K., Paymaster, J. C., Dave, M. J. and Tiwari, R.: Male pseudohermaphrodism with female chromosome complement, J. Clin. Endocr., 21:727-731, 1961

"Ultimate Hermaphrodite"

498. Gartler, S. M., Waxman, S. H. and Giblett, E.: An XX/XY human hermaphrodite resulting from double fertilization, Proc. Nat. Acad Sci., 48:332-335, 1962

499. Giblett, E. R., Gartler, S. M. and Waxman, S. H.: Blood group studies on the family of an XX/XY hermaphrodite with generalized tissue mosaicism, Am. J. Human Genet., 15:62-68, 1963

500. Gorman, J. G., DiRe, J., Treacy, A. M. and Cahan, A.: The application of —Xg^a antiserum to the question of red cell mosaicism in female heterozygotes, J. Lab. Clin. Med., 61:642-649, 1963

501. Waxman, S. H., Gartler, S. M. and Giblett, E.: An XX/XY human hermaphrodite resulting from a double fertilization, Am. J. Dis. Child. 104:512, 1962

X-Y Translocation

502. Gray, J.: Gonadal dysgenesis (Turner's syndrome) with male penotype and XO chromosomal constitution, Lancet, 1:53, 1960

503. Ohno, S., Kaplan, W. D. and Kinosita, R.: Conjugation of the heteropyknotic X and Y chromosomes of the rat spermatocyte, Exp. Cell Res., 12:395-397, 1957

Mosaic Intersexes

504. Blank, C. E., Bishop, A. and Caley, J. P.: Example of XY/XO mosaicism, Lancet, 2:1450, 1960

505. de la Chapelle, A. and Hortling, H.: XY/XO mosaicism, Lancet, 2: 783-784, 1962

506. **Dewhurst, C. H. XY/XO mosaicism, Lancet, 2:783, 1962**

507. Ferrier, P., Ferrier, S., Klein, D. and Fernex, C.: XY/XO mosaicism Lancet, 1:54, 1963

508. Hirschhorn, K., Decker, W. H. and Cooper, H. L.: Human intersex with chromosome mosaicism of type XY/XO, New England J. M., 263:1044-1048,

509. Judge, D. L. C., Thompson, J. S., Wilson, D. R. and Thompson, M. W., XY/XO mosaicism, Lancet, 2:407-408, 1962

510. Lewis, F. J. W., Mitchell, J. P. and Foss, G. L.: XY/XO mosaicism, Lancet, 1-221-222, 1963

511. Miles, C. P., Luzzatti, L., Storey, S. D. and Peterson, C. D.: A male pseudohermaphrodite with a probable XO/XxY mosaicism, Lancet, 2:455, 1962

512. Waxman, S. H., Kelley, V. C., Gartler, S. M. and Burt, B.: Chromosome complement in a true hermaphrodite, Lancet, 1:161, 1962

513. **Willemse, C. H., van Brink, J. M. and Los, P. L.: XY/XO mosaicism, Lancet, 1:488-489, 1962**

Non-chromosomal Intersex

514. Alexander, D. S. and Ferguson-Smith, M. A.: Chromosomal studies in some variants of male pseudohermaphroditism, Pediatrics, 28:758-763, 1961

515. Bergada, C., Cleveland, W. W., Jones, H. W., Jr. and Wilkins, L.: Variants of embryonic testicular dysgenesis: bilateral anorchia and the syndrome of rudimentary testes, Acta. Endocr., 10:521-536, 1962

516. Chu, E. H. Y., Grumbach, M. M. and Morishima, A.: Karyotypic analysis of a male pseudohermaphrodite with the syndrome of feminizing testes, J. Clin. Endocr., 20:1608-1613, 1960

517. Flor, F. S., Schadt, D. C. and Benz, E. J.: Gonadal dysgenesis with male chromatin pattern: testicular feminization syndrome, J.A.M.A., 181: 375-379, 1962

518. Harnden, D. G. and Stewart, J. S. S.: The chromosomes in a case of pure gonadal dysgenesis, Brit. M.J., 2:1285-1287, 1959

519. Hungerford, D. A., Donnelly, A. J., Nowell, P. C. and Beck, S.: The chromosome constitution of a human phenotypic intersex, Am. J. Human Genet., 11:215-236, 1959

520. Jacobs, P. A., Baikie, A. G., Court Brown, W. M., Forrest, H., Roy, J. R., Stewart, J. S. S. and Lennox, B.: Chromosomal sex in the syndrome of testicular feminization, Lancet, 2:591-592, 1959

521. Sasaki, M. and Makino, S.: The chromosomal constitution of a human hermaphrodite, Tex. Rep. Biol. Med., 18:493-500, 1960

522. Shah, P. N., Naik, S. N., Mahajan, D. K., Dave, M. J. and Paymaster, J. C.: A new variant of human intersex with discussion on the developmental aspects, Brit. M.J., 2:474-477, 1961

523. Sukumaran, P. K. and Shah, P. N.: Abnormal hemoglobin in testicular feminization syndrome, Lancet, 1:866-867,

Turner's Syndrome

524. Avin, J.: Male Turner syndrome, Am. J. Dis. Child., 91:630-635, 1956

525. Bahner, F., Schwarz, G., Harnden, D. G., Jacobs, P. A., Heinz, H. A. and Walter, K.: A fertile female with XO sex chromosome constitution, Lancet, 2:100-101, 1960

526. Bloise, W., de Assis, L. M., Bottura, C. and Ferrari, I.: Gonadal dysgenesis (Turner's syndrome) with male phenotype and XO chromosomal constitution, Lancet, 2:1059-1060, 1960

527. Boyer, J. H., Ferguson-Smith, M. A. and Grumbach, M. M.: The lack of influence of paternal age and birth order in the aetiology of nuclear sex chromatin-negative Turner's syndrome, Ann. Human Genet., 25: 215-225, 1961

528. Chu, E. H. Y., Warkany, J. and Rosenstein, R. B.: Chromosome complement in a case of "male Turner syndrcme," Lancet, 1:786-788, 1961
529. Ford, C. E., Jones, K. W., Polani, P. E., de Almeida, J. C. and Briggs, J. H : A sex chromosome anomaly in a case of gonadal dysgenesis (Turner's syndrome), Lancet, 1:711-713, 1959
530. **Fraccaro, M., Ikkos, D., Lindsten, J., Luft, R. and Tillinger, K. G.: Testicular germinal dysgenesis (male Turner's syndrome). Report of a case with chromosomal studies and review of the literature, Act. Endocr., 36-98-114, 1961**
531. Fraccaro, M., Kaijser, K. and Lindsten, J.: Chromosome ccmplement in gonadal dysgenesis (Turner's syndrcme), Lancet, 1: 886, 1959
532. Fraccaro, M., Kaijser, K. and Lindsten, J.: Somatic chromosome comment in continuously cultured cells of two individuals with gonadal dysgenesis, Ann. Human Genet., 24:45-61, 1960
533. Frasier, J. D., Bashore, R. and Mosier, H. D.: Chromatin-negative twins with female phenotype, gonadal dysgenesis and gonadoblastoma: chromosome evaluation, Am. J. Dis. Child., 102:582, 1961
534. Izakovic, V.: Gonadal dysgenesis in two sisters with male nuclear sex pattern and female characteristics in polymorphonuclear leukocytes, J. Clin. Endocr., 20:1301-1303, 1960
535. Morishima, A. and Grumbach, M. M.: Karyotypic analysis in a case of Turner's syndrome in a phenotypic male, Am. J. Dis. Child., 102: 585-586, 1961
536. Oikawa, K. and Blizzard, R. M.: Chromosomal studies of patients with congenital anomalies simulating those of gonadal aplasia, New England J.M., 264:1009-1016, 1961
537. Steiker, D. D., Mellman, W. J., Bongiovanni, A. M., Eberlein, W. R and Leboeuf, G.: Turner's syndrome in the male, J. Pediat., 58:321-328, 1961
538. Stewart, J. S. S.: Gonadal dysgenesis. The genetic significance of unusual variants, Acta. Endocr., 33:89, 1960
539. Tjio, J. H., Puck, T. T. and Robinson, A.: The somatic chromosomal constitution of some human subjects with genetic defects, Proc. Nat. Acad. Sci., 45:1008, 1016, 1959
540. Turner, H. H. and Zanarta, J.: Ovarian dysgenesis in identical twins: discrepancy between nuclear chromatin pattern in somatic and in blood cells, J. Clin. Endocr., 22:660-665, 1962

Chromatin Positive Gonadal Dysgenesis

541. Blank, C. E., Gordon, R. R. and Bishop, A.: Atypical Turner syndrome, Lancet, 1:947-9 8, ³0520
542. **de Grouchy, J., Lamy, M., Frezal, J. and Ribier, J.: XX/XO mosaics in Turner's syndrome—two further cases, Lancet, 1:1369-1371, 1961**
543. Ferrier, P., Gartler, S., Mahoney, C. P., Shepard, T. H., II, and Burt, B.: Study of a case of gonadal dysgenesis with positive chromatin pattern, Am. J. Dis. Child., 102:581-582, 1961

544. **Ferrier, P., Gartler, S. M., Waxman, S. H. and Shepard, T. H. II:** Abnormal sexual development associated with sex chromosome mosaicism, Pediatrics, 29:703-713, 1962

545. Ferrier, P., Shepard, T., Gartler, S. and Burt, B.: Chromatin positive gonadal dysgenesis and mosaicism, Lancet, 1:1170-1171, 1961

546. Vaharu, T., Voorhees, M. L., Leibow, S. G., Cara, J., Patton, R. G. and Gardner, L. I.: XX/XO mosaicism in a girl. Report of the youngest patient, J. Pediat., 61:751-754, 1962

Primary Amenorrhea

547. **Jacobs, P. A., Harnden, D. G., Buckton, K. E., Court Brown, W. M., King, M. J., McBride, J. A., MacGregor, T. N. and Maclean, N.:** Cytogenentic studies in primary amenorrhea, Lancet, 1:1183-1188, 1961

548. Puck, T. T., Robinson, A. and Tjio, J. H.: Familial primary amenorrhea due to testicular feminization: A human gene affecting sex differentiation, Proc. Soc. Exp. Biol. Med., 103:192-196, 1960

XXX and XXXX

549. Carr, D. H., Barr, M. L. and Plunkett, E. R.: An XXXX chromosome complex in two mentally defective females, Canad. M.A.J., 84:131-137, 1961

550. Fraser, J. H., Campbell, J., MacGillivray, R. C., Boyd, E. and Lennox, B.: The XXX syndrome—frequency among mental defectives and fertility, Lancet, 2:626-627, 1960

551. Jacobs, P. A., Baikie, A. G., Court Brown, W. M., MacGregor, T. N., Maclean, N. and Harnden, D. G.: Evidence for the existence of the human "superfemale," Lancet, 2:423-425, 1959

552. **Johnston, A. W., Ferguson-Smith, M. A., Handmaker, S. D., Jones, H. W. and Jones, G. S.: The triple-X syndrome—clinical, pathological and chromosomal studies in three mentally retarded cases, Brit. M. J., 2:1046-1052, 1961**

553. Sandberg, A. A., Crosswhite, L. H. and Gordy, E.: Trisomy of a large chromosome, J.A.M.A., 174:221-225, 1960

554. Stewart, J. S. S. and Sanderson, A. R.: Fertility and oligophrenia in an apparent triplo-X female, Lancet, 2:21-23, 1960

X Chromosome Mosaicism

555. de la Chapelle, A.: Chromosomal mosaicism, X chromosome anomaly and sex chromatin discrepancy in a case of gonadal dysgenesis, Acta. Endocr., 39:175-182, 1962

556. de Grouchy, J., Lamy, M., Yaneva, H., Salomon, Y. and Netter, A.: Further abnormalities of the X chromosome in primary amenorrhea or in severe oligomenorrhea, Lancet, 2:777-778, 1961

557. Ford, C. E., Polani, P. E., Briggs, J. H. and Biship, P. M. F.: A presumptive human XXY/XX mosaic, Nature (Lond.), 183:1030-1032, 1959

558. Grumbach, M. M. and Morishima, A.: An XXX/XX/XO sex chromosome constitution in gonadal dysgenesis and other examples of sex chromosome mosaicism in man, Am. J. Dis. Child., 102:691-693, 1961

559. Hayward, M. D. and Cameron, A. H.: Triple mosaicism of the sex chromosomes in Turner's syndrome and Hirschprung's disease, Lancet, 2:623-627, 1961

Morphologic Abnormalities of X Chromosome

560. Carr, D. H., Barr, M. L. and Rathburn, J. C.: A probable isochromosome in a child with multiple congenital anomalies, J. Pediat., 62:696-702, 1963

561. Fraccaro, M., Ikkos, D., Lindsten, J., Luft, R. and Kaijser, K.: A new type of chromosomal abnormality in gonadal dysgenesis, Lancet, 2: 1114, 1960

562. Jacobs, P. A., Harnden, D. G., Court Brown, W. M., Goldstein, J., Close, H. G., MacGregor, T. N., Maclean, T. N. and Strong, J. A.: Abnormalities involving the X chromosome in women, Lancet, 1: 1213-1216, 1960

563. Lindsten, J.: New type of chromosomal mosaicism in ovarian dysgenesis Lancet, 1:1228-1229, 1961

564. **Lindsten, J., Fraccaro, M., Ikkos, D., Kaijser, K., Klinger, H. P. and Luft, R.: Presumptive isochromosomes for the long arm of X in man. Analysis of five families, Ann. Human Genet., 26:383-405, 1963**

565. Lindsten, J. and Tillinger, K-G.: Self-perpetuating ring chromosome in a patient with gonadal dysgenesis, Lancet, 1:593-594, 1962

566. Muldal, S., Gilbert, C. W., Lajtha, L. G., Lindsten, J., Rowley, J. and Fraccaro, M.: Tritiated thymidine incorporation in an isochromosome for the long arm of the X chromosome in man, Lancet, 1:861-863, 1963

567. Ohno, S.: More about the mammalian X chromosome, Lancet, 2:152-153, 1962

568. Sparkes, R. S. and Motulsky, A. G.: Hashimoto's disease in Turner's syndrome with isochromosome-X, Lancet, 1:947, 1963

Klinefelter's Syndrome

569. Anders, G., Prader, A., Hauschtek, E., Scharer, K., Siebenmann, R. E. und Heller, R.: Multiples Sex-chromatin und Komplexes Chromosomales Mosaik bei einam Knaben mit Idiotie und Multiplen Missbildungen, Helv. Pediat. Acta, 15:515-532, 1960

570. **Barr, M. L., Carr, D. H., Poszonyi, J., Wilson, R. A., Dunn, H. G., Jacobson, T. S. and Miller, J. R.: The XXXXY sex chromosome abnormality, Canad. M.A.J., 87:891-901, 1963**

571. Barr, M. L., Shaver, E. L., Carr, D. H. and Plunkett, E. R.: The chromatin positive Klinefelter syndrome among patients in mental deficiency hospitals, J. Ment. Def. Res., 4:89, 1960

572. Carr, D. H., Barr, M. L. and Plunkett, E. R.: A probable XXYY sex determining mechanism in a mentally defective male with Klinefelter's syndrome, Canad. M.A.J., 84:873-878, 1961

573. Carr, D. H., Barr, M. L., Plunkett, E. R., Grumbach, M. M., Morishima, A. and Chu, E. H. Y.: An XXXY sex chromosome complex in Klinefelter subjects with duplicated sex chromatin, J. Clin. Endocr., 21: 491-505, 1961

574. Davis, T. E., Canfield, C. J., Herman, R. H. and Goler, D.: Thyroid function in patients with aspermiogenesis and testicular tubular sclerosis New England J.M., 268:178-182, 1963

575. Ellis, J. R., Miller, O. J. and Penrose, L. S.: (XXYY male with acromegalic features), *quoted by* Carr, D. H., Barr, M. L. and Plunkett, E. R. (ref. 572)

576. Ellis, J. R., Miller, O. J., Penrose, L. S. and Scott, G. E. B.: A male with XXYY chromosomes, Ann. Human Genet., 25:145-151, 1961

577. Ferguson-Smith, M. A.: The prepubertal testicular lesion in chromatin-positive Klinefelter's syndrome (primary micro-orchidism) as seen in mentally handicapped children, Lancet, 1:219-222, 1959

578. Ferguson-Smith, M. A., Johnston, A. W. and Handmaker, S. D.: Primary amentia and micro-orchidism associated with an XXXY sex-chromosome constitution, Lancet, 2:184-187, 1960

579. Fraccaro, M., Kaijser, K. and Lindsten, J.: A child with 49 chromosomes, Lancet, 2:899-902, 1960

580. Fraccaro, M., Klinger, H. P. and Schult, W.: A male with XXXXY sex chromosomes, Cytogenetics, 1:52-64, 1962

581. Fraccaro, M. Lindsten, J. and Kaijser, K.: A child with 49 chromosomes: further investigations, Lancet, 2:509, 1962

582. Fraser, J. H., Boyd, E., Lennox, B. and Denison, W. M.: A case of XXXXY Klinefelter's syndrome, Lancet, 2:1064-1067, 1961

583. Frøland, A. and Ulrich, K.: (Fertile XXY Klinefelter's), *quoted by* Kaplan, H., Aspillaga, M., Shelley, T. F. and Gardner, L. I. (ref. 586)

584. Gray, J.: Hypospadias with 47/XXY karyotype, Lancet, 1:722, 1961

585. Jacobs, P. A. and Strong, J. A.: A case of human intersexuality having a possible XXY sex-determining mechanism, Nature (Lond.), 183:302-303, 1959

586. Kaplan, H., Aspillaga, M., Shelley, T. F. and Gardner, L. I.: Possible fertility in Klinefelter's syndrome, Lancet, 1:506, 1963

587. Lubs, H. A., Jr.: Testicular size in Klinefelter's syndrome in men over fifty. Report of a case with XXY/XY mosaicism, New England J.M. 267:326-331, 1962

588. Muldal, S. and Ockey, C. H.: The "double male": a new chromosome constitution in Klinefelter's syndrome, Lancet, 2:492-493, 1960

589. Muldal, S., Ockey, C. H., Thompson, M. and White, L. L. R.: "Double male"—a new chromosome constitution in Klinefelter's syndrome, Acta. Endocr., 39:183-203, 1962

590. Polani, P. E., Bishop, P. M. F., Lennox, B., Ferguson-Smith, M. A., Stewart, J. S. S. and Prader, A.: Colour vision studies and the X

chromosome constitution of patients with Klinefelter's syndrome, Nature (Lond.), 182:1092-1093, 1958

591. Raboch, J. and Sipova, I.: The mental level in 47 cases of "True Klinefelter syndrome," Acta. Endocr., 36:404-408, 1961

592. Rowley, S., Muldal, S., Gilbert, C. W., Lajtha, L. G., Lindsten, J,, Fraccaro, M. and Kaijser, K.: Synthesis of deoxyribonucleic acid on X chromosomes of an XXXXY male, Nature (Lond.), 197:251-252, 1963

593. Solnitzky, O.: Disorders associated with chromosomal aberrations. I. True Klinefelter's syndrome, Georgetown Med. Bull., 15:112-127, 1961

Other Anomalies of Male Differentiation

594. Bishop, A., Blank, C. E. and Hunter, H.: Heritable variation in the length of the Y chromosome, Lancet, 2:18-20, 1962

595. Conen, P. E., Bailey, J. D., Allemang, W. H., Thompson, D. W. and Ezrin, C.: A probable partial deletion of the Y chromosome in an intersex patient, Lancet, 2:294-295, 1961

596. Hauschka, T. S., Hasson, J. E., Goldstein, M. N., Koepf, G. F. and Sandberg, A. A.: An XYY man with progeny indicating familial tendency to non-disjunction, Am. J. Human Genet., 14:22-30, 1962

597. Makino, S., Sasaki, M. S., Yamada, K. and Kajii, T.: A long Y chromosome in man, Chromosoma, 14:154-161, 1963

598. Muldal, S. and Ockey, C. H.: Muscular dystrophy and deletion of Y-chromosome, Lancet, 2:601, 1961

599. Muldal, S. and Ockey, C. H.: Deletion of Y chromosome in a family with muscular dystrophy and hypospadias, Brit. M.J., 1:291-294, 1962

600. Sandberg, A. A., Ishihara, T., Crosswhite, L. H. and Koepf, G. F.: XYY genotype. Report of a case in a male, New England J.M., 268: 585-589, 1963

601. Sandberg, A. A., Koepf, G. F., Ishihara, T. and Hauschka, T. S.: An XYY human male, Lancet, 2:488-489, 1961

602. Vaharu, T., Patton, R. G., Voorhees, M. L. and Gardner, L. I.: Gonadal dysplasia and enlarged phallus in a girl with 45 chromosomes plus "fragment," Lancet, 1:1351, 1961

603. van Wijk, J. A. M., Tijdink, G. A. G. and Stolte, L. A. M.: Anomalies in the Y chromosome, Lancet, 1:218, 1962

Sex Chromosome Defects and Mental Deficiency

604. Gustavson, K.-H. and Akesson, H. O.: Mental deficiency and aberrant sex chromatin, Lancet, 2:724, 1961

605. Hamerton, J. L., Jagiello, G. M. and Kirman, B. H.: Sex chromosome abnormalities in a population of mentally defective children, Brit. M.J., 1:220-223, 1962

606. Kaplan, N. M.: Mental deficiency and Klinefelter's syndrome, Lancet 2:1455, 1961

607. Maclean, N., Mitchell, J. M., Harnden, D. G., Williams, J., Jacobs P. A., Buckton, K. A., Baikie, A. G., Court Brown, W. M., McBride, J. A., Strong, J. A., Close, H. G. and Jones, D. C.: A survey of sex chromosome abnormalities among 4,514 mental defectives, Lancet, 1:293-296, 1962

608. Mosier, H. D., Scott, L. W. and Cotter L. H.: The frequency of the positive sex-chromatin patterns in males with mental deficiency Pediatrics, 25:291-297, 1960

609. Raphael, T. and Shaw, M. W.: Chromosome studies in schizophrenia, J.A.M.A., 183:1022-1028, 1963

610. Queries re schizophrenia (editorial), J.A.M.A., 183:1033, 1963

Pertinent discussions will also be found in the following articles: 129, 130 (sex differentiation); 138, 253 (nondisjunction); 144 (Turner's syndrome); 144 (Klinefelter's syndrome); 21 (general discussion); 229 (long Y chromosome); 246 (X-isochromosomes).

Chapter XIII - Unrelated Chromosomal Defects in Families and Individuals

611. **Baikie, A. G., Buckton, K. E., Court Brown, W. M. and Harnden, D. G.: Two cases of leukemia and a case of sex-chromosome abnormality in the same sibship, Lancet, 2:1003-1004, 1961**

612. Benirschke, K., Brownhill, L., Hoffnagel, D. and Allen, F. H., Jr.: Langdon Down anomaly (mongolism) with 21/21 translocation and Klinefelter's syndrome in the same sibship, Cytogenetics, 1:75-89, 1962

613. Breg, W. R., Cornwell, J. G. and Miller, O. J.: The association of the triple-X syndrome and mongolism in two families, Am. J. Dis. Child., 104:534-535, 1962

614. Buckton, K. E., Harnden, D. G., Baikie, A. G. and Woods, G. E.: Mongolism and leukemia in the same sibship, Lancet, 1:171-172, 1961

615. Ford, C. E., Jones, K. W., Miller, O. J., Mittwoch, U., Penrose, L. S. Ridler, M. and Shapiro, A.: The chromosomes in a patient showing both mongolism and Klinefelter's syndrome, Lancet, 1:709-710, 1959

616. German, J. L., III., DeMayo, A. P. and Bearn, A. G.: Inheritance of an abnormal chromosome in Down's syndrome (mongolism) with leukemia, Am. J. Human Genet., 14:31-43, 1962

617. Harnden, D. G., Miller, O. J. and Penrose, L. S.: The Klinefelter-mongolism type of double aneuploidy, Ann. Human Genet., 24:165-169, 1960

618. Johnston, A. W.: The chromosomes in a child with mongolism and acute leukemia, New England J.M., 264:591-594, 1961

619. Johnston, A. W. and Petrakis, J. K.: Mongolism and Turner's syndrome in the same sibship, Ann. Human Genet., 26:407-413, 1963

620. Kemp, N. H., Stafford, J. L. and Tanner, R. K.: Acute leukemia and Klinefelter's syndrome, Lancet, 2:43 -435, 1961

621. Lanman, J. T. and Hirschhorn, K.: Klinefelter's syndrome in an infant with hypogenitalism and mongolism, Am. J. Dis. Child., 100:546, 1960

622. Lanman, J. T., Sklarin, B. S., Cooper, H. L. and Hirschhorn, K.: Klinefelter's syndrome in a 10 month old mongolian idiot. Report of a case with chromosome analysis, New England J. M., 263:887-890, 1960

623. Lehmann, O. and Forssman, H.: Klinefelter's syndrome and mongolism in the same person, Acta. pediat., 49:536-539, 1960

624. Mamunes, P., Lapidus, P. H., Abbott, J. A. and Roath, S.: Acute leukemia and Klinefelter's syndrome, Lancet, 2:26-27, 1961

625. Miller, O. J., Breg, W. R., Schmickel, R. D. and Tretter, W.: A family with an XXXXY male, a leukemia male and two 21-trisomic mongoloid females, Lancet, 2:78-79, 1961

626. Miller, R. W.: Down's syndrome (mongolism), other congenital malformations and cancers among the sibs of leukemic children, New England J.M., 268:393-400, 1963

627. Ross, J. D. and Atkins, L.: Chromosomal anomaly in a mongol with leukemia, Lancet, 2:612-613, 1962

628. Thompson, M. W., Bell, R. E. and Little, A. S.: Familial 21-trisonic mongolism coexisting with leukemia, Canad. M.A.J., 88:893-894, 1963

629. Uchida, I. A. and Bowman, J. M.: XXX-18 trisomy, Lancet, 2:1094, 1961

630. Uchida, I. A., Lewis, A. J., Bowman, J. M. and Wang, H. C.: A case of double trisomy: trisomy No. 18 and triplo-X, J. Pediat., 60:498-502, 1962

631. Wald, N., Borges, W. H., Li, C. C., Turner, J. H. and Harnois, M. C.: Leukemia associated with mongolism, Lancet, 1:1228, 1961

632. Warkany, J., Schubert, W. K. and Thompson, J. N.: Chromosome analyses in mongolism (Langdon-Down syndrome) associated with leukemia, New England J.M., 268:1-4, 1963

633. Wright, S. W., Day, R. W., Mosier, A. D., Koons, A. and Mueller, H.: Klinefelter's syndrome, Down's syndrome (mongolism) and twinning in the same sibship, J. Pediat., 62:217-224, 1963

Pertinent discussions will also be found in the following articles: 358 (XO and D. trisomy)

Chapter XIV - Chromosomal Changes in Neoplasia
General

634. Atkin, N. B.: The relationship between deoxyribonucleic acid content and the ploidy of human tumors, Cytogenetics, 1:113-122, 1962

635. Atkin, N. B. and Ross, A. J.: Polyploidy in human tumors, Nature (Lond.), 187:579-581, 1950

636. Axelrod, A. A.: Genes, chromosomes and antigens in the evolution of malignant cell populations, Canad. M.A.J., 86:1153-1160, 1962

637. Bayreuther, K.: Chromosomes in primary neoplastic growth, Nature (Lond.), 186:6-9, 1960

638. Burch, P. R. J.: A biological principle and its converse: some implications for carcinogenesis, Nature (Lond.), 195, 214-243, 1962

639. Harman, D.: Mutation, cancer and ageing, Lancet, 1:200-201, 1961

640. Hauschka, T. S.: The chromosomes in ontogeny and oncogeny, Cancer Res., 21:957-974, 1961

641. Ishihara, T. and Sandberg, A. A.: Chromosome constitution of diploid and pseudodiploid cells in effusions of cancer patients, Am. J. Human Genet., 16:885-895, 1963

642. Levan, A.: The significance of polyploidy for the evolution of mouse tumors: strains of the TA3 mammary adenocarcinoma with different ploidy, Exp. Cell Res., 11:613-629, 1956

643. McCulloch, E. A.: Viral carcinogenesis, Canad, M. A. J., 86:1148-1153, 1962

644. Morgan, C.: Viral multiplication and cellular hyperplasia, Nature (Lond.), 184:435-436, 1959

645. Nichols, W. W., Levan, A., Hall, B. and Ostergren, G.: Measles-associated chromosome breakage. Preliminary communication, Hereditas, 48: 367-370, 1962

646. Powell, A. K.: Colchicine-type metaphases in HeLa carcinoma cells, Nature (Lond.), 194:109-110, 1962

647. Rabotti, G.: Ploidy of primary and metastatic human tumors, Nature (Lond.), 183:1276-1277, 1959

648. Revesz, L., Glas, U. and Hilding, G.: Relationship between chromosome number and radiosensitivity of tumour cells, Nature (Lond.), 198: 260-261, 1963

649. Revesz, L. and Norman, U.: Chromosome ploidy and radiosensitivity of tumours, Nature (Lond.), 187:861-862, 1960

650. Sibatani, A., Yamana, K., Kimura, K. and Takahashi, T.: Fractionation of two metabolically distinct classes of ribonucleic acids in animal cells and its bearings on cancer, Nature (Lond.), 186:215-217, 1960

Chronic Myeloid Leukemia - the Ph¹ Chromosome

651. Adams, A., Fitzgerald, P. H. and Gunz, F. W.: A new chromosome abnormality in chronic granulocytic leukemia, Brit. M.J., 2:1474-1476, 1961

652. Atkin, N. B. and Taylor, M. C.: A case of chronic myeloid leukemia with a 45-chromosome cell line in the blood, Cytogenetics, 1:97-103, 1962

653. Baikie, A. G., Court Brown, W. M., Buckton, K. E. Harnden, D. G., Jacobs, P. A. and Tough, I. M. A possible specific chromosome abnor-

mality in human chronic myeloid leukemia, Nature (Lond.), 188: 1165-1166, 1960

654. Fitzgerald, P. H.: The Ph¹ chromosome in uncultured leukocytes and marrow cells from human chronic granulocytic leukemia, Exp. Cell Res., 26:220-222, 1962

655. Fitzgerald, P. H.: Chromosomes of two cases of human chronic myeloid leukemia, Nature (Lond.), 194:393, 1962

656. Fortune, D. W., Lewis, F. J. W. and Poulding, R. H.: Chromosome pattern in myeloid leukemia in a child, Lancet, 1:537, 1962

657. Hall, B.: Down's syndrome (Mongolism) with a morphological Philadelphia chromosome, Lancet, 1:558, 1963

658. Nowell, P. C. and Hungerford, D. A.: A minute chromosome in human chronic granulocytic leukemia, Science, 132:1497, 1960

659. **Nowell, P. C. and Hungerford, D. A.: Chromosome studies in human leukemia. II. Chronic granulocytic leukemia, J. Nat. Cancer Inst., 27:1013-1035, 1961**

660. **Tough, I. M., Court Brown, W. M., Baikie, A. G., Buckton, K. E., Harnden, D. G., Jacobs, P. A., King, M. J. and McBride, J. A.: Cytogenetic studies in chronic myeloid leukemia and acute leukemia associated with mongolism, Lancet, 1:411-417, 1961**

661. Tough, I. M., Court Brown, W. M., Baikie, A. G., Buckton, K. E., Harnden, D. G., Jacobs, P. A. and Williams, J. A.: Chronic myeloid leukemia: cytogenetic studies before and after splenic irradiation, Lancet, 2:115-120, 1962

662. Tough, I. M., Jacobs, P. A., Court Brown, W. M., Baikie, A. G. and Williamson, E. R. C.: Cytogenetic studies on bone-marrow in chronic myeloid leukemia, Lancet, 1:844-846, 1963

Other Leukemias

663. **Baikie, A. G., Court Brown, W. M., Jacobs, P.A. and Milne, J. S.: Chromosome studies in acute leukemia, Lancet, 2:425-427, 1959**

664. Bouton, M. J., Phillips, H. J., Smithell, R. W. and Walker, S.: Congenital leukemia in a consanguinous marriage, Brit. M.J., 2:866-869, 1961

665. Castoldi, G. L., Ricci, N., Punturieri, E. and Bosi, L.: Chromosomal imbalance in plasmacytoma, Lancet, 1:829, 1963

666. Court Brown, W. M., Jacobs, P. A., Tough, I. M. and Baikie, A. G.: Manifold chromosome abnormalities in leukemia, Lancet, 1:1242, 1962

667. Gunz, F. W., Fitzgerald, P. H. and Adams, A.: An abnormal chromosome in chronic lymphocytic leukemia, Brit. M.J., 2:1087-1099, 1962

668. **Hungerford, D. A. and Nowell, P. C.: Chromosome studies in human leukemia. III. acute granulocytic leukemia, J. Nat. Cancer Inst., 29:545:565, 1962**

669. Kinlough, M. A. and Robson, H. N.: Studies of chromosomes in human leukemia by a direct method, Brit. M.J., 2:1052-1055, 1961

670. **Nowell, P. C. and Hungerford, D. A.: Chromosome studies in human**

leukemia. IV. Myeloproliferative syndrome and other atypical myeloid disorders, J. Nat. Cancer Inst., 29:911-931, 1962

671. Pearson, H. A., Grello, F. W. and Cone, T. E.: Leukemia in identical twins, New England J. M., 268:1151-1156, 1963

672. Sandberg, A. A., Ishihara, T., Miwa, T. and Hauschka, T.: The *in vivo* chromosome constitution of marrow from 34 human leukemias and 60 nonleukemic controls, Cancer Res., 21:678-689, 1961

673. Sandberg, A. A., Koepf, G. F., Crosswhite, L. H. and Hauschka, T. S.: The chromosome constitution of human marrow in various developmental and blood disorders, Am. J. Human Genet., 12-231-249, 1960

674. Solari, A. J., Sverdlick, A. B. and Viola, E. R.: Chromosome abnormality in myeloid metaplasia, Lancet, 2:613, 1962

675. Speed, E. D. and Lawler, S. D.: (XOPh[1] positive cells in males with chronic myelocytic leukemia), *quoted by* Tough, I. M. *et al.* (ref. 662)

676. Wahrman, J., Schaap, T. and Robinson, E.: Manifold chromosome abnormalities in leukemia, Lancet, 1:1098-1100, 1962

677. Weinstein, A. W. and Weinstein, E. D.: A chromosomal abnormality in acute myeloblastic leukemia, New England J.M., 268:253-255, 1963

Chromosomal Alteration in Solid Tumors

678. Atkin, N. B. and Klinger, H. P.: The superfemale mole, Lancet, 2:727-728, 1962

679. "Chromosome set" in cancer (editorial), New England J.M., 268:954-9555, 1963.

680. Galan, H. M, Lida, E. J. and Kleisner, E. H.: Chromosomes of Reed-Sternberg cells, Lancet, 1:335, 1963

681. Galton, M. and Benirschke, K.: Forty-six chromosomes in an ovarian eratoma, Lancet, 2:761-762, 1959

682. Lewis, F. J. W., MacTaggart, M., Crow, R. S. and Willis, M. R.: Chromosomal abnormalities in multiple myeloma, Lancet, 1:1183-1184, 1963

683. Lubs, H. A., Jr. and Clark, R.: The chromosome complement of human solid tumors. I. Gastrointestinal tumors and technic, New England J.M., 268:908-911, 1963

684. Nakaniski, Y. H., Mizutani, M. and Pomerat, C. M.: Smoke condensates on lung cells in tissue culture with special reference to chromosomal changes, Tex. Rep. Biol. Med., 17:542-590, 1959

685. Spriggs, A. I. and Boddington, M. M.: Chromosomes of Sternberg-Reed cells, Lancet, 2:153, 1962

686. Spriggs, A. I., Boddington, M. M. and Clarke, C. M.: Carcinoma-in-situ of the cervix uteri—some cytogenetic observations, Lancet, 1:1383-1384, 1962

687. Stolte, L. A. M., v. Kessel, H. I. A. M., Selen, J. D. and Tijdink, G. A. J.: Chromosomes in a hydatidiform mole, Lancet 2:1144-1145, 1960

688. Stich, H. F. and Emson, H. E.: Aneuploid deoxyribonucleic acid content of human carcinomas, Nature (Lond.), 184:290-291, 1959

689. Taylor, A. I.: Nuclear sex of embryonic tumors, Brit. M.J., 1:377-378, 1963

Detection of Malignant Cells

690. Goodlin, R. C.: Utilization of cell chromosome number for diagnosing cancer cells in effusions, Nature (Lond.), 197:507, 1963
691. Ishihara, T. and Makino, S.: Chromosomal conditions in some human subjects with nonmalignant diseases, Tex. Rep. Biol. Med., 18:427-437, 1960
692. Jacob, G. F.: Diagnosis of malignancy by chromosome counts, Lancet, 2:724, 1961

Appendix II - Technical Methods

Sex Chromatin

693. **Barr, M. L.: Cytological tests of chromosomal sex; in, Recent Advances in Clinical Pathology (ed. S. C. Dyke), Series III, Little, Brown and Co., Boston p. 334, 1960**
694. Chagula, W. K.: Sexing of skins in east Africans, Nature (Lond.), 193: 802-803, 1962
695. Castro, N. M., Trench, U. S., Sasso, W. S. and Kerbauy, J.: Sex diagnosis by the nuclear structure of the cells of human urinary sediment, Lancet, 2:565-566, 1957
696. **Guard, H. R.: New technic for differential staining of the sex chromatin, and the determination of its incidence in exfoliated vaginal epithelial cells, Am. J. Clin. Path., 32:145-151, 1959**
697. Klinger, H. P. and Ludwig, K. J.: A universal stain for the sex chromatin body, Stain. Technol, 32:235-244 1957
698. Olmstead, E. G.: Sequential analysis in the assignment of chromosomal sex by means of nuclear chromatin patterns in smears of oral mucosa Am. J. Clin. Path., 32:346-349, 1959
699. Sanderson, A. R.: Rapid nuclear sexing, Lancet, 1:1252, 1960
700. Sanderson, A. R. and Stewart, J. S. S.: Nuclear sexing with aceto-orcein, Brit. M.J., 2:1065-1067, 1961
701. Stevenson, A. C. and McClarin, R. H.: Determination of the sex of human abortions by nuclear sexing of the cells of the chorionic villi, Nature (Lond.), 180:198-199, 1957
702. Thuline, H. C.: A technique for nuclear sexing, Lancet, 2:1310-1311, 1961

Karyotyping Using Peripheral Blood

703. **Genest, P. and Auger, C.: Observations on the technique for the study of human chromosomes by the culture of leukocytes from peripheral blood, Canad. M.A.J., 88:302-307, 1963**
704. Hastings, J., Friedman, S., Rendon, O., Cooper, H. L. and Hirschhorn, K.: Culture of human white cells using differential leukocyte separation, Nature (Lond.), 192:1214-1215, 1961

705. Kaijser, K.: Container for cultivating blood for chromosome studies, Lancet, 2:1362, 1961
706. Koulischer, L. and Mulnard, J.: Staining of chromosomes, Lancet, 1 916, 1962
707. Marshall, G. J., Wood, E. M. and Bierman, H. R.: Hyaluronidase as an effective agent for separating chromosomes, Exp. Cell Res., 23:176-180, 1961
708. Mellman, W. J., Moorehead, P. S., Nowell, P. C. and Batipps, D. M.: The analysis of human chromosomes by use of cultures of peripheral leukocytes, Am. J. Dis. Child., 100:614-615, 1960
709. **Moorehead, P. S., Nowell, P. C., Mellman, W. J., Batipps, D. M. and Hungerford, D. A.: Chromosome preparations of leukocytes cultured from human peripheral blood, Exp. Cell Res., 20:613, 1960**
710 Rothfels, K. H. and Siminovitch, L.: An air drying technique for flattening chromosomes in mammalian cells grown *in vitro*, Stain Techn., 33:73-77, 1958
711. Salkinder, M. and Gear, J. H. S.: Fluorescent staining of chromosomes Lancet, 1:107, 1962
712. Schiffer, L. M., Vaharu, T. and Gardner, L. I.: Acridine orange as a chromosome stain, Lancet, 2:1362-1363, 1961

Blood, Micro Methods
713. Edwards, J. H.: Chromosome analysis from capillary blood, Cytogenetics, 1:90-96, 1962
714. Edwards, J. H. and Young, R. B.: Chromosome analysis from small volumes of blood, Lancet, 2:48-49, 1961
715. Frøland, A.: A micromethod for chromosome analysis on peripheral blood cultures, Lancet, 2:1281-1282, 1962

Mail-in Methods
716. Edwards, J. H.: Chromosomal investigation by post, Lancet, 1:725-726, 1963
717. Lycette, R. R., Pearman, G. and Fitzgerald, P. H.: Simplified culture techniques in chromosome analysis, Lancet, 2:1173, 1962

Marrow and Iltra-short Methods
718. Berg, R. B. and Rosenthal, M. S.: The *in vitro* cultivation of cells from human bone marrow, Am. J. Dis. Child., 100:568, 1960
719. Bottura, C. and Ferrari, I.: A simplified method for the study of chromosomes in man, Nature (Lond.), 186:904-905, 1960
720. Kinlough, M. A. and Robson, H. N.: Chromosome preparations obtained directly from peripheral blood, Nature (Lond.), 192:684, 1961
721. Kinlough, M. A., Robson, H. N. and Hayman, D. L.: A simplified method for the study of chromosomes in man, Nature (Lond.), 189:420, 1961
722. Meighan, S. S. and Stich, H. F.: Simplified technique for examination of chromosomes in the bone marrow of man, Canad. M.A.J., 84: 1004-1006, 1961

Lymph Nodes, Autopsy Material

723. Baker, M. C. and Atkin, N. B.: Short term culture of lymphoid tissue for chromosome studies, Lancet, 1:1164, 1963

Secondary Constrictions

724. Saksela, E. and Moorehead, P. S.: Enhancement of secondary constrictions and the heterochromatic X in human cells, Cytogenetics, 1:225-229, 1962

725. Sasaki, M. S. and Makino, S.: The demonstration of secondary constrictions in human chromosomes by means of a new technique, Am. J. Human Genet., 15:24-33, 1963

Reagents

726. Genest, P.: Production of a semi-purified phytohemagglutinin (mucoprotein) of high potency for the study of chromosomes of leukocytes, Lancet, 1:828, 1963

727. Marshall, R. and Capon, B.: Factor stimulating cell division in cultured leukocytes, Lancet, 2:103-104, 1961

728. Punnett, T., Punnett, H. H. and Kaufmann, B. N.: Preparation of a crude human leukocyte growth factor from *Phaseolis vulgaris*, Lancet, 1:1359-1360, 1962

Pertinent discussions will also be found in the following articles: 23, 204, 271, 672 (general methodology); 143 (thionin stain for sex chromatin); 223 (method for solid tissues).

Appendix III - Sources of Error

729. Bender, M. A., Gooch, P. C. and Prescott, D. M.: Aberrations induced in human leukocyte chromosomes by 3H-labelled nulceosides, Cytogenetics, 1:65-74, 1962

730. Court Brown, W. M., Jacobs, P. A. and Doll, R.: Interpretation of chromosome counts made on bone marrow cells, Lancet, 1:160-163, 1960

731. Ford, C. E., Jacobs, P. A. and Lajtha, L. G.: Human somatic chromosomes, Nature (Lond.), 18:1565-1568, 1958

732. Leon, N., Epps, D. R., Becak, M. L. and Becak, W.: Discrepancies between bone marrow and peripheral-blood chromosomal constitution, Lancet, 2:880-881, 1961

733. Sasaki, M.: Observations on the modification in size and shape of chromosomes due to technical procedure, Chromosoma, 11:514-522, 1961

734. Sohval, A. R. and Casselman, W. G. B.: Alteration in size of nuclear sex-chromatin mass (Barr body) induced by antibiotics, Lancet, 2:1386-1388, 1961

735. Taylor, A. I.: Sex chromatin in the newborn, Lancet, 1:912-914, 1963

736. Trujillo, J. M., Stenius, C., Ohno, S. and Nowack, J.: Translocation heterozygosity in man, Lancet, 1:560, 1961

Pertinent discussions will also be found in the following articles: 10, 219, 220 (chromosome counting); 23 (general precautions); 150, 194, 195 (chromatin and drumsticks).

Appendix V - Classification of Known Chromosome Defects

(Included herein are a number of informative isolated case reports not specifically alluded to in other chapters)

737. Barr, M. L., Carr, D. H., Morishima, A. and Grumbach, M. M.: An XY/XXXY sex chromosome mosaicism in a mentally defective male patient, J. Ment. Def. Res., 6:65-74, 1962

738. Bergman, S., Reitalu, J., Nowakowski, H. and Lenz, W.: The chromosomes in two patients with Klinefelter's syndrome, Ann. Human Genet., 24:81-88, 1960

739. Blumel, J., Ohnuki, Y. and Awa, A.: Chromosome anomaly in two cases of cerebral palsy: a brother and a sister, Nature (Lond.), 189:154-155, 1961

740. Bray, P. and Josephine, Sr. A.: An XXXYY sex-chromosome anomaly, J.A.M.A., 184:179-182, 1963

741. Carr, D. H., Morishima, A., Barr, M. L., Grumbach, M. M., Luers, T. and Boschann, H. W.: An XO/XX/XXX mosaicism in relationship to gonadal dysgenesis in females, J. Clin. Endocr., 22:671-677, 1962

742. Cooper, H. L., Kupperman, H. S., Rendou, O. R. and Hirschhorn, K.: Sex-chromosome mosaicism of type XYY/XO, New England J. M.: 266:699-702, 1962

743. Crawfurd, M. d'A.: Chromosomal mosaicism in a case of Klinefelter's syndrome associated with thalassemia, Ann. Human Genet., 25:153-158, 1961

744. Crooke, A. C. and Hayward, M. D.: Mosaicism in Klinefelter's syndrome, Lancet, 1:1198, 1960

745. Day, R. W., Wright, S. W., Larson, W. and Mann, J. D.: Abnormal-sex chromosome complements and the Xg blood groups, Lancet, 1: 655, 1963

746. Elves, M. W. and Israels, M. C. G.: An abnormal large chromosome in a hemophiliac with congenital abnormalities, Lancet, 2:909-911, 1962

747. Engel, E. and Forbes, A. P.: An abnormal medium-sized metacentric chromosome in a woman with primary gonadal failure, Lancet, 2: 1004-1005, 1961

748. Fraccaro, M., Bott, M. G., Salzano, F. M., Russell, R. W. R. and Cranston, W. I.: Triple chromosome mosaic in a woman with clinical evidence of masculinization, Lancet, 1:1379-1381, 1962

749. Fraccaro, M., Taylor, A. I., Bodian, M. and Newns, G. H.: A human intersex ("true hermaphrodite") with XX/XXY/XXYYY sex chromosomes, Cytogenetics, 1:104-112, 1962

750. Ilbery, P. L. T., Lee, C. W. G. and Winn, S. M.: Incomplete trisomy in mongoloid child exhibiting minimal stigmata, M.J. Austral., 2:182-184, 1961

751. Klinger, H. P. and Schwarzacher, H. G.: XY/XXY and sex chromatin distribution in a 60 mm. human fetus, Cytogenetics, 1:266-290, 1962

752. Lejeune, J., Turpin, R. and Decourt, H.: Aberrations chromosomiques et maladies humaines. Syndrome de Klinefelter a 46 chromosomes par fusion centromerique T-T, Compt. rend. Acad. Sci. Paris, 250:2468, 1960

753. Schmid, W. and Hatfield, D.: Normal karyotype/translocation mosaic, Cytogenetics, 1:210-216, 1962

754. Schuster, J. and Motulsky, A. G.: Exceptional sex-chromatin pattern in male pseudohermaphroditism with XX/XY/XO mosaicism, Lancet, 1:1074-1075, 1962

755. Warkany, J., Chu, E. H. Y. and Kauder, E.: Male pseudohermaphroditism and chromosomal mosaicism, Am. J. Dis. Child., 104:172-179, 1962

756. Bray, P. F. and Mukherjee, B. B.: A chromosome anomaly in an infant with a degenerative disease of the nervous system, J. Pediat., 62:230-234, 1963

INDEX

A

Abortion, habitual, 158
Acentric chromosomes, 8, 243
  formation of, 124, 133
Acrocentric chromosomes, 8, 243
  and structural abnormalities, 121
Actinomycin D, 23
Adjacent segregation, 128
  (diagram), 129
Adrenal virilism, 153
Affinity, 59, 243
Ageing, 28
  effects of on disjunction, 106
  effects of on human chromosomes, 138
Alleles, 22, 243
  dominant and recessive, 22
  multiple, 57
  "wild type", 57
Allocycly, 243
  in sex chromosomes, 93
Alternate segregation, 128
  (diagram), 129
Amenorrhea, 154, 216
Anaphase, 243
  meiotic, 41, 42
  mitotic, 34
Anaphase bridges, 124, 134
Anaphase lagging, 117
  radiation and, 140
Aneuploidy, 104
  anaphase lagging and, 117
  causes of, 104
  classification of, in man, 145
    Appendix V, 283
  clones and, 118, 201
  complex, in man, 178, 226
  defined, 30, 243
  genetic control of, 230
  hereditary patterns, 151

  human, etiology of, 137
  meiotic nondisjunction, 107
  mitotic nondisjunction, 113
  premature disjunction, 116
  secondary nondisjunction, 116, 183
  supernumerary chromosomes, 105, 184
Androgens, 66
Antenatal sex determination, 157
Antibiotics, effect on sex chromatin, 76
Arresting, 276
Association, 57, 243
Assortment, 50, 243
Asymmetrical gonadal differentiation
    207, 208
  (table), 209
Asymmetrical translocations, 125
  (diagram), 126
Autoradiography, 91, 243
  chromosome breaks and, 122
  method, 270
Autosomes, 5, 243
Azaguanidine, 142

B

Back cross, 51, 244
Bacteriophages, 143
Balanced translocations, 187
Balbiani rings, 9, 28, 244
Balloons, 77
Barr body (*see also* Sex chromatin), 244
Barr test (*see* Sex chromatin)
Benign congenital myotonia, 177
Bivalents, 37, 244
Biological dosimeter, 157
Blood, use in karyotyping, 82, 256
Blood dyscrasias, cytogenetic evaluation, 156

Bone marrow, use in karyotyping, 82 265
Bouquet, 37
Bromouracil, 142

C

C-mitosis, 34, 142, 244
C trisomy, 176, 197
Carrier state, in mongolism, 151, 188, 192
  sex linkage and, 56
  translocations and, 128, 151
Cell division (*see also* Mitosis; Meiosis), 30
Centric fusion, 127, 244
  isochromosomes and, 130
  (diagram), 131
Centromere, 4, 7, 244
  genetic activity of, 59
  spindle formation and, 34
Centromeric index, 89, 244
  (table), 90
Centrosome, 33, 244
Centrotype, 59
Chemical induction of chromosome defects, 141
Chiasmata, 38, 40, 244
Chimeras, 115, 183, 244
  of blood cells, 115
  whole body, 207
Ch¹ chromosome, 240
Chromatids, 4, 244
  fractures of, 120, 140
Chromatin negative gonadal dysgenesis, 215
Chromatin positive gonadal dysgenesis in females, 214
  vs. Turner's syndrome (table), 214
  in males (Klinefelter's syndrome), 220
Chromatin test (*see* Sex chromatin)
Chromomeres, 5, 244
Chromonema, 5
Chromosomes
  abnormalities of (*see* specific listing)
  autoradiography, 91, 243
    method, 270
  breaks in, 120, 140
  constrictions in

primary (*see also* Centromere), 7
  secondary, 7, 89
    accentuation of, 91, 269
    (diagram), 91
  culture methods (*see also* Karyotyping)
    general, 81
    specific, 256
  differentiation in, 28
  hereditary variations in, 93
  identification of
    general, 87, 89
    specific, 98
    (table), 90
  ideogram of (diagram), 95
  karyotypes, normal (diagram), 97
  mapping, 102
  metaphase figures, normal (diagram) 96
  modal number, 86
  nomenclature, 88
  polytene, 9
  structure of, 4, 5
    (diagram), 5
  supernumerary, 105, 117
Chronic disease, effects of, 145
"Cis" loci, 59, 73
Cistrons (*see also* Subgenes), 23, 244
Claret locus, 138
Classification of chromosome defects
  detail (Appendix V), 283
  general, 145
Cleavage, defined (*see also* Mitosis), 244
Clones, 118, 244
  in man, 201
Colchicine, 34, 85, 142, 244
  effect on chromosome length, 86, 94
  excess, effects on chromosomes, 276
    (diagram), 277
Complete linkage, 52
Congenital anomalies, investigation of, 149
Constrictions (*see* Chromosomes, constrictions in)
Crossing-over, 38, 39, 245
  and linkage, 52
  double, 53
Culture media (*see* Media)
Cytogenetics, defined, 63

Cytogenetic testing, indications, 148
Cytoxan, 142

D

D trisomy syndrome, 165
  clinical features, diagram, 166
    (table), 169
  karyotype in (diagram), 168
  mosaicism in, 181
  translocation in, 193
Davidson-Smith test (*see* Sex chromatin)
Deletions (*see also* Ph¹ chromosome),
    124, 245
  in man
    autosomal, 195
    X chromosome, 219
    Y chromosome, 224
Denver nomenclature, 88, 245
    (table), 90
Deoxyribosenucleic acid, 10, 245
    (diagram), 12
  function of, 20
    (diagram), 20
  in mitosis and meiosis, 31
  replication of, 13
    (diagram), 13
  sex chromosomal, 64
  template, 14
Dermatoglyphics, 245
D/G mongolism (diagram), 190
Diakinesis, 40, 245
Dicentric chromosomes, 124, 140
  from inversions, 134
  from ring chromosomes, 132
Dictyotene ovum, 44, 245
Differentiation of cells, 27
Differential distance, 39, 245
Dihybrid cross, 50
Diploid, 30, 245
  number, in man, 80
Diplotene, 38, 245
Direct tandem inversions, 134
Disjunction, 105, 245
  abnormalities of, 105
  in meiosis I, 41
  in meiosis II, 42
  in mitosis, 34
  premature, 116

D.N.A. (*see* Deoxyribosenucleic acid)
D/N ratio, 79
Dominant alleles, 22, 245
Dominant inheritance
  autosomal, 56
  sex linked, 56
Dosage compensation, 59
Double crossovers, 53
Double nondisjunction, 109
Double trisomy, 179
Down's syndrome (*see* Mongolism)
Drumsticks, 77, 245
Duplication, 130, 145
  in man, 190
Dysproteinemia, 156, 202

E

E trisomy syndrome, 170
  clinical features (diagrams), 171, 172
    (table), 173
  deletions in, 197
  karyotype in (diagram), 175
  translocation in, 193
E.D.T.A., 85
Edwards' syndrome (*see* E trisomy syndrome)
Effusions, cytogenetic study of, 83, 158,
    242
Environment, effects of, 61
Equational division, 42, 245
Equatorial plate
  meiotic, 41
  mitotic, 33
Erythroblastic endopolyploidy, 202
Estrogen, 66
  effect on sex chromatin, 74
Euchromatin, 6, 245
Euploidy, 30, 246
Evocator, testicular, 66
Expressivity, 58, 246

F

F trisomy, 177
Familial mongolism, 188
Fascia, use in karyotyping, 82
Fixed differentiation hypothesis, 70
Free radicals, 139

G

Gamete, defined, 246
Gametogenesis in man, 44
Gene (*see also* Genetic code; Operon), 21, 246
  balance, 59, 73, 161
  concept of inheritance, 3
  defined, 23, 246
  Jacob-Monod model, 24
  length of, 23
  mode of action of, 14, 20
    (diagram), 20
  mutations, 27
Genetic code, 14, 246
  (table), 17
Genetic counselling, 150
Genes and chromosome defects, 138
Genome, 17, 246
Genotype, 48, 246
G/G mongolism (diagram), 191
Gibberish mutations, 27
Gonadal dysgenesis
  in females, 210, 214, 215
  in males, 207, 208, 220
Gonads, differentiation of, 63
Guard stain, method, 255

H

Habitual abortion, 158
Haploid, 30, 104
Haptoglobulins, 39
Healing time, in chromosomes, 122
Hemizygous, 55, 246
Heredity (*see also* Inheritance)
  genes and, 3
Hermaphroditism, true, 153, 204, 206
Heterochromatin, 6, 26, 73, 246
  histones and, 26
  position effects and, 59
  sex chromatin and, 71
Heterogametic sex, 63, 246
Heteroploidy, 104, 246
Heteropyknosis (*see also* Heterochromatin), 6, 246
Heterosomal defects, 130
Heterozygous, 22, 246
Histones, 25
  cell differentiation and, 28

neoplasms and, 233
Holandric inheritance, 55, 246
Homogametic sex, 63, 246
Homosomal defects, 120
Homozygous, 22, 247
Hybrid, 49, 247
Hypomodal counts, 87

I

Identification of chromosomes (*see* Chromosomes, identification)
Ideogram, defined, 247
  (diagram), 95
Incomplete linkage, 52
Independent assortment, law of, 50
Inducible system, 25, 73
  (diagram), 24
Infertility, 155, 217
Inheritance (*see also* Heredity), 47
  genes and, 3
  holandric, 55
  patterns of, 55
  sex-linked, 55
Insertions, 185
  in man, 199
Interference distance, 39, 247
Interkinesis, 35, 247
Interphase nucleus, 31, 247
Intersex, 152, 204, 206
Inversions, 132, 247
  in man, 198
Isochromatid breaks, 120
Isochromosomes, 130, 247
  (diagram), 130
  in autosomes, 198
  in sex chromosomes, 217, 219
  in Waldenstrom's macroglobulinemia, 202

J

Jacob-Monod model, 24
Jost's experiments, 64

K

Karyotype, 81, 247
  normal (diagrams), 97

Karyotyping (*see also* Chromosomes)
  colchicine in, 85
  general principles, 81
  media for, 83
  phytohemagglutinin in, 84
  sources of error, 274, 279
    (table), 275
  using blood
    general, 82
    mail-in method, 264
    micro method, 262
    routine method, 256
  using bone marrow
    general, 82
    routine method, 265
    ultrashort (direct) method, 266
  using tissue
    general, 82
    methods, 267, 268
Kinetochore (*see* Centromere)
Klinefelter's syndrome, 220
  karyotype in (diagram), 221

L

Lampbrush chromosomes, 9, 13, 247
Langdon Down anomaly (*see* Mongolism)
Leptotene, 37, 247
Leukemia, 238
  and mongolism, 227, 229
  and the Ph¹ chromosome, 202, 235
Linkage, 51, 102, 247
  complete *vs.* incomplete, 52
  sex linkage, 54
  three-point studies, 58
  vs. association, 57
Locus, 22, 247
Long arm/short arm ratio, 89
  (table), 90
Lymphocytes, activity in culture media, 82
Lyon hypothesis, 70
Lysogeny, 143

M

Macroglobulinemia, 156, 202
Mapping chromosomes, 102

Maternal age (*see* Ageing)
Matroclinous, 112, 247
Media, 83, 271
Medicolegal cytogenetics, 156
Meiosis, 35, 247
  human, 44
  in sex chromosomes, 64
  in translocations, 125
  meiosis I, 36
    (diagram), 40
  meiosis II, 42
    (diagram), 43
  nondisjunction in, 107
  vs. mitosis, 43
Mendelian inheritance, 247
Mendel, Gregor, 47
Mendel's laws, 48, 247
  first law, 48
  second law, 56
Mental deficiency, 224
Mercado, Luis, 47
Messenger R.N.A., 19, 248
Metacentric chromosomes, 8, 248
Metaphase, defined, 248
  normal (diagrams), 96
  meiotic, 41, 42
  mitotic, 34
Mitogenic agents
  EDTA, 85
  phytogemagglutinin, 84
Mitosis, 31, 248
  (diagram), 32
  nondisjunction in, 113
  vs. meiosis, 43
Mitotic poisons, 142
Modal number, 86, 248
Mongolism, 161
  and leukemia, 227, 229
  familial, 188
    karyotypes in (diagrams), 190, 191
  mosaicism in, 181
  sporadic (trisomic), 161
    karyotype in (diagram), 164
Monosomy, 104, 248
Monohydrid cross, 49, 248
Monosomy, 104, 248
  autosomal, 178
  monosomy X (Turner's syndrome) 210

- trisomy, 179
Mosaicism, 104, 113, 248
  autosomal, 180
  diagnosis, 114
  in mice, sex chromatin and, 71
  intersexes and, 209, 215
  mitotic nondisjunction and, 113
  sex chromosomal, 209, 214, 218
    (tables)—XO/XY, 209
             XO *vs.* XO/XX, 214
  triple stem line, 113
Mullerian development, 65
Multiple alleles, 57
Mutations, 27
Mutator gene, 123, 138
Myeloid leukemia, chronic, 156, 235
Myeloproliferative syndromes, 240

N

Neoplastic diseases, 232
Nitrogen mustard, 142
Nondisjunction, 104
  defined, 105, 248
  determining source of, 111
  double, 109, 110
  etiology of, 105
  familial, 184
  frequency, 112
  meiotic, 107
    (diagram), 109
  mitotic, 113
  secondary, 116, 183
  simple, 109
  successive, 109, 110
  types of, 109
Nonsense mutations, 27
Nucleolus organizers, 121, 139
Nucleotide analogs, 142

O

Oligomenorrhea, 217
Oogenesis, human, 44
  (diagram), 45
Operator subgenes, 24
Operon, 24, 248
  (diagram), 24
Orcein, staining, 253

P

Pachytene, 37, 248
Pachytene cross, 127, 248
Paracentric defects, 120, 248
Paracentric inversions, 133
  meiotic behavior (diagram), 133
Paramutation, 27, 59, 248
Partial trisomy, 136, 179
Patau's syndrome (*see* D trisomy syndrome)
Patroclinous, 112, 248
Pedigree chart (diagram), 61, 62
Penetrance, 249
Pericentric defects, 120, 249
Pericentric inversions, 133
  meiotic behavior of (diagram), 133
Phages, 143
Phaseolus vulgaris, 84
Ph¹ chromosome, 202, 235
  (diagram), 236
Phenotype, 48, 249
Phytohemagglutinin, 84, 249
Ploidy, 30
  of neoplasms, 233
Polar bodies, 45, 46, 249
Polymorphonuclear leukocyte sex chromatin (*see* Sex chromatin)
Polyploidy, 30, 104, 202, 249
Polysomy, 105
  autosomal, 178
  sex chromosomes, 217, 222
Polytene chromosomes (*see* Chromosomes)
Position effects, 58
Premature disjunction, 116
Primary amenorrhea, 154, 216
Primary constriction (*see* Centromere)
Prometaphase, 35
Prophase, 249
  meiosis I, 36
  meiosis II, 42
  mitosis, 32
Prophase chromosomes, identification, 92
Prophase nucleus (diagram), 6
Propinquity effect, 123, 249
Pseudoallelism, 59, 249
Pseudohermaphroditism, 153, 204
Pure lines, 49, 249

R

Racquets, 77
Radiation, 139, 141
    estimating dose of, 158
Radiomimetic drugs, 141
Random segregation, law of, 50
Recessive alleles, 22, 249
Recessive inheritance, 56
    sex-linked, 56
Reciprocal translocations, 125
    (diagrams), 126, 128, 129
Recombination (*see also* Crossing-over)
    57
Reductional division, 36, 39, 249
Regulator subgenes, 24
Relative length of chromosomes, 89, 249
    (table), 90
Repressible systems, 25
    (diagram), 24
Resting phase (*see* Interkinesis; Inter-
    phase)
Restitution, 123, 249
    (diagram), 123
Reversed tandem inversions, 134
Ribosenucleic acid, 18, 249
    functions of, 20
        (diagram), 20
    histones and, 26
    messenger, 19
    ribosome, 19
    transfer, 19
Ribosomes, 20, 249
    R.N.A. and, 19
Ring chromosomes, 132
    in man, 199
R.N.A. (*see* Ribosenucleic acid)
Runt disease, 115

S

Salivary gland chromosomes, 9
Satellites, 8, 250
    (diagram), 91
    abnormalities, 198
    chromosome breaks and, 121
    chromosome identification and, 89
Satellite association (diagram), 121
Schizophrenia, 177

Secondary constrictions (*see* Chromo-
    somes)
Secondary nondisjunction, 116, 183
Segregation distorter gene, 60, 106, 138
Segregation, 50, 250
    adjacent *vs.* alternate, 128
    alteration of ratio by gametes, 60
    -distorter gene, 60, 106, 138
    gene control of, 60
    laws of, 48, 50
Semiconservative duplication, 14
Sessile nodules, 77
Sex chromatin, 68, 250
    abnormalities of, 74
        (diagrams), 72, 74
    in newborns, 75
    in polymorphonuclear leukocytes, 76
        demonstration of, 252
        (diagrams), 75
    interpretation, 78
    morphology, 76
    origin of, 78
    methods of demonstration, 258
        Guard stain, 255
        orcein stain, 253
        thionin stain, 254
    morphology of, 68
        normal variations, 75
    modification by drugs, 75, 76
    origin of, 70
    post partum, 75
    significance, 73
    sources of error, 273, 278
Sex chromosomes, 64
    abnormalities of, 203
        vs. autosomal abnormalities, 228
    identification of, 64, 93, 99, 101
    formation of sex chromatin, 70
    functions of, 66
    in meiosis, 38, 64
    nondisjunction in, 105
Sex, defined, 205
Sex determination, antenatal, 157
Sex differentiation, 63
Sex-linked inheritance, 54, 250
    use in timing nondisjunction, 111
Shifts, 135
Shope rabbit papilloma, 144
Simple nondisjunction, 109

Sister strand reunion, 124
　and isochromosomes, 131
　(diagrams), 123, 131
Sites (*see* Subgenes)
Skin, use in karyotyping, 82
Spermatogenesis, 44
Spindle apparatus, 34, 250
　effect of colchicine, 34, 85
　in meiosis I, 41
Spiralization, 5, 32, 34
Statmodiaeresis, 142
Stein-Levinthal syndrome, 218
Sterility, 155, 217
Stratification, 57
Structural abnormalities of chromo-
　somes, 119, 185
　abnormal size, 200, 224
　deletions, 124
　　in man, 197, 219, 224, 235
　duplications, 130
　　in man, 198
　effect of on hereditary patterns, 60
　etiology of, 119
　　in man, 137
　in man, 185
　　classification
　　　general, 145
　　　specific (Appendix V), 283
　　incidence, 121
　　insertions, 134
　　　in man, 199
　　interchromosome effects of, 139
　　inversions, 133
　　　in man, 198
　　isochromosomes, 130
　　　in man, 198, 202, 217, 219
　　restitution, 123
　　ring chromosomes, 132
　　　in man, 199
　　sister-strand reunion, 123
　　shifts, 135
　　translocations, 125
　　　in man, 188
　　whole arm, 126
Structural subgenes, 24
Sturge-Weber syndrome, 177, 179, 198
Subgenes, 23, 24, 250
Submetacentric chromosomes, 8, 250
Successive nondisjunction, 109

Superfemale, 217
Supernumerary chromosomes, 105, 117,
　184, 250
SV 40 virus, 144, 234
Symmetrical translocations, 125
　(diagram), 126
Synapsis, 37, 39, 250
　in insertions, 135
　in inversions, 133
　in translocations, 127

T

Tandem inversions, 134
Technical methods, general principles,
　81
　specific methods, 252
Telocentric chromosomes, 7, 250
Telomeres, 8, 250
Telophase, 250
　meiotic, 42
　mitotic, 35
Temperate phage, 143
Template D.N.A., 14
Terminalization, 40, 250
Testicular feminization, 154
Testicular function, 65
Tetrad, 38, 250
Tetravalent, 127, 187, 250
Tetra X syndrome, 217
Tetra XY syndrome (table), 222
　X-ray changes in (diagram), 223
Thionin stain, 254
Three point linkages, 53
"Trans" loci, 59
Transducing systems, 102, 250
Transduction, viral, 144
Transfer R.N.A. (*see* Ribosenucleic acid)
Transformation, viral, 144
Translocations, 124, 251
　autosomal, 187
　　mongolism and, 188
　balanced and unbalanced gametes in.
　　187
　(diagrams), 126, 128, 129
　inheritance patterns of, 151
　uncommon, 195
　whole arm, 126
　X/Y, 208

Triplet code, 15
Triploidy, 30, 109, 351
  in man, 179
Triplo X syndrome, 217
  karyotype in (diagram), 218
Trisomy, 104, 251
  complex, 179
  partial, 136, 179
Trisomy syndromes
  D trisomy, 165
  E trisomy, 170
  mongolism, 161
  other, 176
  partial, 136, 179
Tritiated thymidine (*see* Autoradiography)
Trivalents, 128, 187, 251
  (diagram), 129
True hermaphroditism, 153, 204, 206
Tumors, karyotype analysis of, 83, 241
Turner's syndrome, 210
  karyotype in (diagram), 213
  in males, 213
  vs. XO/XX (table), 214
22 Trisomy, 177

U
"Ultimate hermaphrodite," 207
Unbalanced translocations, 187

V
Viral carcinogenesis, 234

Viral effects on chromosomes, 142
  (diagram), 143
Virulent phage, 144
"V type" position effects, 59

W
Waldenstrom's macroglobulinemia, 156, 202
Watson-Crick model, 11
Whole arm interchanges, 126
Wild type alleles, 157
Wolffian development, 65

X
X chromosome (*see* Sex chromosomes)
XO/XX mosaicism (table), 209
X ray (*see* Radiation)
X/TCL ratio, 93
XXX syndrome, 217
  karyotype in (diagram), 218
XXXXY syndrome (table), 222
X/Y translocation, 208

Y
Y chromosome (*see* Sex chromosomes)

Z
Zygote, 35, 251
Zygotene, 37, 251